Alaska

Maps for America
Second Edition, 1981
First Edition published in 1979 as
A Centennial Volume
1879–1979

John Wesley Powell Federal Building
U.S. Department of the Interior
Geological Survey National Center
Reston, Virginia

Second Edition

maps for

Cartographic products of the
U. S. Geological Survey and others

Morris M. Thompson, USGS (retired)

america

GEOLOGICAL SURVEY
FINE FOR DISTURBING THIS MARK
ELEVATION
ABOVE SEA
108 FEET
DATUM
1879
250 DOLLARS
U.S.
B.M.

UNITED STATES DEPARTMENT OF THE INTERIOR

JAMES G. WATT, *Secretary*

GEOLOGICAL SURVEY

DALLAS L. PECK, *Director*

Library of Congress Cataloging in Publication Data
Thompson, Morris Mordecai, 1912–
  Maps for America.
  Bibliography: p.
  Includes index.
  1. Cartography—United States. 2. United States.
  Geological Survey. I. Title.
  GA405.T46 1981   526'.0973   81–607878
                                    AACR2

For sale by the Superintendent of Documents, U.S. Government Printing Office
Washington, D.C. 20402

What is there in this richly endowed land of ours which may be dug, or gathered, or harvested, and made part of the wealth of America and of the world, and how and where does it lie?

CONGRESSMAN A. S. HEWITT, New York

Author of legislation establishing
the Geological Survey, 1879

TABLE OF CONTENTS

SI units		Inch-pound system
LINEAR MEASURES		
millimeter (mm)	= 0.039 37	inch (in)
meter (m)	= 3.281	feet (ft)
	= 1.094	yards (yd)
kilometer (km)	= 0.621 4	mile (mi)
	= 0.540 0	nautical mile (nmi)
AREAL MEASURES		
centimeter^2 (cm^2)	= 0.155 0	inch^2 (in^2)
meter^2 (m^2)	= 10.76	feet^2 (ft^2)
	= 1.196	yards^2 (yd^2)
	= 0.000 247 1	acre
hectometer^2 (hm^2)	= 2.471	acres
	= 0.003 861	section (640 acres or 1 mi^2)
kilometer^2 (km^2)	= 0.386 1	mile^2 (mi^2)

FOREWORD

"Maps for America" was originally published in 1979 as a Centennial Volume commemorating the Geological Survey's hundred years of service (1879–1979) in the earth sciences. It was an eminently fitting Centennial Year publication, for, since its establishment, the Geological Survey has continuously carried on an extensive program of mapping to provide knowledge of the topography, geology, hydrology, and natural resources of our Nation.

This volume contains an organized presentation of information about the maps produced by the Geological Survey and other American organizations, public and private. Such maps are important tools for those in government and in private endeavors who are working to assure the wisest choices in managing the Nation's resources. They are particularly supportive of the Department of the Interior's role as the Nation's principal conservation agency.

The second edition of "Maps for America" is intended primarily to replenish the dwindling supply of copies of the book, but it also contains a number of changes to correct or update the text and to provide more suitable illustrations in certain instances.

1982
U.S. Geological Survey

Dallas L. Peck
Director

PREFACE

This book was first conceived as being devoted entirely to descriptions of the maps produced by the U.S. Geological Survey. As the project developed, however, it became clear that the story of maps is not complete unless it is properly set in the background of the American mapping effort as a whole. Extension of the scope of the book does not preclude placing emphasis on the Geological Survey mapping program, which is treated in full while other programs are treated only in sufficient detail to provide leads for exploring them elsewhere.

At the outset, let it be understood that this book is not intended to explain the detailed procedures for making maps. Procedures are described only to the extent needed for an understanding of map content. The primary objectives are to inform the map user of (1) the meaning of lines, colors, images, symbols, numbers, captions, and notes that appear on maps, (2) the possible errors and anomalies affecting the reliability and interpretation of maps, (3) the different kinds of maps and map data, and (4) the various sources of maps and related information.

Of necessity, this book is based on established practice and explains maps as they exist, not as they might be designed by you or me or anyone else. Therefore, do not expect any hitherto unknown cartographic devices to come to light here. The distinctive feature of the book is that the particular range of subjects included is covered in a single volume for the first time. The text is freely drawn from material already published in technical journals, special reports, leaflets, instruction manuals, and other similar sources. Likewise, the illustrations come from material already published; the map samples used as illustrations are, unless otherwise noted, taken from the Geological Survey 1:24,000-scale 7.5-minute quadrangle map series.

Existing maps and related material, with few exceptions, refer to measurements in customary (inch-pound) units rather than metric units, although the change to metric units (SI) on certain new maps is proceeding rapidly. In a number of instances where the statement of

quantities in both systems would serve no practical purposes, we have dispensed with the exercise of stating quantities in both metric and customary units. A table of metric equivalents for customary linear and areal measurements is given on page viii.

In many places I have changed the wording of previously published material only to the extent needed to adapt it to the new context. For the use of these materials I offer acknowledgment of sources (in the "Selected References"), and I expect that the original authors will be pleased that their expositions are used without significant change.

Finally, I must warn that practices change. Discrepancies between what appears on a map and what is described in this book may result from changes in conditions, materials, or practices. In particular, map colors may differ in hue and intensity; the process used in reproducing the illustrations in this text gives some degradation in quality from the original printing of some of the maps illustrated.

In this second edition of "Maps for America," a number of changes have been made in the text. Some of these changes entail the correction of typographical errors or omissions in the first printing; other changes are intended to update or improve statements presented in the first printing. In addition, certain illustrations have been replaced by more suitable ones, or the original illustrations have been reprocessed to obtain a better quality of reproduction. Cartography is a well-established science, but it is also an art and, therefore, subject to human judgment, discretion, and taste. Considering the dynamic nature of both the technology and the art of cartography, we need to remember that this book discusses the 1981 condition of "Maps for America." For tomorrow, we know only that it will be something else.

MORRIS M. THOMPSON

1982
U.S. Geological Survey

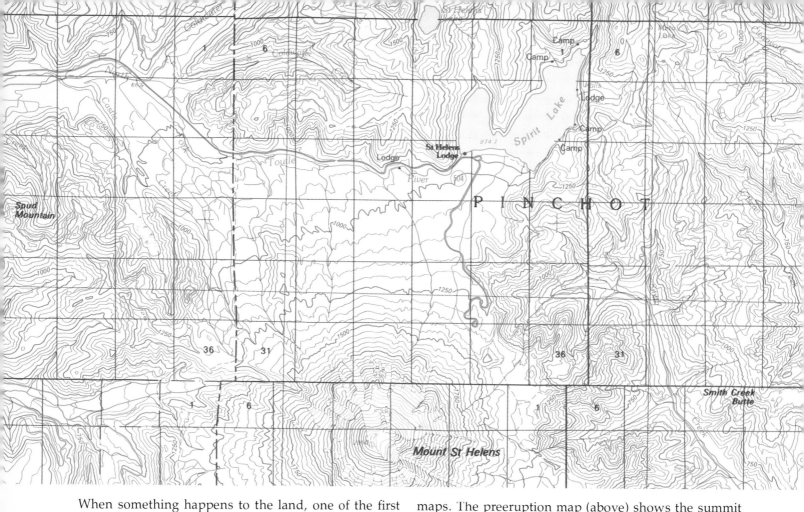

When something happens to the land, one of the first things people reach for is a good topographic map. The enormous change in the configuration of Mount St. Helens, caused by the catastrophic eruption of May 19, 1980, is graphically shown by these two topographic maps. The preeruption map (above) shows the summit elevation to be 2,950 meters (9,677 feet), while the post-eruption map (below) shows the highest elevation to be about 2,550 meters (8,364 feet).

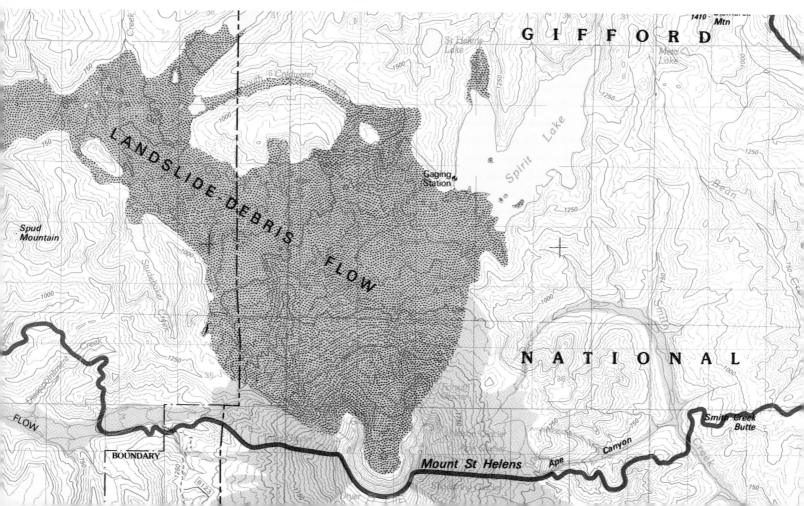

Second Edition

MAPS for America

Cartographic Products of the
U.S. Geological Survey and Others

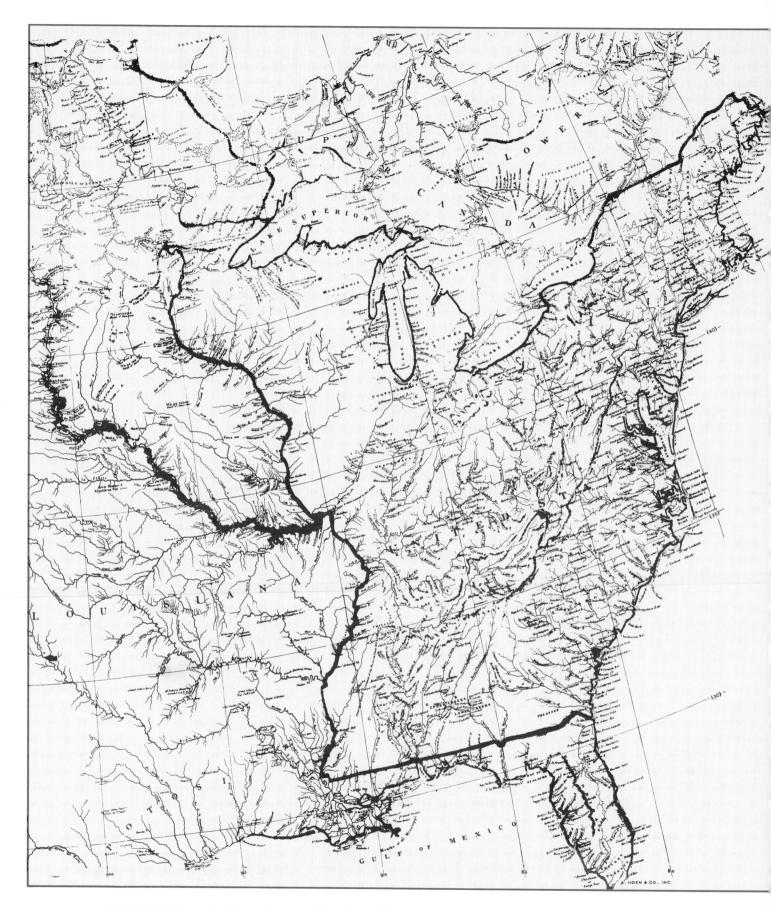

FIGURE 1. Drawn by Aaron Arrowsmith and entitled "A Map Exhibiting all the New Discoveries in the Interior Part of North America," this 1814 edition is considered an outstanding example of early American mapping. *(Reproduction courtesy of the Carnegie Institution of Washington.)*

1:

Development of American Mapping

" . . . the Federal Government formally recognized [in 1807] a new responsibility: The development and dissemination of maps and charts to promote the safety and welfare of the people."

Survey of the Coast

When President Thomas Jefferson signed a bill on February 10, 1807, establishing the Survey of the Coast, the Federal Government formally recognized a new responsibility: The development and dissemination of maps and charts to promote the safety and welfare of the people (fig. 1). The primary motivation in the enactment of this legislation was an urgent need to provide safety for mariners, ships, passengers, and cargoes. The waterborne commerce of the Atlantic Coast was the young Nation's lifeblood; but without complete information on the location of reefs, wrecks, and other navigational hazards, shipwrecks were all too frequent (fig. 2). Because the new Survey was important to the economic well-being of the Nation, as well as to the safety of its citizens, it was placed under the Treasury Department which was then headed by Albert Gallatin. The organization retained the name Survey of the Coast until 1836 when it was renamed U.S. Coast Survey. From 1878 until 1970 it was known as the U.S. Coast and Geodetic Survey, the name which appears on thousands of maps and charts produced during those 92 years. In 1970, the organization was incorporated into the National Oceanic and Atmospheric Administration, Department of Commerce, and the name was changed to National Ocean Survey.

With the establishment of the Survey of the Coast, the first requirement was to select a qualified person to head the agency. On the basis of proposals for organizing the Survey submitted by several men of high scientific reputation, President Jefferson appointed Ferdinand R. Hassler as the first Superintendent. This was a fortunate appointment, for Hassler was a man of inventive genius, keen insight, and rare initiative, who established and maintained extremely high standards. Thus, the Survey of the Coast began with a firm foundation upon which it and its descendant agencies have built a continuing tradition of careful and accurate operation.

Ferdinand Hassler, often called the "father of the Coast Survey," was a Swiss engineer who came to the United States in 1805 to become a professor of mathematics at the new U.S. Military Academy at West Point. The proposal which led to his appointment in 1807 to head the Survey of the Coast called for dividing the agency into three branches—geodesy, topography (of the coast), and hydrography. As the geodetic (precision surveying) operation controlled the value of the topographic and hydrographic operations, he assigned first priority to geodesy.

Because of lack of funds, the disruption of the War of 1812, and political juggling of the agency, the Survey of the Coast was unable to mount a substantial program until 1832. At that time, Hassler returned from a 14-year break in his superintendency, and significant work was undertaken in all three branches. The available techniques (fig. 3) were crude by today's standards—geodesy by huge, clumsy theodolites and astronomical instruments, topography by planetable, and hydrography by lead-line soundings from a sailing vessel—but the results were excellent because of the rigid requirements of Hassler's directives. By the time Hassler died in 1843, Coast Survey triangulation extended from Rhode Island to Chesapeake Bay, embracing an area of 9,000 mi² (23,300 km²) containing a network of 1,200 geodetic stations. Topographic mapping was completed along 1,600 mi (2,575 km) of shoreline. Completed hydrographic surveys included New York Bay, Long Island Sound, Delaware Bay, and the Delaware River. Hassler's legacy was a scientifically sound base upon which succeeding generations of the Coast Survey could build (fig. 4).

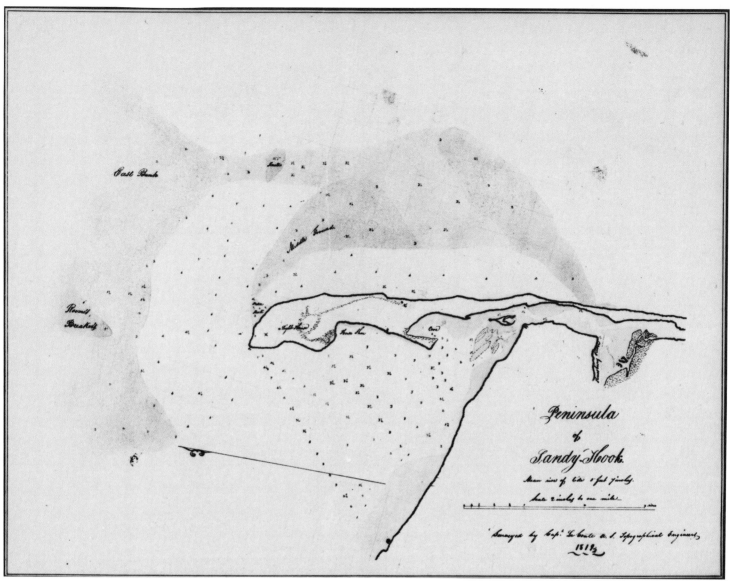

FIGURE 2. The survey work for this early map of Sandy Hook was performed during the period when Ferdinand Hassler was the Superintendent of the Survey of the Coast.

The heads of the Coast Survey who followed Hassler gave form and direction to his plan. As the country grew, the task of coastal mapping expanded tremendously; for example, when Alaska was purchased in 1867, the length of our tidal shoreline increased by 33,904 mi (54,563 km), nearly doubling the total survey job. To meet the growing need, geodetic control, topographic mapping, and hydrographic surveys were stepped up in all coastal areas. Innumerable technical improvements were implemented to keep pace with the explosion in mapping demand. The fleet of sailing vessels (fig. 5) used at first for hydrographic surveys was augmented with steam-powered survey ships. New kinds of bottom samplers, deep-sea thermometers, and depth lines were introduced. A new automatic recording tide gage was placed in operation. A new method of determining latitude with the zenith telescope produced greater accuracy. The newly invented telegraph permitted the determination of longitude differences by flashing time signals between distant points. These are but a few of the many technical changes that marked the growth of the Coast Survey.

FIGURE 3. William Young's transit, the first to be made in the United States, Philadelphia, 1831.

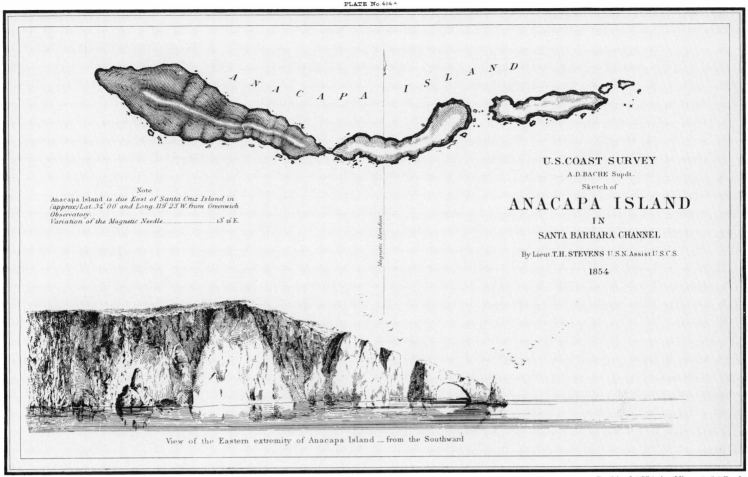

U.S.COAST SURVEY

A.D.BACHE Supdt.

Sketch of

ANACAPA ISLAND

IN

SANTA BARBARA CHANNEL

By Lieut. T.H. STEVENS U.S.N. Assist U.S.C.S.

1854

Note

Anacapa Island *is due East of Santa Cruz Island in (approx.) Lat. 34° 00' and Long. 119° 23' W. from Greenwich Observatory.*
Variation of the Magnetic Needle _____ 13° 21' E.

Magnetic Meridian

View of the Eastern extremity of Anacapa Island — from the Southward

Dr⁰ᵍ by W.B. M°Murtrie   Engᵍ by J.A.Whistler J.Young & C.A.Knight

FIGURE 4. U.S. Coast Survey chart of Anacapa Island, 1854.

FIGURE 5. Brig *Washington*, the U.S. Coast Survey's first hydrographic survey vessel, 1840 (*above*); and the National Oceanic and Atmospheric Administration Ship *Surveyor*, 1977 (*right*).

During the Civil War, unprecedented demands for maps and charts strained the resources of the Coast Survey. Annual chart production grew from a pre-war count of less than 10,000 copies to 66,000 copies by 1863. The Coast Survey performed defense surveys of the areas around Washington, Baltimore, St. Louis, Philadelphia, and other cities. Coast Survey maps played important roles in such operations as Grant's running of the batteries at Vicksburg and Sherman's march to the sea.

Following the Civil War, the Coast Survey embarked on an era of great expansion and continuous improvements in equipment and techniques that extends to the present day (fig. 5). In the meantime, along with continuing needs for coastal and geodetic surveys, new needs were developing for maps of the interior of the country.

Early Surveys of the West

Prior to the Civil War, the Federal Government conducted limited surveys in the vast hinterland between the coasts. The earliest surveys, usually under the sponsorship of the Army, were exploratory in nature, partly to extend geographic knowledge of the country and partly to gather information for military purposes. Early survey projects included the explorations of Lewis and Clark in the Northwest (1804–06), the Zebulon Pike expedition to the Rocky Mountains (1805–07), the Stephen H. Long expedition to the Rocky Mountains (1819–20), the geologically oriented field trips of George W. Featherstonhaugh to the Ozark Mountains (1834–35), and the examination of the mineral lands of the Upper Mississippi Valley by David Dale Owen (1839–40, 1847–49) and other geologists. In the 1840's and 1850's, the Corps of Topographical Engineers Office of Explorations and Surveys carried out surveys for wagon roads, railroad routes to the Pacific, and international boundaries.

The westward migration that followed the Civil War spawned an urgent need for detailed information about the resources and the natural features of the western portion of the country. Responding to this need, Congress authorized four Federal territorial surveys to explore various parts of the West. These surveys, known as the King, Hayden, Powell, and Wheeler Surveys, each named after its leader, operated as follows:

1. *GEOLOGICAL EXPLORATION OF THE FORTIETH PARALLEL* (*King Survey*). The Act of March 2, 1867 (14 Stat. L., 457) provided for a geologic and topographic survey of the territory between the Rocky Mountains and the Sierra Nevada Mountains, including alternate routes for the proposed Pacific Railroad. Although under the jurisdiction of the War Department,

the director (Clarence King) and his scientific assistants were civilians. Results were published in 1870–80 in seven volumes, eight annual reports, and an atlas.

2. *GEOLOGICAL AND GEOGRAPHICAL SURVEY OF THE TERRITORIES* (*Hayden Survey*). The Act of March 2, 1867 (14 Stat. L., 471, sec. 2) provided for a geologic survey of Nebraska, under the direction of the Commissioner of the General Land Office. F. V. Hayden was assigned to this work and subsequently was designated U.S. Geologist for the territories of Colorado and New Mexico; the survey's scope was extended by the Congress to include all the territories, and work was done in New Mexico, Colorado, Wyoming, Montana, and Idaho. Although primarily geological, the Hayden Survey also included topography, paleontology, ethnology, philology, botany, and allied sciences. Results were published in a series of volumes, issued from 1867 to 1883.

3. *GEOGRAPHICAL AND GEOLOGICAL SURVEY OF THE ROCKY MOUNTAIN REGION* (*Powell Survey*). In 1867, John Wesley Powell began his explorations in the West. On July 11, 1868, a joint resolution of the Congress was approved (15 Stat. L., 253), which authorized the Secretary of War to issue rations for 25 men of Powell's expedition to explore the Colorado River (fig. 6). Additional appropriations were provided in 1870–73, with the expedition coming under the control of the Smithsonian Institution. After the completion of the Colorado River expedition, Powell was authorized by the Act of June 23, 1874 (18 Stat. L., 707) to continue the survey in Utah under the direction of the Secretary of the Interior; subsequent appropriation acts extended the survey to the "Rocky Mountain region." The survey covered southern Wyoming, central and southern Utah, southeastern Nevada, and northern Arizona. Although primarily geographical, the survey established geodetic points and included work in topography, ethnology, geology, botany, paleontology, and related sciences. Results of this survey were published in reports by Powell, Gilbert, and Dutton.

4. *GEOGRAPHICAL SURVEYS WEST OF THE ONE HUNDREDTH MERIDIAN* (*Wheeler Survey*). The Act of June 10, 1872 (17 Stat. L., 367) authorized a "continuance of the military and geographical surveys and explorations west of the one hundredth meridian of longitude," under the War Department's jurisdiction, with Lt. George M. Wheeler of the Engineer Corps in charge. This survey included the western parts of the Dakotas, Nebraska, Kansas, and Texas; the Rocky Mountain States; and California. Although mainly geographical or topographical, this survey was made to obtain:

FIGURE 6. John Wesley Powell's Grand Canyon survey party negotiating Colorado River rapids, about 1870.

. . . there remained one more step necessary to give the highest efficiency and most harmonious balance to the National geological work. It was the discontinuance of the several Geological Surveys under personal leadership, and the foundation of a permanent bureau charged with the investigation and elucidation of the geological structure and mineral resources and productions of the United States.

The Hayden-Wheeler rivalry precipitated a hearing in 1874 before the House Committee on Public Lands, focusing on the question of whether it would be most practicable to consolidate the western surveys or restrict the geographic limits of each. There followed a 5-year period of proposals, counterproposals, and acrimonious debate. In the end, President Hayes signed the bill on March 3, 1879, which discontinued the three remaining territorial surveys and gave birth to the U.S. Geological Survey.

With the establishment of the Geological Survey an accomplished fact, the controversy shifted to the appointment of a Director. After considerable political maneuvering by supporters of King and Hayden, Clarence King was appointed as the first Director.

Topographic Mapping

When Clarence King assumed his position as Director, he realized that the legislation establishing the Geological Survey did not define in detail the duties of the new organization. After discussing these functions with members of Congress, King concluded that the intention of Congress was to begin a rigid scientific classification of the lands of the national domain for the general information of the people of the country and to produce a series of land maps which would show all those features upon which the intelligent agriculturists, mining engineers, and timbermen might hereafter base their operations and which obviously would be of the highest value to all students of the political economy and resources of the United States. Accordingly, topographic mapping was included in the work of the Geological Survey. From 1879 to 1888, Survey funds were allotted for mapping surveys. Since 1889, Congress has made annual appropriations to the Survey specifically for topographic surveys.

Major John Wesley Powell, who succeeded King as Director in 1881, proposed to Congress that a 20-year mapping program be authorized and financed in order to provide a sound framework for scientific study and national resource development. Although this 20-year program did not receive specific Congressional approval, the impetus given to the topographic mapping program by King and Powell determined the eventual direction of Geological Survey mapping activities.

. . . at the same time and as far as practicable without greatly increasing the cost, all the information necessary before the settlement of the country, concerning the branches of mineralogy and mining, geology, paleontology, zoology, botany, archeology, ethnology, philology, and ruins (Chief of Engineers, 1878).

This survey was discontinued in 1879, and its results were published in 1875-89 under varying titles.

U.S. Geological Survey

In the early 1870's a bitter rivalry arose between Hayden and Wheeler, mainly over personal prestige and appropriations. As Clarence King (1880, p. 4) later described the situation:

The earliest maps produced by the Survey were published in quadrangle form at a scale of 1:250,000 for 1-degree maps and 1:125,000 for 30-minute maps (see p. 21–23). Gradually, the scale of much of the mapping was increased to meet demands for more detailed mapping. In 1894, for example, the Survey map output covered 35,650 mi² (92,333 km²), of which 66 percent were 15-minute maps at a scale of 1:62,500, 31 percent were 30-minute maps at a scale of 1:125,000, and 3 percent were 1-degree maps at a scale of 1:250,000. The scale of 1:62,500 continued as the prevailing scale until the 1950's, when a continuing requirement for more detail resulted in a shift to a standard scale of 1:24,000, although maps at other scales continued to be published for some areas.

The pioneer Geological Survey mapmakers worked with crude procedures, such as tape-and-compass traverse and elevation determination by aneroid barometer. The accuracy of these surveys later was increased by the introduction of improved planetables equipped with telescopic alidades with vertical-angle arcs (fig. 7). The Survey was authorized by Congress, in 1896, to determine elevations by the use of leveling instruments and to set permanent bench marks for the control of mapping. Transportation of men and equipment presented a difficult and costly aspect of the mapping procedure. Many of the areas to be mapped could be reached only by means of strenuous effort via packtrain (fig. 8).

FIGURE 7. Mapping with planetable and telescopic alidade, early 1900's.

FIGURE 8. U.S. Geological Survey packtrain carrying men and equipment up a steep slope for mapping the Mount Goddard, Calif., quadrangle, 1907.

FIGURE 9. Photographer and pilot (*right*) preparing to take off on an aerial photography mission, about 1922. Camera (*on ground*) was installed on a swivel mount (*on far side of cockpit, not visible*) for taking either vertical or oblique photographs. (Courtesy W. Sidney Park, the pilot on this mission.)

During World War I, many Survey topographers were commissioned for duty with the Army Corps of Engineers. Some of these officers played important roles in developing techniques for using aerial photography for intelligence purposes. Returning to the Survey after the war, these topographers applied their interest in aerial photography to its potential use in the civilian topographic mapping program. Throughout the 1920's, they experimented with applications of the relatively new science of photogrammetry and succeeded in making a few maps from aerial photographs (fig. 9).

Meanwhile, Congress recognized the need for increased production of topographic maps by passing the Temple Act in 1925. This act, strongly supported by engineering organizations and other interested groups, authorized a program for completion of the mapping of the United States in 20 years. Unfortunately, funds were not appropriated in sufficient amount to carry out the program at the authorized rate of progress.

Photogrammetric Applications

A great surge in the application of photogrammetry to mapping occurred in the 1930's. When the Tennessee Valley Authority (TVA) was established in 1933, one of its immediate needs was map coverage of the entire valley. In cooperation with the TVA, the Survey undertook the preparation of planimetric maps of this area, using five-lens aerial photographs (fig. 10) and radial-line plotting methods. The planimetric maps filled the immediate need but there was still a long-range requirement for complete topographic maps. To meet this need, the Survey acquired its first multiplex equipment for photogrammetric mapping using single-lens aerial photographs. The value of these instruments was soon demonstrated, and in 1936 a fully equipped multiplex mapping office (fig. 11) was established in Chattanooga, with a program of topographic mapping of the entire Tennessee River Valley in cooperation with TVA. Thus began a revolutionary swing away from field methods as the basic mapmaking procedure. During the war years of 1941–45, the Survey performed important strategic mapping assignments, using its well-established photogrammetric plant and personnel.

FIGURE 10. Five-lens aerial camera, about 1930.

FIGURE 11. First U.S. Geological Survey multiplex mapping equipment in operation, Chattanooga, Tenn., 1937.

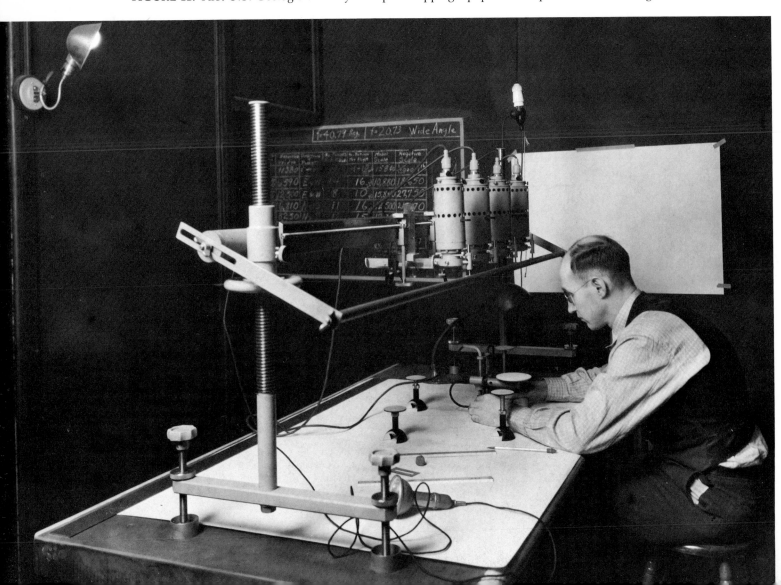

Following World War II, the development of photogrammetric practices by the Survey continued at an ever-increasing pace. The multiplex system was superseded by a succession of improved plotting instruments: the Kelsh plotter, the ER-55 plotter, and various instruments of Swiss, German, and Italian manufacture. The emergence of powerful computer systems led to a revolution in photogrammetric methods for analytically extending survey control, which had been performed by an optical-mechanical analog system. The development by the Survey of the concept of orthophotography and the successful building of a practical orthophotoscope led to the widespread use of a new kind of cartographic product: the orthophotographic map. (See glossary.) New techniques utilizing electronic image correlation for the automation of photogrammetric operations (fig. 12) and the digitization of data made possible the production of cartographic data in numerical form—the digital terrain model. The application of space technology to mapping has resulted in the production of useful small-scale cartographic products from remote-sensing data obtained via space vehicle.

Meanwhile, the great increase in mapping resulting from improved photogrammetric techniques gave rise to increased demand for field-survey control. Here, too, necessity spawned invention. The old systems of measuring distance by tape, stadia, or tacheometer gave way to new systems of electronic distance measurement using microwaves and lasers. Still under development are sophisticated systems based on an inertial navigation package which will automatically record the x, y, and z coordinates at any point as a vehicle proceeds along a given course.

Military Mapping

The country's need for military maps dates from the Revolutionary War when George Washington realized that accurate maps were of prime importance in planning his campaigns. To provide for Washington's map needs, a Military Cartographic Headquarters was established in 1777 at Ringwood, N.J., under the leadership of Robert Erskine, and, later, Simon DeWitt.

Following the Revolutionary War, DeWitt repeatedly sought Congressional appropriations for military mapping, but no funds were forthcoming until the great sea battles of the War of 1812 led to efforts to set up an agency for publishing American aids to navigation. As a result, the Navy Depot of Charts and Instruments was established in 1830, with Lt. Goldsborough as its head. Shortly thereafter (1838) the Corps of Topographical Engineers was activated in the Army under Col. John James Abert.

FIGURE 12. A modern image-correlator mapping machine. This system uses electronic correlation of images to produce orthophotos, contours, and digitized terrain models. The operator communicates with the equipment by means of the console, which displays the image on a cathode ray screen. Editing is accomplished by means of a manual device. The main elements in the system consist of twin scanners (*far left*), an electronic image correlator, a computer, and a magnetic tape input/output device. Not shown in the picture is the printer, which is located in a separate darkroom.

By the time the war with Mexico broke out, the Topographic Corps and the Naval Depot had carried out important work in surveying routes for the transcontinental railroads and in gathering data for charts of the Atlantic and Pacific Oceans. The Vera Cruz campaign in the Mexican War was (for its time) a vast amphibious operation. In preparing for this campaign, the mapmakers of the Army and the Navy learned how to coordinate land map and nautical chart data.

During the Civil War, topographers, cartographers, and hydrographers on both sides of the conflict made important contributions to the military efforts. In 1861, the Union Army carried out the first known application of photographic aerial reconnaissance in the United States by photographing from a tethered balloon all the countryside in Virginia between Richmond and the Chickahominy River. The planning of every major campaign of the war depended on the availability of reliable maps and charts (fig. 13).

The tremendous growth of commerce that followed the Civil War gave rise to a vital need for more and better aids to navigation. The Navy's Hydrographic Office, established in 1866, undertook the compilation of charts of the two oceans and negotiations for the international exchange of data. When the Spanish-American War broke out, American military cartographers had their first, if limited, experience of mapping foreign soil.

In the early 1900's, military mapping became a vital element of the Army Corps of Engineers, and the Navy Hydrographic Office developed a comprehensive program for issuing nautical charts. A perceptive look at the potential of military aerial mapping occurred with the establishment in 1907 of the Aeronautical Division of the Army Signal Corps.

World War I brought a new dimension to American military mapping—the need for extensive mapping of foreign areas. At the same time, the development of the airplane as an advantageous platform for viewing and

FIGURE 13. Aerial reconnaissance was first used by the U.S. Army in 1861. This sketch of rebel camps and batteries on the west bank of the Potomac River below Washington, D.C., was drawn from balloon observations for the Commander of the Union forces.

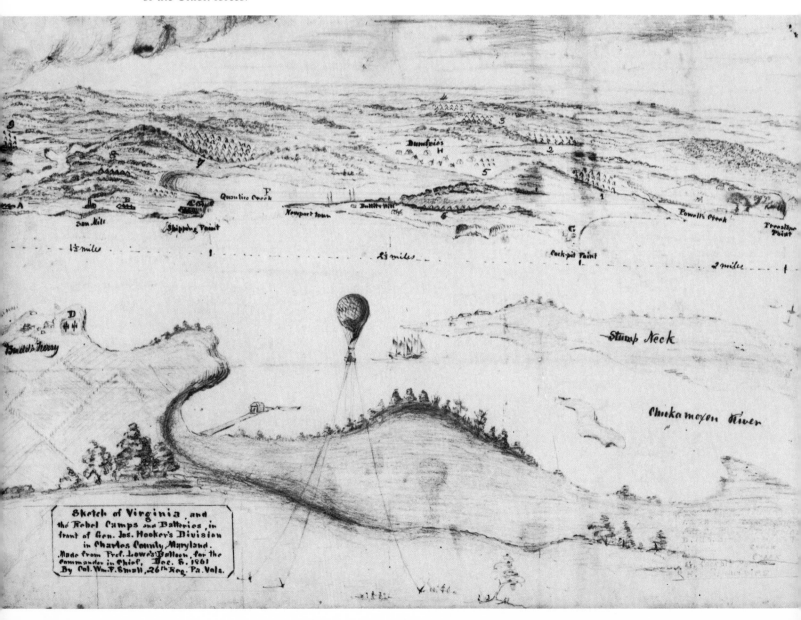

photographing terrain extended immensely the range of practical mapping. The science of photogrammetry could now be applied to produce more, better, and cheaper maps.

With the outbreak of World War II, the need for military maps became truly global and immediate. The civilian mapping agencies of the United States pooled their efforts with those of the Army Map Service (established within the Corps of Engineers early in the war) and the Navy Hydrographic Office, which resulted in a vast production of maps for the war effort, based mostly on ingenious applications of the young science of photogrammetry.

During World War II and immediately thereafter, aeronautical charts for military use were prepared under the sponsorship of the Army Air Corps. In 1951, the Aeronautical Chart and Information Service was established in the U.S. Air Force, thereby formally adding an aeronautical charting arm to the existing arms for land mapping and sea charting. In 1972, the Department of Defense combined its various elements engaged in map production and distribution under one command—the Defense Mapping Agency, comprising the Topographic, Hydrographic, and Aerospace Centers.

Surveys of Public Lands

Public lands are those which, after inuring to the United States, have remained in public ownership, or, after private acquisition, have been returned to public ownership and the status of public land by law.

Surveys of lands owned by the Federal Government have been conducted since 1785 (Cazier, 1976). The initial activity—the establishment of a beginning point where the west boundary of Pennsylvania crosses the north bank of the Ohio River—was carried out under the supervision of the Geographer of the United States in compliance with the Ordinance of May 20, 1785. In these early surveys, only the exterior lines of the 6-mile-square (36 mi² or 93 km²) township were surveyed, and only mile corners were established. Township plats were marked by subdivisions into 1-mile-square sections commencing with section 1 in the southeast corner of the township and running from south to north in each file of sections to section 36 in the northwest corner of the township.

Under the Act of May 18, 1796, a Surveyor General was appointed with responsibility for surveying the public lands northwest of the Ohio River. The act specified that half of the townships were to be subdivided into 2-mile-square blocks (4 mi² or 10.4 km²). Further-more, the rule for numbering of sections within each township was changed to the system followed today in which the sections are numbered beginning with section 1 in the northeast corner, and proceeding west and east alternately through the township to section 36 in the southeast corner. Subsequent legislation modified the system of surveys to provide for additional subdivision (640 acres per section) and gradual refinement of the system to its present form. At first, the Surveyor General was under the supervision of the Secretary of the Treasury; later, the office came under the direction of the Commissioner of the General Land Office. Eventually a Surveyor General was appointed for each of many public-land States and Territories, with the same duties as the original Surveyor General.

The Act of July 4, 1836, placed the overall direction of the public-land surveys under the principal Clerk of Surveys in the General Land Office, Department of the Interior. The General Land Office continued to function for more than a century, until it was finally abolished and replaced by the Bureau of Land Management which was established in the Department of the Interior on July 16, 1946. The Bureau of Land Management's Division of Cadastral Surveys exercises technical supervision, through State and service center directors, of surveying the public lands.

The tangible products of a public-land survey consist of the field notes and the plat. These provide a technical record of the survey procedure. They also provide a report on the character of the land, soil, and timber traversed by the survey, and the topographic features along line, with accurate connections showing the relation of the rectangular surveys to other surveys, to natural objects, and to improvements. Occasionally the plat may constitute the entire record of the survey and, hence, has great economic and legal significance.

Other Federal Mapping Programs

In recent years, various government agencies have been faced with special requirements for maps in connection with their specific missions. Many of these maps are highly specialized and quite different from the standard products of the Geological Survey, the National Ocean Survey, the Bureau of Land Management, and the Defense Mapping Agency. In a great many instances, the existing maps, such as those of the Geological Survey, are suitable to meet the entire need of the other agency or to serve as bases for additional cartographic data. In other instances, when suitable standard products are not available, the other agency sometimes funds an accelerated Geological Survey program or undertakes its own mapping program to meet an urgent need.

Federal agencies performing specialized mapping when necessary to meet specific needs include:

Bonneville Power Administration
Bureau of the Census
Bureau of Indian Affairs
Bureau of Mines
Bureau of Reclamation
Department of Energy
Department of State
Environmental Protection Agency
Federal Communications Commission
Federal Energy Regulatory Commission
Federal Highway Administration
Federal Insurance Administration
Heritage Conservation and Recreation Service
    (formerly Bureau of Outdoor Recreation)
International Boundary Commission, United States
    and Canada
International Boundary and Water Commission,
    United States and Mexico
Mississippi River Commission
National Aeronautics and Space Administration
National Park Service
Soil Conversation Service
Tennessee Valley Authority
U.S. Army Corps of Engineers
U.S. Coast Guard
U.S. Fish and Wildlife Service
U.S. Forest Service

In each of the agencies, a cartographic base was needed as a medium for planning and carrying out the broad mission of the agency, and this need could not be met in a timely manner by maps already available. As a result, separate special mapping programs have been developed.

State, Regional, and Local Mapping Programs

In recent years the increasing complexity of the technical programs of public administration has produced a new recognition of the vital role of maps for the States, regional planning commissions, and local jurisdictions. If the requirement is for maps of the types produced by Federal mapping agencies, the completion of the needed maps can be speeded up through cooperative programs. Federal agencies (for example, U.S. Geological Survey and National Ocean Survey) cooperate with local jurisdictions on projects that contribute to national mapping and charting, including special products such as geodetic control, as well as standard series maps. States, their political subdivisions, and their agencies may enter into cooperative agreements in which map production costs are split between the State agency and the Federal Government. The cost of publication normally is borne by the Federal Government. The effect of cooperative agreements is to expedite mapping of areas of particular interest to the cooperating agency, since the cooperators help select new project areas.

If the needed maps cannot be obtained through Federal assistance, States and other jurisdictions must use other means. Some States have their own mapping organizations, some obtain their maps by contract with commercial mapping organizations, and others use a combination of these two methods.

Commercial Mapping

Since the early days of the Union, private mapmakers have produced and sold maps, usually of local areas. These efforts have generally been very limited, however, because of the skill and long hours of labor required to develop a map manuscript. Only a few companies have been able to support mapping enterprises on a national or international scale.

The first extensive opportunity for American commercial cartographers came with the Nation's westward expansion in the latter part of the 19th century. As the railroads pushed westward, the lands along the rail lines assumed a new value and a new potential for profitable development, which in turn gave rise to a special kind of mapping that emphasized the railroad and its stations.

Road Maps

With the development of the automobile, and a universal thirst for mobility, the 20th century saw a cartographic phenomenon that is peculiar to America: the free road map. Every major oil company produced its own series of highway maps, thereby providing a fertile market for commercial cartographers. In the 1970's, however, dramatic changes in the petroleum supply and resultant cost increases have ended the oil companies' eagerness to supply free road maps.

Government and Private Cartographic Cooperation

In any event, commercial mapping enterprises depend to a large extent on government maps and source data as a basis for their cartographic products. The exception is the large-scale map for engineering or planning purposes, which can be efficiently produced by highly competent engineering, mapping, or photogrammetric organizations. For small- and medium-scale commercial mapping, however, government maps are generally recognized as the indispensable beginning point. As one officer (Voisin, 1976) of a prominent commercial mapping organization states:

A strong and effective commercial cartographic environment which the United States enjoys today could not exist without a strong and healthy national mapping program. Without this, the cartographic publisher would be deprived of his most important basic ingredient, source documentation, for it is here where it all begins. Aerial photography, topographic coverage, census data—all are fundamental to the skilled cartographer who, without them, could not proceed. The equally important aspect of timely revision must be provided as well, and serious cartographers are keenly concerned that appropriate levels of funding are provided to maintain the national programs, both for original mapping and in revision.

General Atlases

The same observer also offers an interesting statement regarding the production of general atlases in America:

The general atlas has been one of the prime services provided by the private mapping sector in America. The spectacular success of mass-geography with maps experienced by the National Geographic Society's magazine and atlas publishing program is renowned. This successful formula has been unique in the world, although efforts now in Mexico and Brazil are being made to emulate the pattern. Three American map publishers today share in the general atlas publishing scene, General Drafting, Hammond Map Company and Rand McNally. While atlases may appear with the imprint of another publisher, they will usually be found to be the work of one of these houses or possibly from a company outside the United States.

It is noteworthy that only in America do private mapping companies have complete freedom to use government cartographic products as a base for further cartographic development without the payment of fees of any kind (other than the price of a copy of the map). In some countries only the central cartographic authorities may issue maps. In other countries the national mapping organization holds a copyright on the work, and any mapmaker wishing to adapt it must secure permission and pay fees.

National Mapping Program

The last few decades have witnessed a dramatic increase in the Nation's needs and uses for maps. New kinds of map users have brought forth requirements for new kinds of maps. Local and regional planning commissions and environmental and resource groups have been formed across the land, each with a need for maps to suit a particular purpose. Many of these map needs have been brought about by the country's growing awareness of the impact of the Nation's population on its resources and the effect of expanded resource development on our environment.

Mapmakers are now being called on to produce coastal maps, large-scale urban maps, county maps, land use maps, orthophotographic maps, slope maps, and thematic maps of countless varieties. The availability of data acquired by satellites has spurred a demand for maps giving synoptic representations of the Earth, the Moon, and the planets.

In its continuing program to assure responsiveness to these needs and to improve programing and coordination of mapping in the Federal Government, the Office of Management and Budget sponsored a comprehensive study of the civil agency mapping and surveying programs. This study, carried out by a Federal Mapping Task Force (FMTF) is documented in a full report (Office of Management and Budget, 1973). The report made significant recommendations for Federal mapping, charting, and geodesy program improvements and organizational changes.

In response to the FMTF findings, the Department of the Interior, in 1975, modified, extended, and renamed its National Topographic Program to meet better the basic cartographic data needs of the country. This new program, the National Mapping Program, includes those activities necessary to make available basic map data and a family of general-purpose maps.

The Geological Survey was named by the Department of the Interior as the lead agency for the administration of the National Mapping Program. This includes coordinating, defining, and approving the National Mapping Program categories, and assuring the availability of the resulting map data and materials to users.

Certain of these map-data categories (such as roads, structures, topography, streams, lakes, and shorelines) are identified as base map-data categories. Other map data of public value may also be incorporated into the National Mapping Program and will be identified as nonbase categories. The nonbase categories will be developed and maintained by the responsible agencies and will be made available under cooperative agreement for the preparation of maps and other forms of cartographic display through the National Mapping Program's coordination and dissemination arrangements.

COLOR COMPOSITE. Detail from Landsat image (combined multispectral scanner–return beam vidicon) of a part of the San Francisco Bay area.

2:

Kinds of Maps and Kinds of Map Data

Map users seek information. It may range from the location of likely fishing spots to the site features for planning a giant hydroelectric plant. So there are many kinds of maps. Samples reproduced throughout this book are ordinarily from the Survey's 1:24,000-scale 7.5-minute quadrangle series.

Most map users have one motive in common: They are seeking information. But the information they seek may range from the location of likely fishing spots to the site features for planning a giant hydroelectric plant. The kind of map needed may be a rough sketch (fig. 14A) showing only a few general features, or it may be an extremely accurate topographic map (fig. 14B) showing all the terrain features of an area in minute detail, or it may be any variety of map lying between or beyond these examples. Map samples reproduced throughout this book are ordinarily taken from the U.S. Geological Survey 1:24,000-scale 7.5-minute quadrangle series. Any exceptions are noted on that particular map.

Americans are usually familiar with road and street maps (showing how to get from place to place), political maps (showing the boundaries of countries and subdivisions and the locations of communities), and physiographic maps (showing the locations of mountains, valleys, rivers, lakes, and seashores). They are less likely to know of the many map products that are needed for technical and economic planning and countless specialized uses. The primary emphasis in *Maps for America* is on topographic maps and map data of the kind produced by the U.S. Geological Survey; however, other kinds of maps are considered.

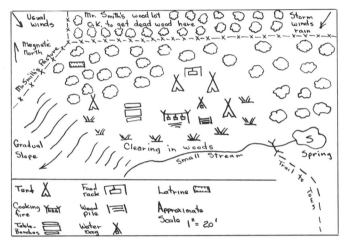

FIGURE 14. The sketch above (reduced) has the essential attributes of a topographic map; it has a legend, a scale, and a north arrow and presents information on relief, hydrology, woodland, and natural resources (*Handbook for Boys*, Boy Scouts of America). The portion below of a modern topographic map accurately shows all terrain features in detail.

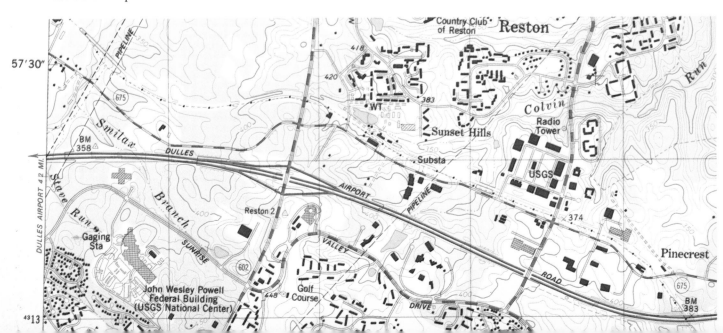

In the changing setting of modern times, the demand for conventional line maps continues, but it is accompanied by a burgeoning parallel demand for new cartographic products. These products include not only new types of line maps at a broad range of scales, but also accurate photomaps, remote-sensor maps, and cartographic data presented in digital form. The types of maps that can be made for different uses are practically unlimited. Generally, however, maps can be classified in one or more of the following categories: Planimetric, topographic, thematic, digital, line, or photographic.

Planimetric Maps

Planimetric maps present the horizontal position of selected features but do not show relief in measurable form. Examples of planimetric maps are base, cadastral, line-route, and outline maps.

Base maps are used to plan or to compile data for the production of specialized maps.

Cadastral maps show the boundaries of subdivisions of land (usually with bearings and lengths and the areas of individual tracts) for describing and recording ownership. One type of cadastral map is the plat, which often constitutes, or is an essential part of, a legal description of a parcel of land. The Bureau of Land Management is the major single producer of land plats.

Line-route maps are used by utility companies. They show the routes and type of construction of pipelines or wire circuits, plus the locations of facilities such as switchboards, valves, and pumping stations.

Outline maps present only the information needed to provide a basis for the compilation of additional data. Outline maps often show only national and State boundaries and major drainage systems.

Topographic Maps

In addition to the features shown on planimetric maps, topographic maps portray the shape and elevation of the terrain, usually by contours, formlines, shading, color gradients, or hachures. Any map portraying relief by one of these conventions can be called a **hypsometric map.** A map on which the elevations are referred to a specific datum is called a **hypsographic map.** Standard topographic maps are in both categories.

In the United States the best known topographic maps are the Geological Survey quadrangle series, which range in scale from 1:20,000 to 1:250,000. The **quadrangle series** are used for various purposes, such as selecting industrial sites, planning highways, routing utility lines, selecting damsites, and locating communication facilities. They are also popular in recreation for hunting, fishing, hiking, and camping.

Other types of topographic maps are engineering, flood-control, landscape, and bathymetric. **Engineering maps** are used for planning and for estimating project costs. **Flood-control and storm evacuation maps** are special-purpose topographic maps used to study areas subject to flooding. **Landscape maps** are used by architects to plan buildings that will conform to the topography of the site. Gardeners use landscape maps to maintain parks, playgrounds, and private estates. **Bathymetric maps** show water depths and underwater topography. Water depth ranges are generally portrayed by various colors or shades. Usually, uniform depth intervals are connected by solid lines called bottom contour lines. The Geological Survey and the National Ocean Survey produce bathymetric maps.

Special Role of Topographic Maps

Because of their vital role in the development of the Nation's economy and environment, topographic maps are reviewed in greater depth than other kinds of maps, important though these others may be. Some of the uses of conventional topographic maps are indicated in figure 15.

Topographic maps are classified generally by publication scale, and each scale series fulfills a range of map needs. Map scale defines the relationship between the measurements of the features as shown on the map and as they exist on the Earth's surface. Scale is generally stated as a ratio or fraction—1:24,000 or 1/24,000. The numerator, customarily 1, represents map distance, and the denominator, a large number, represents horizontal ground distance. Thus the scale 1:24,000 states that any unit, such as 1 inch or 1 cm on the map, represents 24,000 of the same unit on the ground. Figure 16 shows the contrast between maps of large, intermediate, and small scale.

Large-scale maps, such as the 1:24,000-scale maps, are especially useful for highly developed areas or rural areas where detailed information is needed for engineering planning or similar purposes.

Intermediate-scale maps, ranging in scale from 1:50,000 to 1:100,000, cover larger areas and are especially suited for land management and planning.

Small-scale maps, such as those made at scales of 1:250,000, 1:500,000, and 1:1,000,000, cover very large areas on a single sheet and are useful for comprehensive views of extensive projects or for regional planning.

Thematic Maps

Thematic maps are also called geographic, special-purpose, or distribution maps. They emphasize a single topic, such as geology, climatology, or crop distribution, and the entire map is devoted to presenting this distribution or concentration. Geographers use thematic maps to show the distribution of subjects such as population,

FIGURE 15. Some uses of conventional topographic maps.

FIGURE 16. Comparison at various scales of maps covering the Gorham, Maine, area.

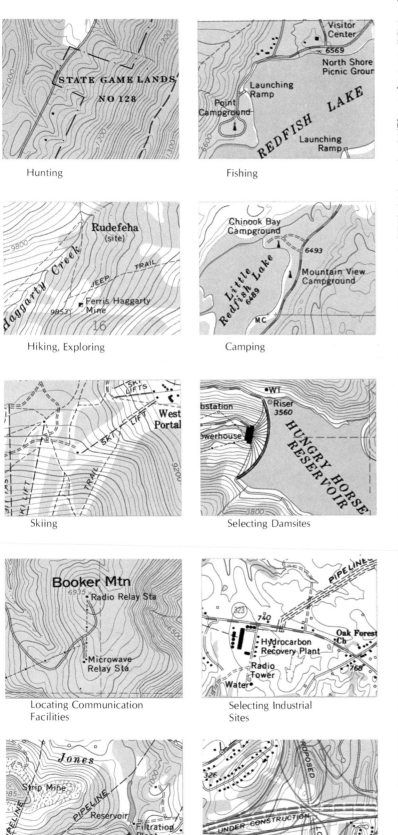

Hunting

Fishing

Hiking, Exploring

Camping

Skiing

Selecting Damsites

Locating Communication Facilities

Selecting Industrial Sites

Routing Pipelines

Planning Highways

1:24,000 scale,
1 inch=2,000 feet.
Area shown,
1 square mile.

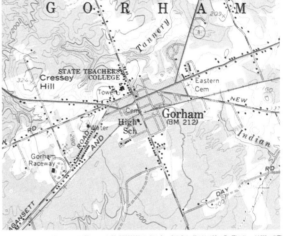

1:62,500 scale,
1 inch=about 1 mile.
Area shown,
6¾ square mile

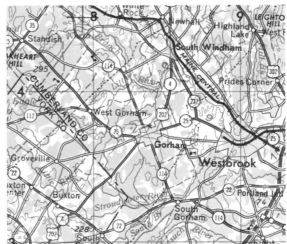

1:250,000 scale
1 inch=about 4 miles.
Area shown,
107 square mile

1:1,000,000 sca
1 inch=nearly 16 miles.
Area shown,
1,712 square m

languages, crop production, soil, climate, vegetation, land use, and industry. The distributions are shown by several methods, including dot patterns, choropleths, or isopleths.

Dots are used to represent quantities such as 1,000 people or 500 acres of corn. The size and value of dots are selected so that the dots coalesce in areas of densest distribution. Sometimes dots of varying sizes are used for different quantities.

Choropleth maps are thematic maps in which sections determined by civil boundaries or other arbitrary divisions are colored, shaded, dotted, or hatched to make darker or lighter areas in proportion to the density of a given subject's distribution. Because of this arbitrary delineation of thematic sections, choropleth maps can be somewhat misleading since they show an abrupt change between sections where in fact the change is gradual.

Isopleth maps are used to show numerical values for continuous distributions (such as rainfall and temperature) rather than discrete variables. Isopleths are lines connecting places of equal value and have the same inherent virtues and deficiencies as contour lines. They provide exact information throughout their entirety but do not provide values in the intervals. Tinting or shading is sometimes used between isopleths.

Types of thematic maps include geologic, forestry, soil, land use, slope, and historical. **Geologic maps** portray geologic conditions in an area. **Forestry maps** show the size, density, kind, and economic values of trees in a given area. **Soil maps** portray soil conservation parameters. **Land use maps** depict land usage by means of colors, letters, or numbers within small areas. **Slope maps** use colors or shades to represent different degrees of slope graphically and are used in studies related to land use. Slopes can be determined mechanically by the distance between contours on a relief map, or they may be generated by computer printout from digital terrain data.

Thematic maps dedicated to the explanation of the past are called **historical maps.** They show such features as battlefields, military routes, and boundary changes. Although all maps are in a sense "historical" because of the time interval between compilation and publication or use, not all historical maps are thematic. Only those intended to illustrate statistics can be classified as thematic.

Digital Maps and Map Data

The development in recent years of powerful data-processing systems has made it possible to store digitized map data in a computer bank and retrieve desired information either in graphic form as a digital map or in numerical form as a body of data. For example, the location and elevation of all bridges in a given area can be obtained from the data bank and automatically plotted on a map or listed in terms of horizontal and vertical coordinates.

Line Maps

Any map produced from scribed, inked, or pasted-on line copy is considered a line drawing or **line map.**

Photomaps

The photomap is an alternative to the line map—it shows nonselective details requiring photointerpretation by the user. Any aerial photographic image can be considered a photomap. However, although aerial photographs are map substitutes because they show surface features, they may contain serious scale distortions caused by camera tilt or topographic relief. Most photomaps include some cartographic enhancement to help the user—perhaps only marginal information, or an overprinted line drawing, or place names.

Image distortions on photographs caused by camera tilt in an aircraft can be removed by a simple rectification process. Distortions caused by relief (the varying heights of ground features) can be removed by an orthophotoscope or other differential-rectification system which produces orthophotographs, correct in scale and relative position. Various cartographic products derived from orthophotographs are defined in the glossary and discussed on pages 135–142.

National Cartographic Programs

National programs of nautical and aeronautical charting, geodetic control, and topographic mapping have long been recognized as the responsibility of the Federal Government, for they produce information that serves the common needs of Federal agencies, State and local governments, and the general public. Cartographic products developed by State and local governments and by private mapmaking organizations are, to a very large extent, based on original surveys and cartographic compilations performed by the Federal Government and made available to the public.

The principal varieties of maps and map data produced by government agencies are outlined in table 1. Information concerning specific maps may be obtained from the publishing agency. Some of the Federal maps are available from the Superintendent of Documents, U.S. Government Printing Office. Addresses of publishing and distributing agencies (with abbreviations keyed to table 1) are given on **page 247.**

TABLE 1. Map products and sources

[Addresses of Federal, State, and other agencies identified by acronyms in this table begin on page 247.]

Products	Producing agency	Available from
Aeronautical charts	NOS	NOS
Boundary information:		
United States and Canada	IBC	IBC
United States and Mexico	IBWC	IBWC
Boundary and annexation surveys of incorporated places with 2,500 or more inhabitants	BC	GPO
Civil subdivisions and reservations	BLM	BLM
State/Federal	DOS	DOS
Census data (social and economic)	BC	GPO
Climatic maps	NWS	NWS
Earthquake hazard maps	USGS	USGS
Federal property maps:		
Water and Power Resources Service	WPRS	WPRS
Fish and Wildlife Service	FWS	FWS
National Aeronautics and Space Administration	NASA	NASA
National forests	FS	FS
National Park Service	NPS	NPS
Military reservations:		
Air Force	USAF	USAF
Army	USA	USA
Coast Guard	USCG	USCG
Marines	USMC	USMC
Navy	USN	USN
State maps of lands administered by Bureau of Land Management	BLM	BLM
U.S. maps of lands administered by Bureau of Land Management	BLM	BLM
Flood-plain maps	DRBC	DRBC
	FIA	FIA
	MRC	MRC
	NOS	FIA
	SCS	SCS
	USCE	USCE
	USGS	USGS
Geodetic control data	NOS	NOS
	USCE	USCE
	USGS	NOS/ NCIC
Geologic maps:		
Coal investigations	USGS	USGS
General geologic	SGA	SGA
	USGS	USGS
Geophysical investigations	NOAA	EDIS
	NOAA	ERL
	USGS	USGS
Mineral investigations	USGS	USGS
Mines	BM	BM
Oil and gas investigations	USGS	USGS
Geographic maps:	NOS	NOS
Land use	USGS	USGS
Highway maps:		
Indian lands	BIA	BIA
Federal lands	FHWA	FHWA
Federally funded roads	FHWA	GPO
Federal primary and secondary	FHWA	GPO
Interstate	FHWA	FHWA
Federal highway maps of the U.S.	FHWA	GPO

Products	Producing agency	Available from
Historical maps and charts	LC / All Federal agencies	LC / NARS
Hydrographic charts and bathymetric maps:	NOS	NOS
	USCE	USCE
	USGS	USGS
Hydrographic surveys	NOS	NOS
	USGS	USGS
Nautical charts	NOS	NOS
	USCE	USCE
Navigable waterways maps	USCE	USCE
River and stream surveys	MRC	MRC
River basin/watershed studies	ERC	ERC
	SCS	SCS
	USGS	USGS
River surveys	WPRS	WPRS
	USGS	USGS
Wildlife and scenic river jurisdiction	BLM	BLM
Hydrologic investigations atlases	USGS	USGS
Indian reservations:		
Land surveys	BIA	GPO
U.S. maps of Indian lands	BIA	GPO
Land plats	BLM	BLM
	BLM	NARS
	NPS	NPS
	USCE	USCE
National Atlas of the U.S.	USGS	USGS
Photographic products:		
Aerial photographs	ASCS	ASCS
	BLM	BLM
	BLM	EDC
	BPA	BPA
	DMA	DMA
	NASA	EDC
	FHWA	FHWA
	FS	EDC
	FS	NCIC
	FWS	EDC
	FWS	NCIC
	NOS	NOS
	NPS	NPS
	SCS	SCS
	USCE	USCE
	FS	FS
	USGS	NCIC/ EDC
Orthophotomaps	BIA	BIA
	NOS	NOS
	USGS	USGS
Space imagery:		
Landsat (ERTS)	NASA	ASCS
	NASA	EDC
	NASA	EDIS
NASA manned spacecraft	NASA	EDC
Nimbus	NWS	NWS
Skylab	NASA	ASCS
	NASA	EDC
Tiros	NWS	NWS
Recreation maps	BLM	BLM
	HCRC	HCRC

TABLE 1. Map products and sources *(continued)*

Products	Producing agency	Available from	Products	Producing agency	Available from
Seismicity maps and charts	ERL	**ERL**	**Miscellaneous data:**		
	USGS	**USGS**	Clinometric (slope) maps	USGS	USGS
Soils	SCS	**SCS**	Gravity survey charts	EDIS	EDIS
				NOS	NOS
Soils—substation quality	BPA	**BPA**		USGS	USGS
Topographic maps	USGS	**USGS**	Income distribution maps	BC	GPO
	MRC	**MRC**	Isogonic charts	USGS	USGS
	NASA	**NASA**	Isomagnetic charts	NOS	NOS
Utilities:			Magnetic charts	EDIS	EDIS
Ground conductivity maps of the U.S.	FCC	**GPO**	National science trail maps	SCS	SCS
Principal electric-facilities maps of the U.S.	ERC	**GPO**	State indexes of fish hatcheries and national wildlife refuges	FWS	FWS
			Storm evacuation maps	NOS	NOS
Principal natural-gas-pipelines maps of the U.S.	ERC	**GPO**	Tree danger (to powerlines) detection maps	BPA	BPA
Water resources development data	USGS	**USGS**	U.S. location maps of fish hatcheries and national wildlife refuges	FWS	FWS

KEY STEP IN MAP PREPARATION. A technician scribes contour lines on coated surface of a plastic sheet.

3:

Characteristics of Geological Survey Maps

As lead agency of the National Mapping Program, the U.S. Geological Survey makes available both basic map data and a family of general-purpose maps for a wide variety of industrial, scientific, commercial, and recreational needs.

The Geological Survey, lead agency of the National Mapping Program, makes available both basic map data and a family of general-purpose maps. As these products are intended for a wide variety of uses—industrial, scientific, commercial, and recreational—the map specifications are designed to satisfy a broad range of public needs.

The National Mapping Program is designed to cover a wide variety of terrain and cultural development. In the areas involved, embracing the United States, Puerto Rico, the Virgin Islands, and other regions of interest, almost every kind of terrain is included—from the Tropics to the Arctic, and from the plains to the mountains. Cultural development ranges from large cities to virtually uninhabitable wasteland. To map all these areas adequately yet economically requires a flexible program that includes several publication scales.

Publication Scales

In map planning, scale is the first consideration and the most important specification. Scale determines the size of the map sheet for a given ground area, the accuracy needed in the surveys, and the amount of detail that can be represented on the map. It is closely related to the contour interval and therefore affects the amount of topographic information that can be shown. Scale directly affects the cost and rate of progress of the work.

Maps in the national topographic map series have been published at the scales shown at the right.

The history of the publication scales for Geological Survey topographic quadrangle maps is graphed in figure 17, which shows that both map scales and production rates have increased in response to modern needs. The trend has been toward the use of larger scales, reflecting the need by map users for more detailed information about the land surface. This need has been caused by the increase in population, construction proj-

ects of various kinds, more intensive and scientific use of land, and other factors. The demand for increased map coverage, which encourages the use of smaller publication scales, however, conflicts with the need for more detail.

The effect of larger scales on the production rate can be plainly seen in figure 17. After the first decade the overall rate declined steadily until around 1930 in spite of wider support for the mapping program and generally greater mapping activity. The wider use of photogrammetric methods brought about a moderate increase in production during the 1930's and early 1940's. The significant increase since 1950 is due to both expanded activity and more efficient mapping procedures.

Inch-pound System	
Scale	*1 inch represents*
1:3,168,000	50 miles
1:2,500,000	40 miles (approx.)
1:1,000,000	16 miles (approx.)
1:500,000	8 miles (approx.)
1:250,000	4 miles (approx.)
1:125,000	2 miles (approx.)
1:63,360	1 mile
1:62,500	1 mile (approx.)
1:31,680	0.5 mile
1:30,000	2,500 feet
1:24,000	2,000 feet

Metric System	
Scale	*1 cm represents*
1:100,000	1.00 km
1:50,000	0.50 km
1:25,000	0.25 km
1:20,000	0.20 km

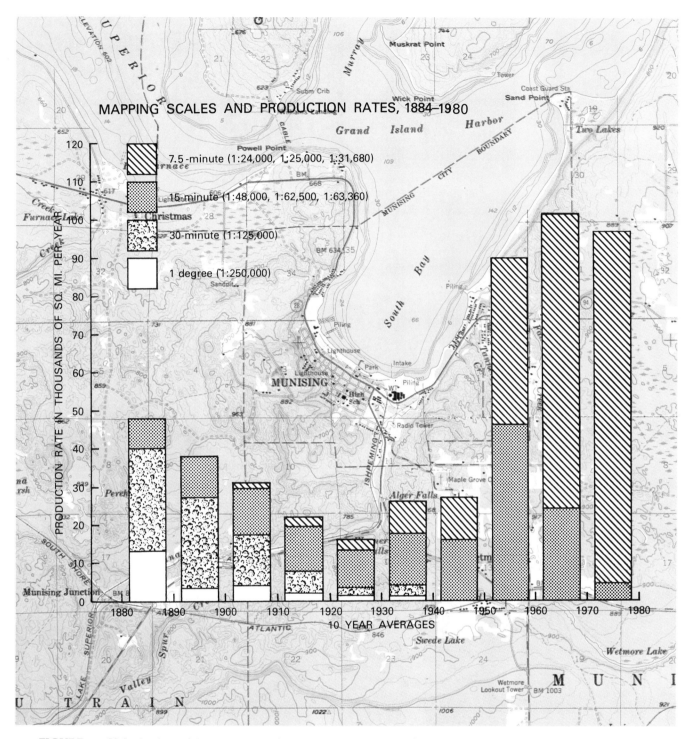

FIGURE 17. U.S. Geological Survey map scales and production rates shown as 10-year averages between 1884 and 1980.

Quadrangle System of Map Layout

Although publication scales have changed, the system of subdividing areas for mapping purposes is the same as originally devised in 1882. The universal coordinate lines of latitude and longitude form the boundaries of four-sided figures called quadrangles, the units of area adopted for topographic mapping. Each map sheet is the map of a quadrangle, and the maps themselves are called quadrangle maps.

The system of subdivision provides quadrangles of different sizes suited to mapping areas at various scales. Generally, the larger quadrangles are bounded by the degree lines of latitude and longitude, and smaller ones are obtained by subdividing the larger, as shown in figure 18*A*. Thus a 1-degree quadrangle comprises four 30-minute quadrangles; a 30-minute quadrangle, four 15-minute quadrangles; and a 15-minute quadrangle, four 7.5-minute quadrangles (see also Appendix B, p. 246). Because the meridians (lines of longitude) converge toward the north in the Northern Hemisphere (see fig. 18*B*), the shape of a quadrangle is actually that of a trapezoid, although the variation from a true rectangle is very small.

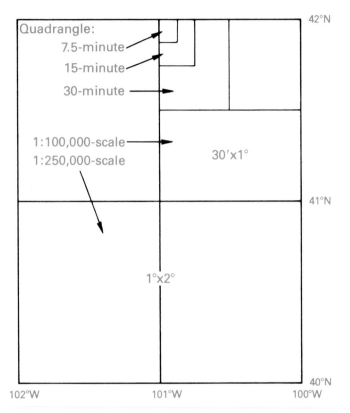

FIGURE 18 *A*. Quadrangle system of map layout.

FIGURE 18 *B*. Meridians encircling the Earth converge toward the North Pole and the South Pole.

Although the quadrangle size in terms of latitude and longitude is generally constant, the ground area covered varies considerably. Quadrangles in the northern part of the country cover a smaller area than those in the southern part; quadrangle size (that is, latitudinal and longitudinal dimensions), therefore, is not equivalent to quadrangle area. The variation in areas for several common quadrangle sizes at latitudes 30° and 49° is tabulated as follows:

Quadrangle size	Area	
	Lat. 30°	*Lat. 49°*
1°×1°	4,109.06 mi² (10,642.42 km²)	3.110.69 mi² (8,056.65 km²)
30'×30'	1,029.85 mi² (2,667.30 km²)	781.60 mi² (2,024.33 km²)
15'×15'	257.78 mi² (667.65 km²)	195.89 mi² (507.35 km²)
7.5'×7.5'	64.48 mi² (167.00 km²)	49.03 mi² (126.98 km²)

There is a systematic relationship between the quadrangle size, and the publication scale at which the map is printed. Considering the quadrangles in order from large to small, both the size and the scale vary in a regular ratio (except for the 7.5-minute quadrangle), as follows:

Not all quadrangles, however, have the same dimensions in latitude as in longitude. For example, the north-south dimension (measuring between lines of latitude) of Alaska maps in the 1:63,360-scale series is 15 minutes, but the east-west dimension (measuring between lines of longitude) varies from 20 to 36 minutes, depending on the latitude. The larger dimensions in longitude are needed to avoid excessively narrow maps in the higher latitudes. A look at a globe will "explain" the problem at once. The regular quadrangle shape is also modified in many areas to include islands and small coastal features. The 1:100,000-scale series is produced in a 30-minute by 1-degree format and the 1:250,000-scale series in a 1- by 2-degree format.

Quadrangle size	1	30'	15'	7.5'
(Ratio)	(1)	(1/2)	(1/4)	(1/8)
Publication scale	1:250,000	1:125,000	1:62,500	1:24,000/ 1:25,000
(Ratio)	(1)	(2)	(4)	(10.4/10)

If the publication scale is doubled and the quadrangle size is halved, the paper area required for printing a map remains the same. Thus the regular ratios between quadrangle sizes and publication scales make it possible to print maps in the first three sizes on paper of the same dimensions, which is a convenience in production, shipping, using, and filing. It is useful, also, to be able to measure distances on different maps and convert to other scales by a simple whole-number multiplication or division.

The regular sequence of scales was not followed, however, for the 7.5-minute series. Instead of twice the 15-minute scale of 1:62,500, two scales were adopted—initially 1:31,680 and later 1:24,000, with 1:24,000 scale remaining standard for this series of maps until the shift to the metric system and to the 1:25,000 scale. A larger sheet of paper is needed for the 1:24,000 scale, but it is useful when the maps are employed directly as planning bases, and the even ratio of inches to feet (1 inch = 2,000 feet at the scale of 1:24,000) is convenient in engineering work based on the customary system of measurement. With the changeover to the metric system, a scale of 1:25,000 (1 cm = 0.25 km) is appropriate.

Series Maps and Special Maps

A map series is a set of maps that conform generally to the same specifications and cover an area or a country in a systematic pattern. The maps of a series have the same format, quadrangle size, and system of symbolization and usually the same scale. Adjacent maps of a series can be combined to form a single large map; the features will match across the joined edges because the symbols and treatment are the same.

Map series may be designated by special titles, quadrangle sizes, or publication scales. A series may be referred to by the quadrangle size only if the quadrangles have the same dimensions in both latitude and longitude; for example, the term "15-minute series" means that all the quadrangles in that series measure 15 minutes by 15 minutes. Otherwise the series must be identified by its scale; for example, "the Alaska 1:63,360-scale series."

Although the great majority of Geological Survey published maps are series maps, some are published at special scales, cover special areas, or have some unique feature so that they cannot be included in a series; these are called "special maps" and are listed individually in map indexes.

Map Sources

Except for a few in the 1:250,000-scale series, maps in the national topographic map series are original Geological Survey products. Until about 1940, field methods—principally planetable sketching—were intensively used to obtain the information shown on the maps, but now the information is obtained by combinations of photogrammetric and field methods. As much information as possible is taken directly from aerial photographs, and the photogrammetrically compiled manuscripts are completed and checked on the ground. Whatever the methods, the maps represent the actual ground conditions as completely and exactly as practicable.

There are many variations in the methods of producing maps, depending on such factors as terrain characteristics, quality of available ground control, kind of product desired, and availability of equipment and manpower. Figure 19 shows a typical sequence of operations for producing a conventional topographic quadrangle map. Figure 20A illustrates stereoscopic aerial photographs of an area to be mapped and figure 20B depicts the principle of photogrammetric mapping with one type of mapping instrument, a double-projection plotter. Modern mapping procedures are described in detail in Slama (1980) and in other technical texts.

Some published maps, especially small-scale maps, are prepared from other maps by selecting and transferring the information by various methods. Small-scale maps prepared in this way are called compiled maps to differentiate them from maps made from original surveys, but the term "compiled" is also widely used now in referring to maps drawn from aerial photographs.

Maps at scales smaller than 1:250,000 are usually compiled from larger scale maps. Maps of this type published by the Survey include the sheets of the International Map of the World, State base maps of various kinds, and Territorial maps.

Series conversion is the process of preparing a map of one series from four or more maps of a larger-scale series. For example, four 7.5-minute maps may be combined, reduced in scale, and redrafted to produce one 15-minute map. The scale reduction usually makes it necessary to use a larger contour interval; most 15-minute maps prepared by series conversion have a contour interval twice as large as the 7.5-minute source maps.

At the time of reprinting or revision, a map may be converted from one scale to another; for example, from

FIGURE 19. Sequence of standard topographic mapping operations.

1:62,500 to 1:50,000. This procedure, called scale conversion, is essentially a process of photographic enlargement, and redrafting is not usually needed.

A few of the quadrangle maps published by the Survey are produced by other Federal agencies. The number of these maps changes from year to year, and the degree of responsibility assumed by the Survey for the content of the maps also varies.

Some maps prepared by other agencies are only distributed by the Survey. Others are both edited and published by the Survey and still others are field-checked before publication. Credit notes on the map margins identify the responsible agencies and give the extent of Geological Survey participation in preparing the maps. However they are prepared, these maps are intended to conform to the standards of accuracy, symbolization, and format for their series.

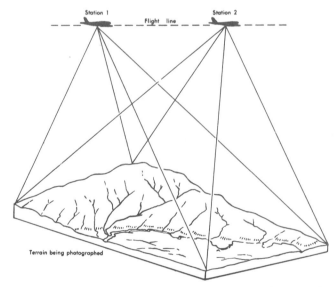

FIGURE 20A. Overlapping aerial photographs provide stereoscopic coverage of area to be mapped.

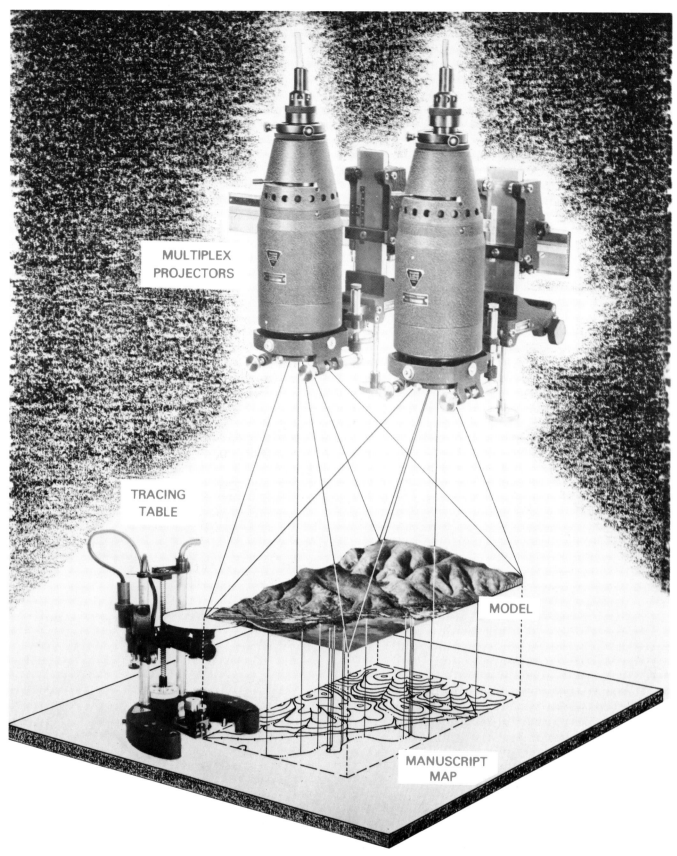

FIGURE 20B. Double-projection mapping instrument. Transparent prints of overlapping aerial photographs are placed in the projectors in the same orientation they had when the pictures were taken. The projected images are viewed stereoscopically on the surface of a tracing table, giving a three-dimensional impression (model) of the terrain. Map features and contour lines are traced as they appear in the stereoscopic model and reproduced on the map sheet. Instruments of this type, used extensively in the 1930's (see fig. 11), 1940's, and 1950's, have been replaced by modern equipment applying advanced optical, mechanical, and electronic techniques to the same principle (for example, see fig. 12).

National Topographic Map Series

National mapping requirements are the basis for the National Mapping Program, which includes a number of individual map series. The following topographic series are prepared, revised, and distributed by the Geological Survey:

7.5-minute	United States
Puerto Rico 7.5-minute	International Map of the
15-minute	World (IMW)
Alaska 1:63,360-scale	National Park
1:250,000-scale	Antarctica
State	Miscellany (special areas)

Maps in the following series are generally not revised or reprinted. Copies of these maps, and maps replaced by revision, are held in the historical file, and monocolor copies are supplied to the public on request at the cost of reproduction:

30-minute	Alaska reconnaissance
1-degree	Metropolitan Area

Additional series may be established as needed. Full descriptions of the series are given in the section "Topographic Maps" (p. 108–149).

Complete coverage of the United States exists or is planned for the 1:250,000-scale, State, and IMW series. Complete coverage at 1:24,000 scale is planned for the conterminous States and Hawaii, and complete 1:63,360-scale coverage is planned for Alaska; 1:25,000-scale coverage in Alaska is provided in areas of special need. The amount of coverage at 1:62,500 scale depends on demonstrated need and demand; however, if initial publication is at 1:62,500 scale, manuscripts are prepared at 1:24,000 scale with accuracy, content, and contour interval suitable for future publication in the 7.5-minute series. Copies of the manuscripts are held as open-file material available in the form of monocolor copies.

Maps in the standard series are published in one or more of the following editions:

Contour. This edition contains impressions of all color-separation plates, except that the woodland overprint is omitted on a limited number of copies.

Orthophotographic maps. This edition consists of maps that portray planimetric data primarily by photoimagery in correct orthographic ground positions. These maps may or may not include contours.

Shaded relief. This edition includes a form of shaded overprint that enhances the impression of relief. The shaded-relief treatment is applied only to selected maps.

Maps in some series are published in editions that vary from those described above; examples are the United States, State, and IMW maps. Also, some maps are published in a monocolor edition.

Terrain Relief

Contour lines, connecting points of equal altitude, are the standard method of portraying terrain relief. Because of wide variations of relief, it is frequently impractical to specify a single contour interval for a given map. Therefore, several types of contour intervals are established as follows:

Basic. The basic contour interval selected for each map is that which most clearly portrays the predominant terrain of the area. Basic intervals for the several map series are given in "Relief Information" (p. 28–35). Two basic intervals may be used on maps of areas containing abrupt contrasts in relief, provided that an adequate key or statement is given in the legend.

Supplementary. Contours that subdivide the basic interval are used if needed for adequate portrayal of the terrain. In portions of maps where supplementary contours are used, both the basic and supplementary contours must meet the accuracy standards for the smaller interval.

Underwater. Contours compiled before areas are inundated by the construction of dams are retained as useful hypsographic information. These areas are overprinted with blue tint.

Depth curves. Depth curves are differentiated from underwater contours because depth curves are measured down from a specific water surface; underwater contours are measured from the datum of mean sea level. Depth curves are shown along coastlines and on inland bodies of water when the data are available from hydrographic charts or other reliable sources.

Accuracy

Maps at scales of 1:100,000 and larger (such as 1:24,000 scale) are prepared by methods designed to meet the National Map Accuracy Standards. These standards have been issued by the Office of Management and Budget (formerly Bureau of the Budget) and are given in "Map Accuracy Standards" on page 104.

Maintenance

To preserve the usefulness of published maps, they must be revised or replaced periodically. The program for maintaining maps on an up-to-date basis is described in "Map Maintenance" on pages 96–102.

Natural and Cultural Features on Topographic Maps

The cartographer selects the natural and cultural features that are most valuable to the user. The smaller the map scale, the more critical and difficult the selection problem becomes.

Selection of Mappable Features

The major problem in map presentation is to make the best use of available space. The space cannot be crowded with lines and symbols beyond a definite limit without making the map unreadable, yet the amount of information that might be useful or desirable is almost unlimited. The cartographer selects the features that are the most valuable to the map user. The smaller the map scale, the more critical and difficult the problem of selection becomes.

Special-Purpose Maps

Topographic maps are often made for a particular purpose. For example, a map made for the purpose of designing a new highway would show the type of woodland cover and the classification of soil and rock along the route. Information about drainage, property lines, and buildings would be shown in detail as required. The map would be in the shape of a strip and would cover a relatively small ground area. This map is a special-purpose map because it has limited value for other uses.

General-Purpose Maps

Unlike special-purpose maps, the quadrangle maps produced by the Survey are designed to be used for many purposes. Scales, contour intervals, accuracy specifications, and features that are shown on the maps have been developed gradually to satisfy the requirements of government agencies, industry, and the gen-

eral public. Because these maps serve a wide variety of uses, they are called general-purpose maps. The functions a map is intended to serve determine which features should be mapped, but other factors are taken into account before it is decided what features actually can be shown. Among the most important considerations are the permanence of the features, the cost of compiling the information, and map legibility. The legibility requirement means that small features must be represented by symbols that are larger than true scale size. For example, roads are shown at least 90 feet wide on 1:62,500-scale maps despite the fact that they are actually narrower. Buildings and other structures also are depictd by symbols that may be larger than the scale size of the features. If smaller objects were represented at their true scale size, the symbols would be too small to be legible.

Symbols larger than scale size take up extra map space; therefore, where small features are close together, the less important features are omitted in congested areas.

The extent to which some kinds of map features are shown is determined partly by the cost of compiling the information. Aerial photographs are the source of most map information, but features that cannot be identified on photographs must be mapped by field methods, an expensive procedure. As an example, not all section corners are shown; they are too small to be seen on aerial photographs, and the cost of mapping them using field surveys would be excessive.

Not only the original compilation cost but also the cost of keeping the map up to date is considered in deciding which features to map. Generally, the more features depicted, the more quickly the map becomes out of date. Cultural features are especially subject to change. If the maps are to have a reasonably long useful life, the features portrayed must be restricted, to some extent, to relatively permanent objects.

Many kinds of features are shown on some maps, but omitted from others, because of their landmark character. In this sense a landmark is an object of sufficient interest in relation to its surroundings to make it stand out. For example, buildings may be considered landmarks when they are used as schools or churches or when they have some other public function. They may be landmarks also because of their outstanding size, height, or design; or they may be landmarks because of their history, such as old forts or the birthplaces of famous people.

The same principle is applied to features other than buildings. The adjacent area always is considered in relation to the object in deciding whether it qualifies as a landmark. Where map features are few, objects that would not be shown in more congested districts may be mapped as landmarks.

Map Symbols, Colors, and Labels

A topographic map, as distinguished from other kinds, portrays by some means the configurations and elevations of the terrain—the shapes into which the Earth's surface is sculptured by natural forces. Geological Survey topographic maps usually represent elevations and landforms by means of contour lines. Other features are shown by a variety of conventional signs, symbols, lines, and patterns printed in appropriate colors and identified by names, labels, and numbers. Figure 21 shows the standard symbols used on the topographic maps of the Survey.

The features shown on quadrangle maps are divided into three general classes, each printed in a different color. Topographic or hypsographic information—collectively the **relief features**—is printed in brown. **Water features** are shown in blue, and **cultural features**—manmade objects—in black. The system of division is not rigid, however. Levees, earth dams, and some other manmade features are also topographic features and are printed in brown, not black.

Besides the colors used for the three main classes of features, green is used to show woodland—timber, brush, vineyards, and orchards—and red is used to show public-land subdivision, built-up areas, and the classification of the more important roads.

Linear features are represented by lines of various weights and styles (solid, dashed, dotted, or some combinations). Structures or individual features are portrayed by a system of pictographs or symbols. The symbols originated as plan views of the objects they represent, and they retain something of this character although they are now formalized. The building symbol, for example, is a solid or open square. The railroad symbol is a line with evenly spaced crossties. The dam and levee symbols look approximately like dams or levees as seen from the air.

Because lines and symbols cannot represent map information completely, they are supplemented by the names of places and objects. Notes are added to explain some features that cannot be depicted clearly by symbols alone. In mapping topographic features the information portrayed by contour lines is supplemented by elevation figures. Letters and numbers are essential to map interpretation, but they tend to obscure other map information. Therefore, they are selected and positioned carefully on the map so that interference with other detail is kept to a minimum.

Relief Information

The two main reasons for showing relief information on maps are to furnish coordinated data for computing problems involving terrain dimensions and to present a graphic picture of the ground surface. The two objectives are related but distinct, and sometimes they may be conflicting.

For engineers or scientists who are interested in exact measurement, topographic maps furnish dimensional information about elevations, areas, grades, and volumes. The approximate elevation of any point can be read directly or interpolated from contours. A series of elevations on a line determines the grade or profile of the line, and areas and volumes can be computed by combining line profiles in various ways. The relief information shown by contours is sufficient for calculating the storage capacity of a reservoir, the area of a drainage basin, or the volume of earth to be moved in a large road cut or fill.

On the other hand, many persons who use maps are not concerned with exact ground elevations but are more interested in the general appearance and shape of the land. For them contours are the graphic means of visualizing the terrain and an aid in locating positions on the map.

Contour Lines

Contour lines are the principal means used to show the shape and elevation of the land surface. Other means are spot elevations, relief shading, hachures, and pattern symbols for special kinds of relief features that are not suited to contouring.

Primary highway, hard surface

Secondary highway, hard surface

Light-duty road, hard or improved surface

Unimproved road

Trail

Railroad: single track

Railroad: multiple track

Bridge

Drawbridge

Tunnel

Footbridge

Overpass—Underpass

Power transmission line with located tower

Landmark line (labeled as to type)   TELEPHONE

Dam with lock

Canal with lock

Large dam

Small dam: masonry — earth

Buildings (dwelling, place of employment, etc.)

School—Church—Cemeteries   Cem

Buildings (barn, warehouse, etc.)

Tanks; oil, water, etc. (labeled only if water)   Water Tank

Wells other than water (labeled as to type)   Oil   Gas

U.S. mineral or location monument — Prospect

Quarry — Gravel pit

Mine shaft—Tunnel or cave entrance

Campsite — Picnic area

Located or landmark object—Windmill

Exposed wreck

Rock or coral reef

Foreshore flat

Rock: bare or awash

Horizontal control station

Vertical control station   BM ×671   ×672

Road fork — Section corner with elevation   429   +58

Checked spot elevation   × 5970

Unchecked spot elevation   × 5970

Boundary: national

State

county, parish, municipio

civil township, precinct, town, barrio

incorporated city, village, town, hamlet

reservation, national or state

small park, cemetery, airport, etc.

land grant

Township or range line, U.S. land survey

Section line, U.S. land survey

Township line, not U.S. land survey

Section line, not U.S. land survey

Fence line or field line

Section corner: found—indicated   +   +

Boundary monument: land grant—other

Index contour	Intermediate contour
Supplementary cont.	Depression contours
Cut — Fill	Levee
Mine dump	Large wash
Dune area	Tailings pond
Sand area	Distorted surface
Tailings	Gravel beach

Glacier	Intermittent streams
Perennial streams	Aqueduct tunnel
Water well—Spring	Falls
Rapids	Intermittent lake
Channel	Small wash
Sounding—Depth curve 10	Marsh (swamp)
Dry lake bed	Land subject to controlled inundation

Woodland	Mangrove
Submerged marsh	Scrub
Orchard	Wooded marsh
Vineyard	Bldg. omission area

FIGURE 21. Topographic map symbols of the Geological Survey; variations may be found on older maps.

Contours are lines of equal elevation. They always are continuous lines and may form closed loops. A contour may be variously described as:

Δ An imaginary line on the ground, every point of which is at the same elevation above a specified datum surface (mean sea level for topographic maps of the Geological Survey).

Δ A coastline or shoreline of level water.

Δ An assumed shoreline resulting from the assumed rising of a body of level water.

However it is described, a contour is the line traced by the intersection of a level surface with the ground. A series of contours is traced by a series of level surfaces, a different contour for each elevation. Each contour line on the map represents a definite ground elevation measured from mean sea level, and the contour interval is the difference in elevation between adjacent contours. The contour interval, together with the spacing of the contour lines on the map, indicates the slope of the ground. On steep slopes the lines are spaced more closely than on gentle slopes. The basic characteristics of contours are illustrated in figure 22 which shows a bird's-eye view of a river valley and the adjoining hills, and the same features shown on a topographic map.

FIGURE 22. Ground configuration (*above*) shown by contours (*below*).

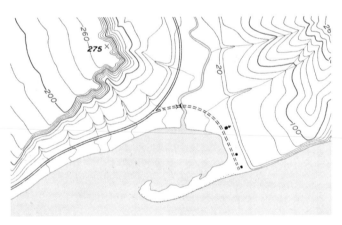

The river flows into a bay partly enclosed by a hooked sandspit. On both sides of the valley are terraces with stream-cut gullies. The hill on the right has a smoothly eroded form and gradual slope above a wave-cut cliff, whereas the one on the left rises to a steep slope from which it falls off gently and forms an inclined tableland crossed by a few shallow gullies. An unimproved dirt road and bridge provide access to a church and two houses situated across the river from an improved light-duty road that follows the sea coast and curves up the river valley. Elevations are represented on the map by contour lines; the vertical difference between any two contours is the contour interval, or 20 feet in this case.

To make maps more readable, contours are classified and the classes are distinguished by different weights and styles of lines.

Index contours—every fourth or fifth contour, de-pending on the basic interval—are accentuated by making the line wider than the other contours. Elevation figures are shown on the index contour lines at frequent intervals to facilitate their identification, as well as to assist in determining the values of adjacent contours.

Supplementary contours, used on the flatter areas of some maps to portray features that cannot be shown with the basic interval, are shown as dashed or dotted lines.

Depression contours, closed contours surrounding a basin or sink, are denoted by right-angle ticks (hachures) pointing inward (downslope).

Approximate contours, shown by dashed lines, are used in limited areas where accurate contours are not feasible.

Carrying contours are single lines representing two or more contour lines, used to show vertical or near-vertical topographic features, such as cliffs, cuts, and fills.

Contour Intervals

The amount of relief information that can be shown depends largely upon the scale of the map and the contour interval used to portray the relief. If a great amount of relief detail is required, the scale must be large and the contour interval small; but regardless of the scale and contour interval, all information concerning the ground surface cannot be shown on maps.

A satisfactory contour interval is one that shows the important topographic features adequately, yet does not result in closely spaced contours that are difficult to read. For a given scale and contour interval, the slope of the ground determines the spacing of contours on the map. Therefore, the most appropriate contour interval depends on the scale and the average ground slope in the quadrangle.

If slopes vary considerably within a quadrangle, the interval chosen may not give enough information in flatter areas because the contours are too far apart. Where this occurs, supplementary contours—at one-half, one-fourth, or one-fifth of the basic interval—are added in the flat areas. On the other hand, if the interval based on average slope causes too much congestion of contours in the steeper areas, intermediate contours may be dropped for short distances to avoid coalescence in printing. This treatment is called "feathering."

The contour interval determines not only the amount of relief information that can be shown but also the allowable tolerances in the vertical accuracy of the map. The two are directly related.

Small irregularities of the ground surface are omitted from the map by drawing the contours as smooth lines through these areas. The technique of ignoring the very small features and drawing the contour lines so that the larger features are emphasized is called "generalization."

Generalization is used to some extent in contouring at any map scale, because it is obviously impossible, even at the largest scale, to show every irregularity of the ground surface. The amount of detail omitted varies inversely with the map scale; some of the relief detail mapped at the scale of 1:24,000 may be omitted at the scale of 1:62,500. Figure 23 illustrates an area contoured at these two scales; a greater amount of detail is shown at the larger scale (1:24,000) by using a contour interval of 20 feet, rather than the 40-foot interval (used at the smaller 1:62,500 scale).

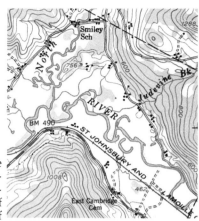

FIGURE 23. Two maps of the same area, each covering 4 mi². The upper map (Mount Mansfield, Vt., 15-minute quadrangle) is at a scale of 1:62,500 with a contour interval of 40 feet; the lower one (Jefferson-ville, Vt., 7.5-minute quadrangle) is at a scale of 1:24,000 with a contour interval of 20 feet.

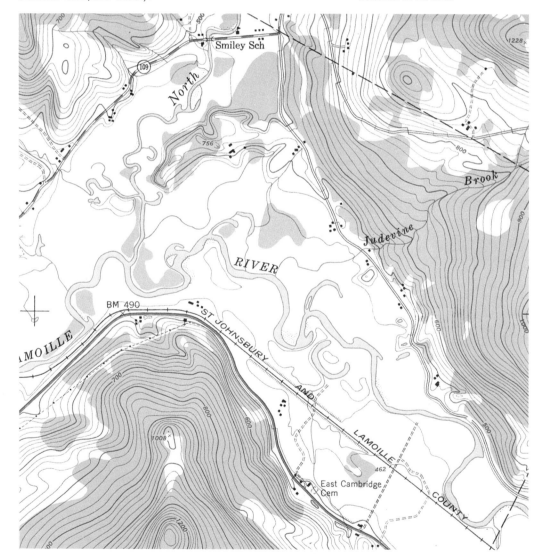

For the national topographic map series, several standard contour intervals have been established, with provision for supplementary contours where necessary.

7.5- AND 15-MINUTE SERIES. For many years the standard contour intervals for both series were 5, 10, 20, and 40 feet; in addition, the 80-foot interval was used in the 15-minute series for maps of areas of predominantly steep terrain. Maps prepared in the metric system have basic contour intervals of 1, 2, 5, 10, and 20 m.

1:100,000-SCALE SERIES. This intermediate-scale series is compiled in the metric system. The contour intervals are 1, 2, 5, 10, 20, and 50 m.

1:250,000-SCALE SERIES. Except for Alaska, the maps in this series were formerly compiled by the Army Map Service (now the Defense Mapping Agency) and published for civil use by the Geological Survey. In 1958, the Survey assumed responsibility for maintaining the series. Whenever a map in this series is revised, it may be necessary to change the contour interval in order to portray the terrain more adequately. The contour intervals used for older maps in the series are 25, 50, 100, or 200 feet. Half-interval supplementary contours may be used with any of these intervals except the 25-foot interval. Newer maps, prepared in the metric system, have basic contour intervals of 10, 20, 50, and 100 m.

STATE SERIES. For the 1:500,000-scale topographic editions of the State series, contour intervals of 50, 100, 200, and 500 feet are used, depending on the amount of relief. The 50-foot interval is used for the Florida and Louisiana maps. On maps of other States east of the Rocky Mountains, the 200-foot interval is used, with the first 100-foot supplementary contour added where necessary to portray flat coastal areas. Mountainous western States are mapped with the 500-foot contour interval. Alaska is not mapped at this scale. For newer State maps prepared in the metric system, the basic contour intervals are 10, 20, 50, 100, and 200 m.

INTERNATIONAL MAP OF THE WORLD ON THE MILLIONTH-SCALE (IMW) SERIES. The treatment of relief for the IMW series is distinctive from that used on other topographic maps in that the contours are not shown at regular or constant intervals. Instead, contours are shown at specified elevations designed to emphasize the elevation of land areas rather than slope. This treatment is described in the following paragraphs quoted from the specifications (United Nations, 1963):

> Contours shall be drawn at vertical intervals reckoning from mean sea level. The 100 m, 200 m, 500 m, 1,000 m, 1,500 m, 2,000 m, 2,500 m, 3,000 m, 4,000 m, 5,000 m, and 6,000 m contours, called principal contours, must be shown whenever practicable because they are required as the limits of hypsometric tints. When a map has been published using a contour interval different from the above, the existing intervals may be retained for reprinting, provided that when this map is extensively revised, the contours shall be recompiled at the above intervals.
>
> At any altitudes, auxiliary contours may be added, but they shall be at regular vertical intervals of 10, 20, 50, or 100 m.

This IMW series now includes the 1:1,000,000-scale maps prepared by the Defense Mapping Agency, which do not conform to all IMW specifications. These are considered preliminary IMW editions and will eventually be revised to meet IMW specifications.

ALASKA 1:250,000-SCALE SERIES. A contour interval of 200 feet is specified, and the 100-foot interval may be used for maps of flat terrain provided that the source data will yield standard-accuracy 100-foot contours. For newer maps, prepared in the metric system, the basic contour intervals are 50 and 100 m.

ALASKA 1:63,360-SCALE SERIES. Contour intervals of 25, 50, 100, or 200 feet may be used, depending on the character of the terrain. Supplementary contours, including 12.5-foot contours, may be used where appropriate. Basic contour intervals for newer maps in this series are 10, 20, 50, and 100 m.

ALASKA 1:25,000-SCALE SERIES. This is a recently established series using the metric system. The contour intervals are 1, 2, 5, 10, 20, and 50 m.

PUERTO RICO 7.5-MINUTE SERIES. The Commonwealth of Puerto Rico is completely mapped in the Puerto Rico 7.5-minute series, at 1:20,000-scale (originally published at 1:30,000-scale). The contour intervals are 1, 5, and 10 m, with supplementary contours where needed.

Other Means of Portraying Relief

Although contours are the best method of showing most topographic features, symbols must be used to represent features that cannot be shown clearly or economically by contours. Hachures and patterns are frequently used to depict relief in areas having a predominance of distinctive ground features that are either too intricate or too small to be individually or accurately shown at the scale or contour interval selected for the map.

HACHURES. Hachures, short lines drawn in the direction of the ground slope, are used to show gravel or borrow pits too small to contour, piles of waste material, such as mine dumps (fig. 24), small banks or escarpments that are prominent but not high enough to be shown by the selected contour interval, and similar relief features.

A slightly different form of hachure is used to depict small earth dams, small levees, spoil banks, and cuts and fills along roads or railroads. Contoured depressions are distinguished from hills by short ticks at right angles to the contours, pointing toward the center of the depression.

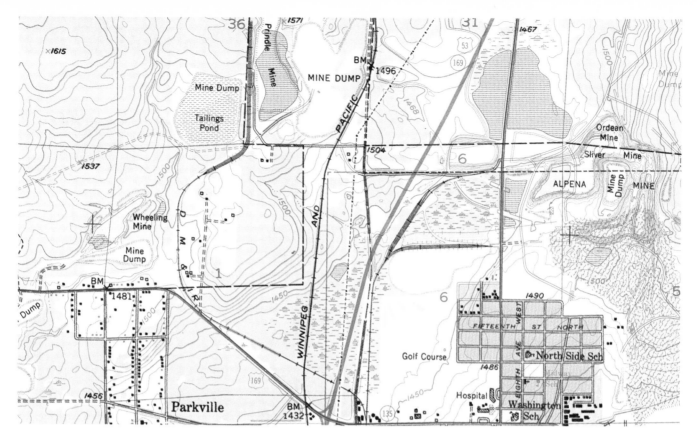

FIGURE 24. Iron mines in the Mesabi district of Minnesota. Hachures show the piles of ore and waste material. Depression contours, with short right-angle ticks, show the open-pit mines. Purple overprint, added at time of interim revision, shows disturbed area *(lower right)* and worked mines *(dot pattern)* filled with water since the previous map was published. (Virginia, Minn., quadrangle.)

AREA PATTERNS. Intricate surface areas too irregular to contour except in a very generalized manner, such as lava beds, sand dunes, and open strip mines, are shown by a variety of symbolic patterns. The patterns are made up of dots, hachures, or formlines that indicate the typical appearance of the area. If patterns are used, no attempt is made to represent the topography in detail. Figure 25 shows a volcanic area with many craters and lava beds. The lava beds are represented by a surface pattern and generalized contours.

FIGURE 25. Lava beds shown by intricate-surface pattern. (Medicine Lake, Calif., quadrangle.)

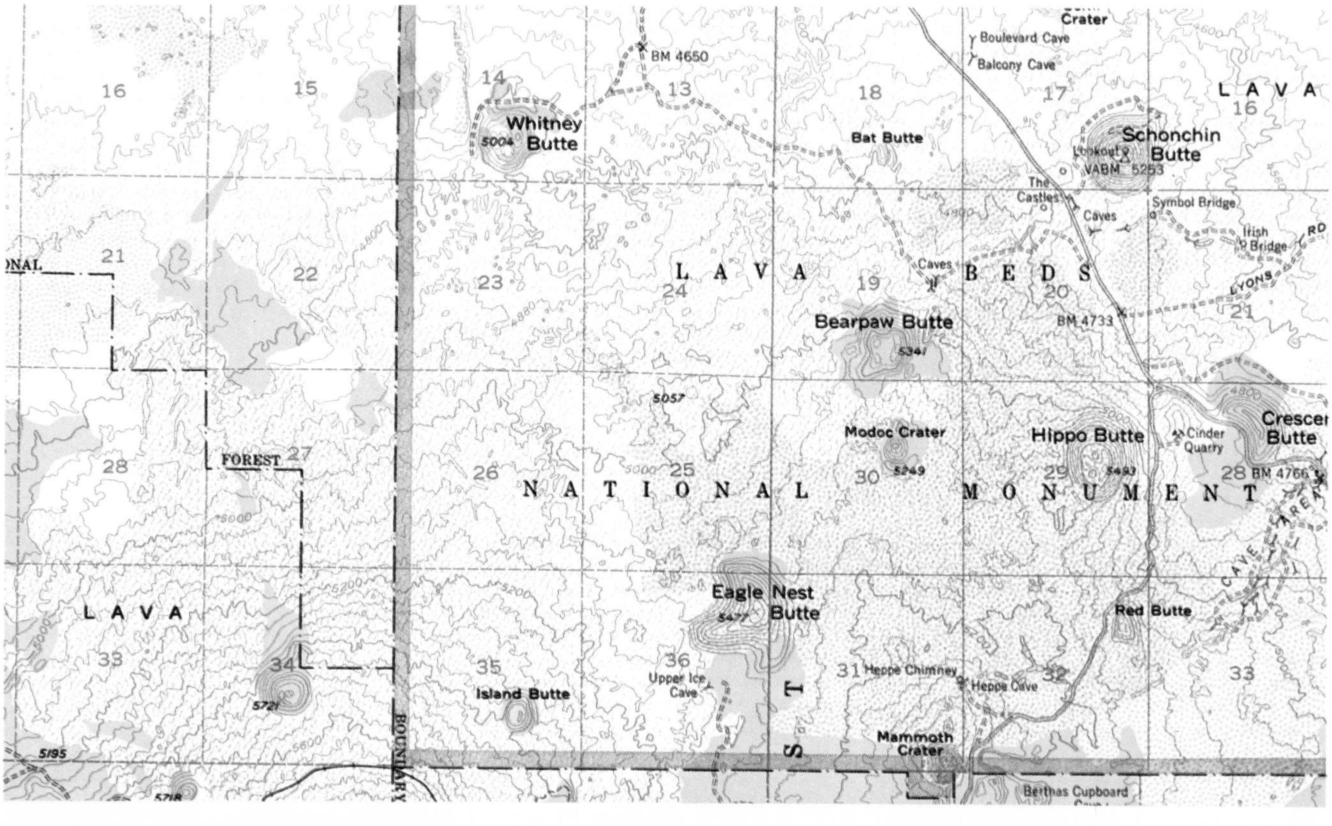

RELIEF SHADING. The pictorial effect of some maps is emphasized by relief shading, a halftone overprint that simulates the appearance of sunlight and shadows on the terrain and provides the illusion of three-dimensional topography. Shaded relief copy is prepared after the rest of the map has been produced in the conventional way. Selected maps are published in shaded-relief editions; an example is shown in figure 26.

DEPTH CURVES. Geological Survey practice provides for depth curves to be shown on standard topographic maps of coastal and navigable-water areas whenever the data can be obtained from hydrographic surveys or charts. Depth curves should not be confused with underwater contours, shown in areas submerged by dams. A depth curve is a line connecting points of equal water depth. The datums for depth curves in tidal waters (fig. 36) are mean low water (Atlantic and Gulf coasts) and mean lower low water (Pacific coast). The datum for inland water bodies is the mean low-water elevation of the surface. On navigable rivers above tidal reaches, the datum conforms with the stream gradient. On older Survey maps, depth curves are shown in feet even though the source materials may show them in other units. On newer maps, depth curves are shown in meters. Each curve is labeled because the curves generally are shown at irregular intervals. On maps of coastal areas, depth curves are not shown below 100 fathoms; this restriction does not apply to inland lakes.

ELEVATIONS. Elevations shown on the published map are of three types: bench mark, spot, and water surface.

Bench-mark elevations are established by methods compatible with geodetic accuracy standards (Federal Geodetic Control Committee, 1974). On the ground, bench marks are metal tablets or other permanent-type markers; elevations are measured at the top of the markers. On the map, they are shown by black crosses; corresponding elevations are in black vertical type.

Spot elevations on discrete map points or features provide more accurate elevations than those interpolated from contours and present additional hypsographic information in the flat areas where contours are widely spaced. These elevations are of a lower order of accuracy than bench-mark elevations but are more accurate than contours. Most spot elevations are established by field surveys, but photogrammetric elevations may be shown as spot elevations on the map if, on the basis of the procedure used, they are considered to be accurate within three-tenths of the contour interval. Spot elevations, except those established on standard tablets, refer to the ground surface, even though a marker such as a section-corner pipe may locate the spot. Regardless of the methods used to establish spot elevations, their locations are shown on the map by small black crosses, unless the locations are obvious, and the elevations are printed in black slanted type.

Water-surface elevations are established, if possible, from reliable records or field surveys. However, photogrammetric spot elevations may be published for lakes, ponds, and other such inland water features in remote and inaccessible areas. Elevations on all natural water features, except coastal waters, are based upon the normal stage. Water-surface elevations are printed in black slanted type, whereas soundings are printed in blue slanted type.

FIGURE 26. Shaded-relief gives pictorial effect of relief to map. (Cumberland, Md.-Pa.-W. Va., quadrangle.)

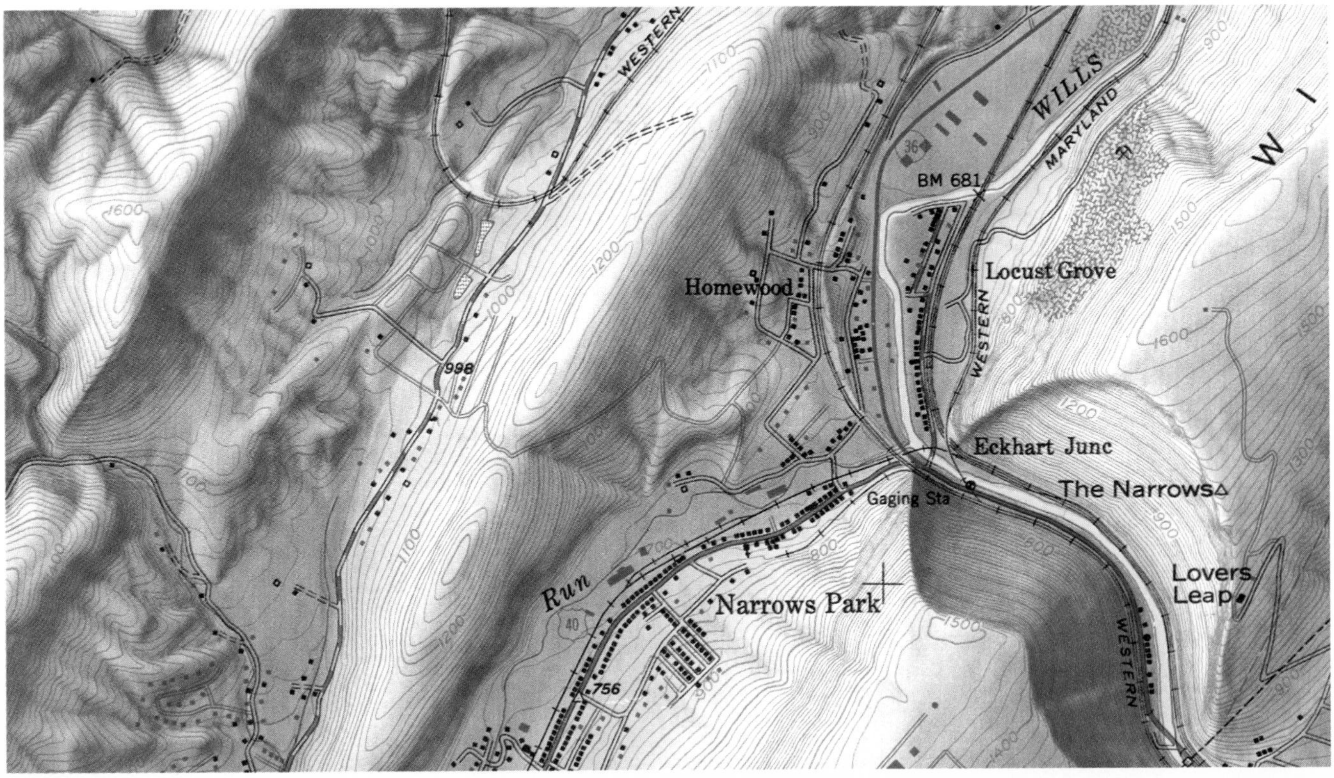

The location and number of spot elevations on the map depend on the scale, contour interval, terrain characteristics, and the amount of existing monumented control. An even distribution of elevations for publication is established where feasible, with preference given to bench-mark, field-survey, and photogrammetric elevations, in that order.

Spot elevations are usually located on features that are easily and positively identifiable and recoverable, such as road intersections, railroad crossings, and boundary markers. Prominent tops, saddles, depressions, and other critical hypsographic points also provide appropriate locations. Except in very flat areas, spot elevations at unidentifiable points add little to the elevation data of the map and usually are not shown.

Generally the proportion of field to photogrammetric spot elevations is greater in areas of low relief and dense cultural detail. Maps compiled at contour intervals larger than 20 feet in areas of difficult access may have a larger proportion of photogrammetric spot elevations because of the relative ease of establishing these points by photogrammetric techniques.

Water Features

Unlike other natural features, most of which are reasonably stable, water features—shown in blue on the map—change from time to time. The levels of rivers, lakes, and reservoirs fluctuate during the year, according to the amount of rainfall and runoff. Smaller streams

and springs may be entirely dry for a part of the year. Daily or even hourly variations in streamflow and water level occur in areas where melting snowfields or glaciers feed the streams or where streams are controlled for irrigation or industrial purposes.

Streams

Rivers, creeks, branches, and runs are shown on standard topographic maps with symbols designed to reflect their width and classification. Perennial streams—those containing water throughout the year except in severe drought—are symbolized by solid blue lines or solid blue lines and light-blue fill. Intermittent streams—those containing water only part of the year—are symbolized by blue dashes separated by three dots.

Aerial photographs for mapping generally are not taken at a time of flood or extreme low water. Photogrammetric compilation of hydrographic features, including streambanks, therefore usually reflects normal conditions. If gaging records for a river are available, the mapped shorelines, contour crossings, and water-surface elevations are based on these records. (Contour crossings pertain to the water surface elevation, not the stream bottom.) The map user who needs specific information on the conditions under which the map was compiled should direct his questions to the Geological Survey.

Figure 27 shows a river with the shoreline corresponding to the normal stage of the river and with the sandbars exposed. Figure 28 shows an intermittent river

FIGURE 27. River shoreline corresponding to normal water stage. (Columbus, Nebr., quadrangle.)

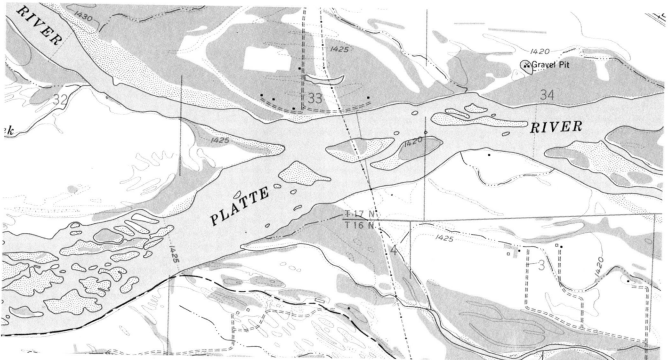

which normally is a dry bed, as indicated by the brown dry-wash symbol. The map user, however, can readily recognize, from the presence of the whiskered brown levee symbol, that this dry bed can contain a torrent in the flood season. The map tells the user that the water feature changes and that he must take this changeability into account. This illustration, incidentally, shows another type of water feature, manmade aqueducts. The dashed single line tells the map user that the aqueducts are buried underground in the flat area, and the dashed double line indicates that they are carried through a tunnel in the mountains.

FIGURE 28. Intermittent river indicated by dry-wash symbol. (San Jacinto, Calif., quadrangle.)

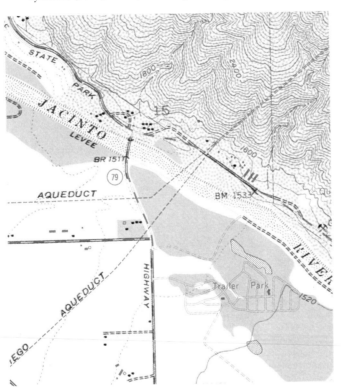

Stream courses that subdivide into interlacing channels are shown as they appear on the aerial photographs used for map compilation. The braided stream shown in figure 29 shows the actual channels at the time the photographs were taken. This gives a reliable portrayal of the general nature of the braided stream, but the map user should recognize that the channels will change.

FIGURE 29. Interlacing channels of a braided stream. (Bottomless Lakes, N. Mex., quadrangle.)

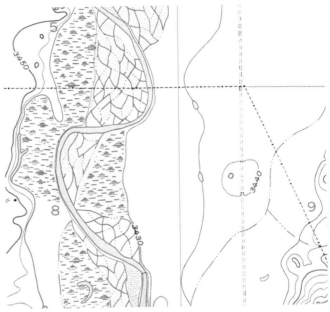

Natural Lakes and Ponds

Perennial lakes and ponds are symbolized by a solid-blue outline with a light-blue tint covering the water area. In figure 30A, numerous perennial lakes and ponds are shown, with the shoreline corresponding to normal water stages. Names and water-surface elevations are shown on selected lakes.

FIGURE 30A. Perennial lakes and ponds depicted by a solid-blue outline surrounding light-blue tint. (Audubon, Minn., quadrangle.)

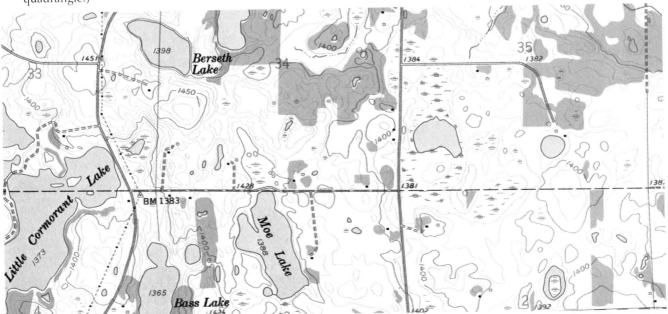

The principal problems related to the depiction of lakes and ponds stem from variations in the quantity of water. These variations affect two very important aspects of map portrayal, the shoreline of the lake and the elevation of the water surface.

For perennial lakes, the shorelines and water-surface elevations shown on the map are intended to correspond to the normal water stage. For some water bodies, however, the normal water stage is difficult to determine and may even be controversial. Various guidelines are used in determining what surface elevation and shoreline are shown on the map. For example, a sharp vegetation line is usually a good guide for locating the shoreline. If gage records are available, the mapped shoreline is based on the gaging data. In any case, the published water-surface elevation is consistent with the shoreline shown on the map.

Water-surface elevations are usually established from reliable records or field surveys. However, in remote and inaccessible areas, where this would entail prohibitive costs, photogrammetric spot elevations are published. If the normal stage of the water body cannot be determined, a dated elevation may be shown. Although water-surface elevations are established and published for as many lakes and ponds as practicable, preference is given to the larger water bodies and those with names, because it is not feasible to show an elevation on every water body.

Intermittent lakes and ponds are depicted by a dashed blue outline with light-blue diagonal hatching inside the outline. Shorelines of intermittent lakes are mapped to correspond to the apparent high water line. Water-surface elevations are not published for intermittent lakes. Figure 30B illustrates the use of the dashed outline to depict intermittent lakes and ponds.

A special case of intermittent lakes is the dry lake, which almost never contains water and then only as a direct result of local storms. They are symbolized with dashed blue outlines and brown dotted fill. Spot elevations are usually shown for large dry lake bottoms.

Manmade Lakes and Reservoirs

Manmade works for impounding water for power production, recreation, flood control, navigation, or water supply are of concern to many map users. The Geological Survey series maps show not only the extent of the manmade water body but also the manner of its making. Identified on the maps are the dams, spillways, canals, locks, power stations, dikes, and gaging stations. If suitable information is available, the configuration of the bottom of the lake is show by underwater contours or depth curves or both.

In figure 31A, the map shows a concrete dam large enough to be outlined to scale. The outline is filled with a line pattern that indicates the sloping downstream face of the dam. Also depicted are a road on top of the dam, underwater contours, the old river course, an aqueduct, a power plant, a substation, power transmission lines, and a gaging station. The concrete dam shown in

FIGURE 31A. Large concrete dam outlined to scale. (Folsom, Calif., quadrangle.)

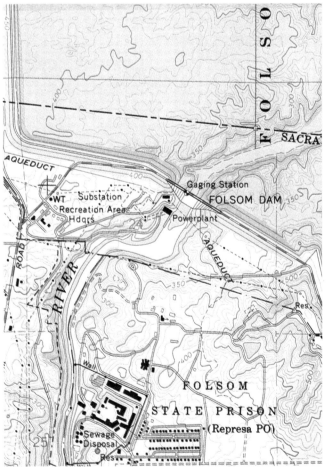

FIGURE 30B. Intermittent ponds shown by dashed outlines at apparent high water lines. (Scranton SW., N. Dak., quadrangle.)

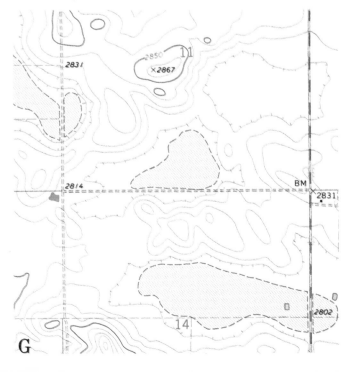

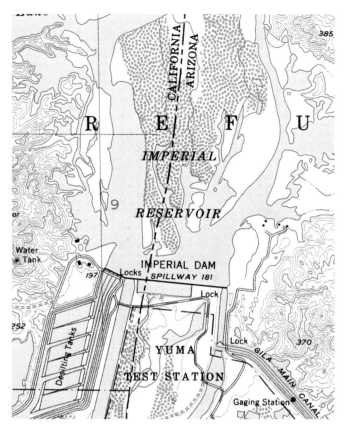

FIGURE 31B. Concrete dam less than 40 feet wide shown as heavy black line. (Imperial Reservoir, Ariz.-Calif., quadrangle.)

figure 31B is less than 40 feet wide and is therefore shown as a heavy black line. The map also shows the locks, a canal, the spillway elevation, desilting tanks, and a gaging station. The desilting tanks and locks are mapped to scale. It should be noted that for concrete or masonry dams, the contours are dropped at the edge of the dam symbol, where they intersect with the masonry part of the dam.

Figure 31C illustrates a large earth dam depicted by contours. (Masonry sections of such dams are shown in black.) The water outline is carried parallel to contoured earth dams, but is dropped where it intersects with masonry sections. This map shows underwater contours, a gaging station, a powerplant, powerlines, and a road on top of the dam. Areas subject to controlled flooding are shown by a dashed light-blue pattern, with the upper limits indicated by a dashed dark-blue line and elevation figures.

The determination of water-surface elevations to be shown on maps is an even more difficult problem for manmade reservoirs than it is for natural lakes because many reservoirs are controlled to operate at different levels to meet varying circumstances. The objective is to determine the level at which the reservoir operates under normal conditions. Sometimes the responsible agency has established a normal operating level. If the reservoir is operated at two normal levels, one for winter and one for summer, the summer level is shown on the map.

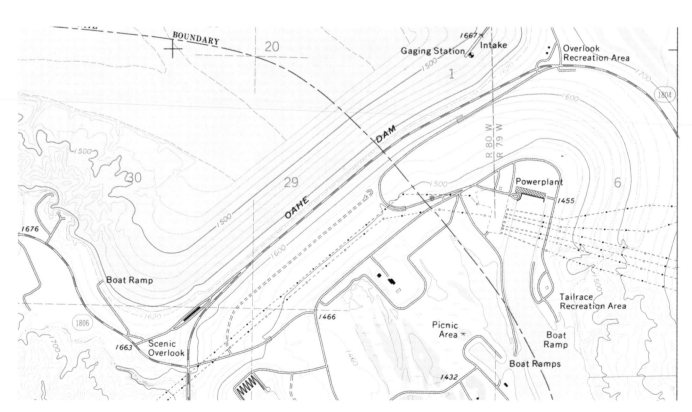

FIGURE 31C. Earth dam shown by contours. (Oahe Dam, S. Dak., quadrangle.)

If a reasonable value for the normal operating level cannot be established, the spillway elevation is shown rather than the normal pool elevation. Examples include a flood-control reservoir that impounds water only when runoff exceeds a predetermined amount, or a storage reservoir for irrigation in which the water level fluctuates considerably. In some situations, as when power generation and flood control are involved, both the normal pool and spillway elevations are given, as shown in figure 32A; in this figure, submerged contours, double-lined stream channels, boundaries, and land lines are shown by their normal symbols within the reservoir area. This is in keeping with the practice of preserving, as much as possible, such information from older Geological Survey maps and other available source maps. The underwater contours are printed in brown under the standard blue water tint.

Figure 32B shows both underwater contours and depth curves. Depth curves, shown in blue, differ from underwater contours in that the depth curves are meas-

ured down from the level of the normal water surface of the reservoir, whereas underwater contours are measured up from a sea level datum. Underwater contours and depth curves are not shown for the same area, but both may be shown in the same body of water as long as they do not overlap. A typical example of including both types of vertical representation would be a newly created reservoir in which depth curves are shown within the limits of the old river channel, and underwater contours are shown in the rest of the water area.

Canals, Aqueducts, and Ditches

Manmade works to control the flow and distribution of water play a vital role in the effective use of the water environment. To the extent that it is practical to do so, the Geological Survey series maps show aqueducts, canals, irrigation systems, ditches, flumes, penstocks, risers, siphons, and weirs.

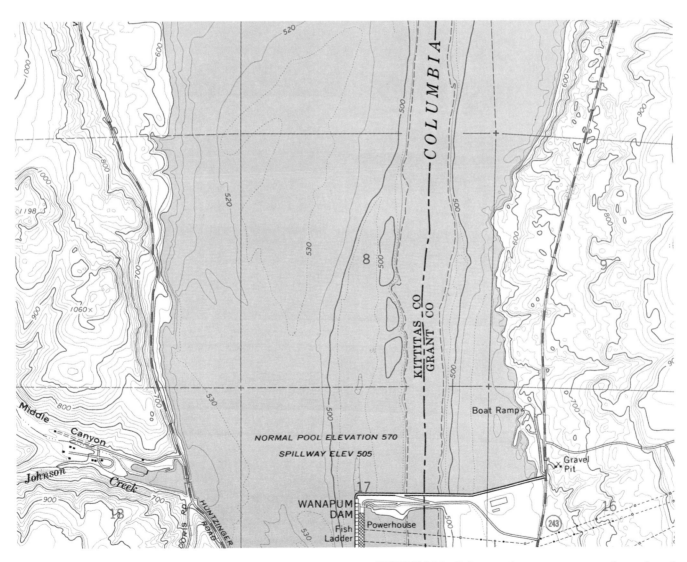

FIGURE 32A. Submerged contours, stream channel, and boundaries shown by normal symbols in reservoir area. (Vantage, Wash., quadrangle.)

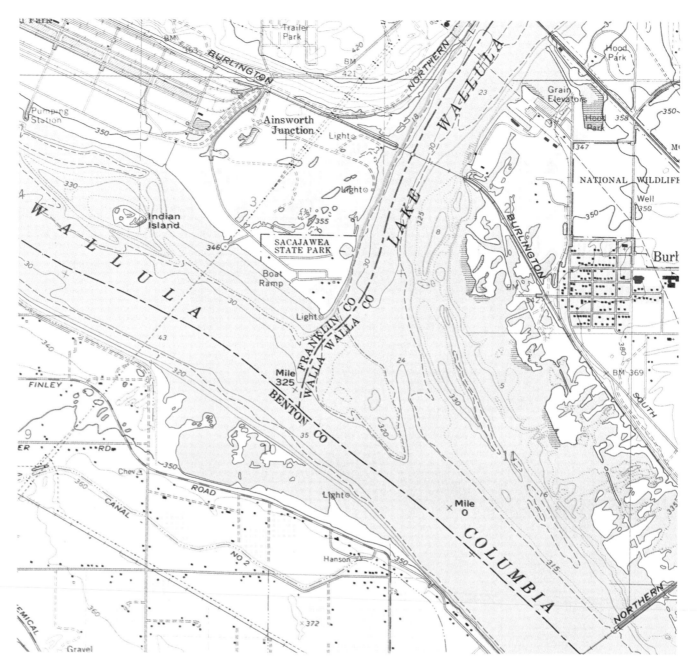

FIGURE 32*B*. Underwater contours used with depth curves. (Pasco, Wash., quadrangle.)

Figure 33 shows the map treatment for irrigation and drainage systems. The main canals and ditches and their major branches (laterals) are shown, but distributaries carrying water to individual fields are omitted. The irrigation system transfers water from the supply source and distributes it directly on the land. The drainage system drains excess water from the surface or lowers the water table. The map shows both perennial and intermittent canals and drains. If the watercourse is more than 40 feet wide, it is shown by double-lined symbols (on 1:24,000-scale maps); otherwise, single-lined symbols are used. As map scale decreases, the stream width requiring double-lined symbols increases.

Elevations shown at road, railroad, and aqueduct crossings and at junction points enable the map user to interpret the gradient. Elevations given for canals and ditches indicate the normal water level for perennial features, the bottom elevations for intermittent features.

Permanent structures built to control or divert the flow of water are shown on 1:24,000-scale maps if they have a major dimension of 40 feet or more. Included in this category are head gates, check gates, sluice gates, diversion weirs, and overflow spillways. For smaller scales, these structures are shown if their dimensions are proportionally larger.

Natural and Cultural Features on
Topographic Maps

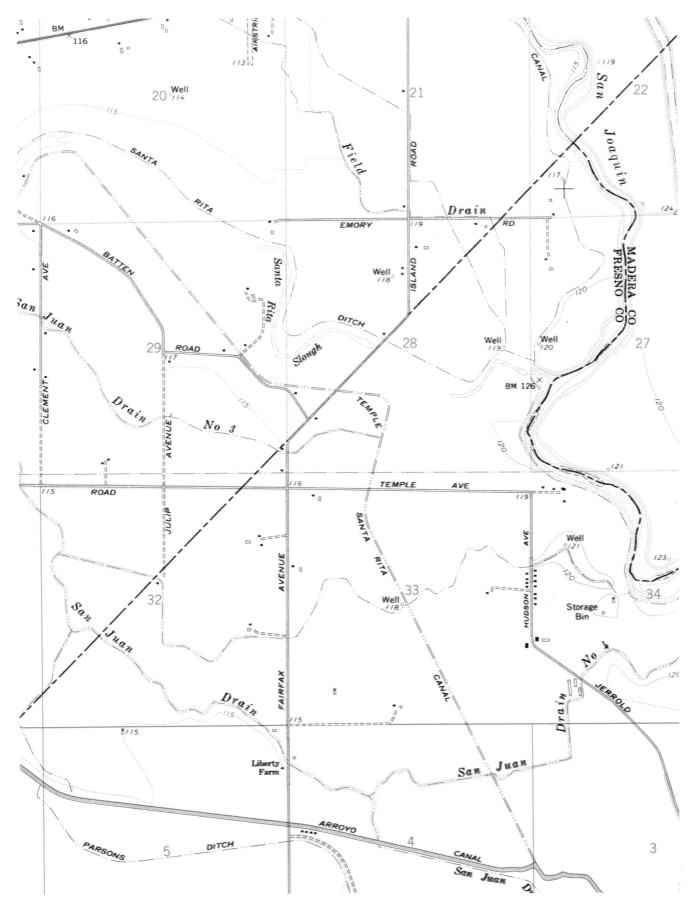

FIGURE 33. Irrigation and drainage system showing canals, ditches, and laterals. (Santa Rita Bridge, Calif., quadrangle.)

Miscellaneous Water Features

Springs and wells are shown on the maps if they are an important part of the water resources of the region or if they are useful landmarks. If springs or wells are numerous, only the more important ones are shown. In arid regions, all springs and wells are shown. Names and elevations of landmark springs and wells are published on the map. Springs and wells are labeled "salt," "alkali," "mineral," or "hot," if appropriate.

Various structures for water use are shown on the maps if they are large enough to plot (50 feet long or longer for a scale of 1:24,000). Figure 34 shows a sewage disposal plant, including settling beds and other related features. The outline is plotted to scale, and the major separations are shown; the water area is filled with a light-blue hatching, and the plant is labeled. Sewage ponds used for natural treatment of sewage by oxidation are mapped as perennial ponds, except that they are outlined in black if walls are masonry or concrete.

Other water-use structures shown on the maps include salt evaporators, fish hatcheries, swimming pools, and miscellaneous diked flood areas. In each case, the water area is shown with either a light-blue hatching or pattern, and the feature is labeled. Structural outlines are usually shown in black for masonry construction and in brown for earth construction.

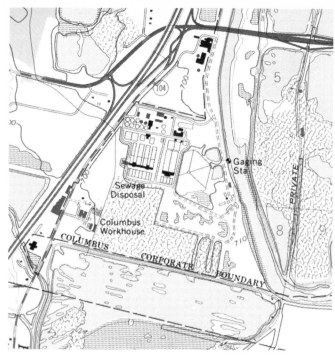

FIGURE 34. Sewage disposal plant and related features. (Southwest Columbus, Ohio, quadrangle.)

Figure 35 shows a glacier outlined by a blue dashed symbol with contours shown in blue across the snow and ice. Crevasses are shown by solid blue lines and are selectively labeled. Moraines are shown by a brown mottled dot symbol.

FIGURE 35. Glaciers, moraines, and crevasses. (Juneau C–1, Alaska, 1:63,360-scale 15-minute quadrangle.)

Coastal Features

The Geological Survey series maps portray, in as much detail as the map scale permits, coastal features such as beaches, inlets, estuaries, bays, islands, spits, coastal marshes, tidal flats, rocks, and reefs. In mapping these coastal areas, the Geological Survey cooperates with the National Ocean Survey and other agencies concerned with the preparation of nautical charts. Most of the topographic maps of the coastal areas are compiled from a combination of sources: current nautical charts (usually National Ocean Survey), new aerial photographs, and fieldwork.

Figure 36 shows that a coastal beach extends from the lower low-water line to the inland limit of wave-deposited debris, generally above the higher high-water line and within the backshore. Foreshore features shown on Geological Survey series maps are obtained from hydrographic or nautical charts. Backshore features are derived from hydrographic charts or aerial photographs or by field methods. The mean high water line is shown as the shoreline on nautical charts of the National Ocean Survey and topographic maps of the Geological Survey.

Figure 37A shows a coastal beach and marsh area. The tidal flats and foreshore area are shown in black, and backshore beach is shown in brown. The channels through the marshes are shown, but the minor channels in the tidal flats are omitted. The shoreline indicated is the approximate line of mean high water (always higher than mean sea level). In areas where the mean high water line is indefinite, the outer edge of vegetation is considered the shoreline.

The map section in figure 37B depicts a coastal area with a jagged rock symbol indicating its rocky nature. The map shows a lighthouse, tidal flats, exposed rocks, soundings, and depth curves. All this information was derived from charts of the National Ocean Survey. It should be noted that the selected foreshore and offshore hydrographic information shown on Geological Survey series maps is not intended for navigational use.

Depth curves and soundings are shown in feet (not fathoms) on older topographic maps; newer maps are prepared in the metric system. For offshore areas, the information is obtained from National Ocean Survey charts. It is referenced to the datum of mean low water (Atlantic and Gulf coasts) or to mean lower low water

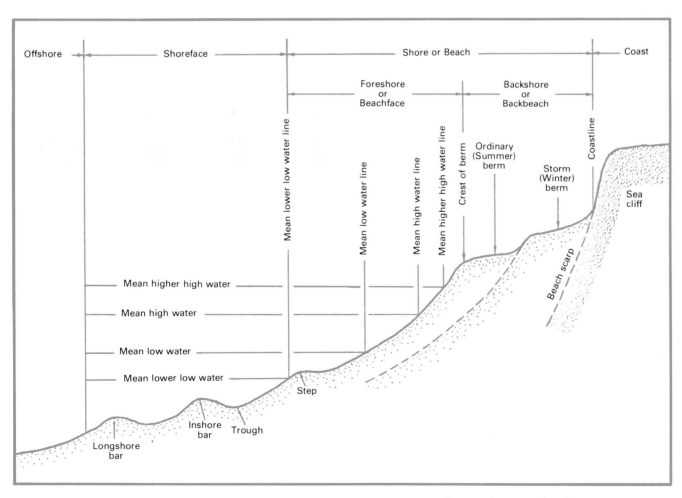

FIGURE 36. Zones of a coastal beach.

Water Features

43

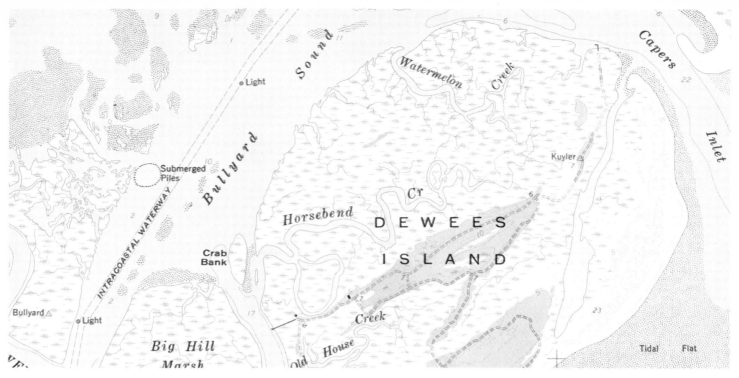

FIGURE 37*A.* Coastal beach and marsh areas. (Capers Inlet, S.C., quadrangle.)

(Pacific coast). For the Great Lakes the information is taken from U.S. Lake Survey charts; it is referenced to the datum shown on the charts.

Depth curves and soundings are also shown for certain inland lakes, based on information provided by State sources, such as a conservation commission. If the information is available, the deepest part of the lake and other selected soundings are shown in blue, and the water-surface elevation is shown in black.

The Geological Survey series maps normally show lighthouses and other lighted beacons; seawalls, breakwaters, and jetties; wharves and piers; dredged channels; cribs; wrecks; seaplane landing areas; water-intake aqueducts; cable and pipeline areas; and ferry routes (figs. 37C and D). Numerous additional features that are shown on nautical charts are omitted from the Geological Survey maps.

FIGURE 37*B.* Rocky coastline mapped with jagged rock symbol. (Hull, Mass., quadrangle.)

FIGURE 37*C.* Fixed lights shown as located objects. (Beaufort, S.C., quadrangle.)

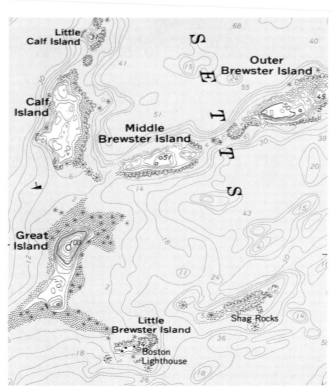

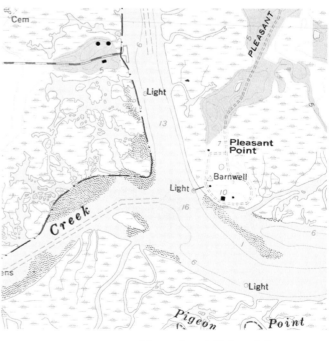

Natural and Cultural Features on Topographic Maps

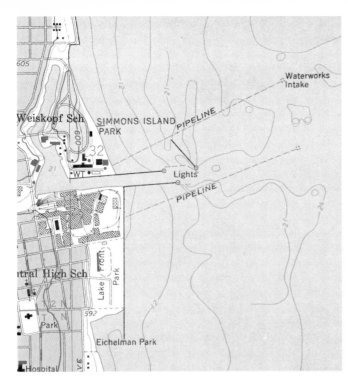

FIGURE 37D. Breakwater and jetties shown if longer than 100 feet (30 m). Water intakes are located from nautical charts. (Kenosha, Wis., quadrangle.)

Roads and Railroads

Roads and railroads are among the most important features shown on topographic maps. On Geological Survey maps roads are classified and symbolized according to their importance as routes of travel and according to their surfacing, weatherability, and construction. Railroads are symbolized according to operating status, gage, and number of tracks.

Road Classification

The five classes of roads shown on Geological Survey 7.5- and 15-minute maps are defined as follows:

Class 1—Primary highways, all-weather, hard surface. All officially designated Interstate and Federal routes (including alternates), primary State routes, and other routes of equivalent importance, such as expressways, throughways, turnpikes, freeways, and parkways, are included. In States where highway systems are divided into two or more classes by State officials, only the highest ranking class is mapped as class 1. In other States, the State routes included in class 1 are selected on the basis of importance.

Class 2—Secondary highways, all-weather, hard surface. Secondary State routes, primary county routes, and other comparable through roads important to statewide or countywide travel are included. These roads are important connecting routes between principal towns and cities, and supplement the primary arterial highway system.

Class 3—Light-duty roads, all-weather, improved surface. Paved roads not included in a higher class and loose-surfaced improved roads passable in all kinds of weather and used mostly for local traffic are included. These roads are adjuncts to the primary and secondary highway systems. Light-duty, as used in this classification, deals with the amount of traffic rather than load weight. Regularly maintained public roads, streets not included in class 1 or 2, service roads, and the more important private roads, such as improved main logging or industrial roads, are also included in class 3.

Class 4—Unimproved roads, fair or dry weather. Unsurfaced and unimproved roads passable in fair or dry weather and confined mostly to local traffic are included. Examples are roads providing access to isolated areas, farm buildings, and ranches; logging roads in the immediate logging area; fire roads; and track roads in desert areas.

Class 5—Trails. Foot trails, bridle and pack trails, ski trails, historic trails, one-lane roads on levees, maintenance roads along transmission lines, and roads passable only with a 4-wheel-drive vehicle are included. Bridle, pack, ski, and jeep trails are identified by labeling.

Roads included in classes 1, 2, and 3 are always shown on the map. Some roads in classes 4 and 5 are shown, others are not. Whether an unimproved road or trail is mapped or not depends on its local importance as a travel route.

As a general rule, class 4 roads leading to mapped features, or providing the only access to a particular area, are shown. However, if two such roads lead to the same feature in approximately the same direction, only the better road is shown and the poorer road is dropped, except in recreational areas where added detail is of interest to hikers and sportsmen.

A second consideration is the amount of cultural detail in an area, particularly one with a dense network of unimproved roads. To map such an area legibly, it is customary to select the better or more direct roads and omit the others. However, in undeveloped areas where travel routes are few and therefore important, all roads that may be useful are shown.

Abandoned roads, which have been replaced by newer roads or are grown over and no longer used, are not mapped unless they are local landmarks.

Field and mine roads, intended for private use only, are shown if they lead to some mapped feature or if they provide the only access to an isolated area. Examples are field roads leading to a spring, windmill, or building or providing access to a substantial area of bottomlands.

Fire roads are mapped on the recommendation of forest officials, or if they are locally important in areas of sparse culture. Fire roads of minor importance may be shown as trails.

Lumber or logging roads are shown if they are useful permanent routes (maintained in wet climates), if they are connecting roads, or if they lead to camps or sawmill sites. In sustained-yield logging areas, the permanent road net is mapped, but the temporary feeder roads within the tract usually are not.

Service roads along pipelines or power-transmission lines are mapped if they provide access to isolated areas. They are shown as trails unless their construction warrants inclusion in class 4.

Because roads are travel routes, they are shown as continuous features. For example, if a class 4 road enters and follows the bed of an intermittent stream, both symbols are shown.

Road Symbolization

Each class of road has a distinctive type of symbol, though the details of the symbols may vary according to the physical dimensions of the roads.

Δ **Class 1 roads.** Solid-line black casing and solid red fill.

Δ **Class 2 roads.** Solid-line black casing and dashed red fill.

Δ **Class 3 roads.** Solid-line black casing without red fill.

Δ **Class 4 roads.** Dashed-line black casing without red fill.

Δ **Class 5 trails.** Dashed black single line.

JEEP TRAIL

Whenever possible, roads are symbolized at true scale. However, most roads are too narrow for clear delineation to scale, so that minimum total symbol widths (representing 40 feet on the ground at 1:24,000 scale, and 80 feet at 1:62,500 scale) are used. Road widths, when they can be scaled, refer to the following:

Δ **City streets.** Distance from curb to curb.
Δ **Paved roads.** Width of the traffic surface, excluding the shoulders.
Δ **Gravel or dirt roads.** Width of the graded surface intended for traffic, excluding the shoulders.

Except for city streets, short stretches of road less than 0.5 mile long are not changed to show minor variations in width.

For roads 16 feet or more in width, the number of lanes marked by stripes or signs, or designated by highway authorities, is accepted regardless of the measured width of the roadway. This information on the number of lanes also applies to roads under construction if they are approved for publication by the State highway department.

For unmarked roads which appear wide enough to accommodate more than two lanes, information on the number of lanes is obtained from official road maps or local authorities.

For roads of more than two lanes and dual highways with dividing strips shown as a single line, the number of lanes is shown by a label, for example, "3 lane." Dual highways with dividing strips shown as a double line are labeled to indicate the number of traffic lanes in either direction, if more than two lanes, and arrows show the direction of flow.

A change in the number of lanes is indicated by a tick and a label. Variations in the number of lanes, including reduction at critical points as safety measures, are disregarded for short stretches of road (less than 0.5 mile).

If the identification or position of access ramps at interchanges or of service roads may be obscured or displaced by holding to the minimum symbol size (0.020 inch), a small departure from this minimum is necessary. Use of the reduced-width road symbol is restricted to service roads (roads paralleling limited-access highways), interchanges, ramps, and alleys.

Dual highways have opposing traffic lanes separated by curbs or median strips. They are shown by a three- or four-line symbol (fig. 38A), depending on the total width of the roadways and the dividing strip.

FIGURE 38A. Dual highways are shown by three- or four-line symbols, depending on widths of roadways and dividing strips. (Hinsdale, Ill., quadrangle.)

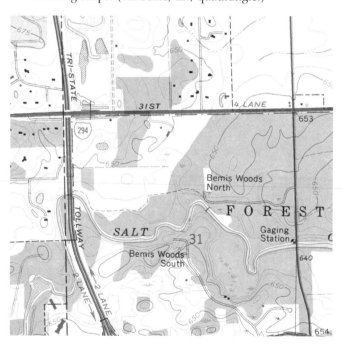

Limited-access highways may be closely paralleled by roads that serve adjoining residential and business sections. These service roads are not considered part of the highway and are therefore mapped separately as roads or streets. If a road is constructed over another, the double-decked structure is shown by the standard road symbolization appropriate to its class and labeled "Double-deck."

Natural and Cultural Features on Topographic Maps

FIGURE 38B. Symbols of underpassing routes at grade-separation crossings are broken; overpassing route symbols are continuous. (Sapulpa North, Okla., quadrangle.)

For **roads intersecting on the same level,** the casing lines of both roads are connected and the intersection is left clear. If a road and railroad intersect on grade, the two symbols are allowed to cross. At grade-separation crossing of two roads or of a road and a railroad, the symbol of the underpassing route is broken and the symbol of the overpassing route is continuous (fig. 38B).

Traffic interchanges, cloverleaves, and **traffic circles** are mapped to scale, showing the actual conditions (fig. 38C). Traffic-interchange ramps carry a red fill consistent with the classification of the limited-access road which they serve.

FIGURE 38C. Traffic interchanges are mapped to scale. (Norman, Okla., quadrangle.)

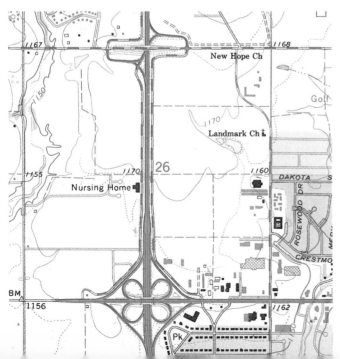

Road intersections that form triangular islands are mapped to scale, showing the actual conditions, if the triangle can be shown clearly without displacing the road casing line. Normally it is impractical to show triangles with a minimum dimension less than 80 feet. Traffic islands and other traffic-regulating structures are not shown unless they are large enough to plot to scale.

Road Identification

Interstate, Federal, and **State highways** are identified by route markers (route numbers within shields or circles). County route numbers are not shown, unless the routes are part of the State system. If a road is a combination of routes, each route number is shown.

Memorial and commemorative highway names on numbered Federal and State routes are not shown, except in urban areas where the names are frequently well established as part of the street naming system. Such names as Lincoln Highway and Blue Star Memorial Highway are omitted in favor of the Federal or State route numbers. However, authentic historical names, such as Santa Fe Trail, Wilderness Road, National Road, and Chisholm Trail, are shown if the name is needed to preserve continuity with the labeled original route that may depart from, or follow in part, the Federal or State numbered routes, provided that the location of the historical route is certain. Names are also shown for prominent expressways and turnpikes, such as the Pennsylvania Turnpike, the New York State Thruway, and the Santa Ana Freeway.

Names of roads in rural and remote areas are shown as posted. If none are posted, the road names are shown if they are well known and accepted by local residents.

In populated places and urban areas, as many road and street names are published as space allows after other requisite nomenclature has been selected. Ordinarily, the names of all the main arteries of traffic and other important through streets are shown, as are the names of as many others as space permits.

Destination Data

Mileages to road destinations outside the map area are shown to enable the map user to relate the map to well-known surrounding features (fig. 39). Double destination mileages are shown in the margin for all class 1 and 2 roads, except in areas of dense culture where the margin would be congested. In areas of sparse culture, single destination mileages may be shown for class 3 and 4 roads and, in rare cases, for trails.

Double mileages are shown for the next immediate and the next important destinations. Usually the important destination is a city. An immediate destination need not be a populated place, but may be the name or route number of an intersecting road. Limited-access highways passing through adjacent quadrangles are

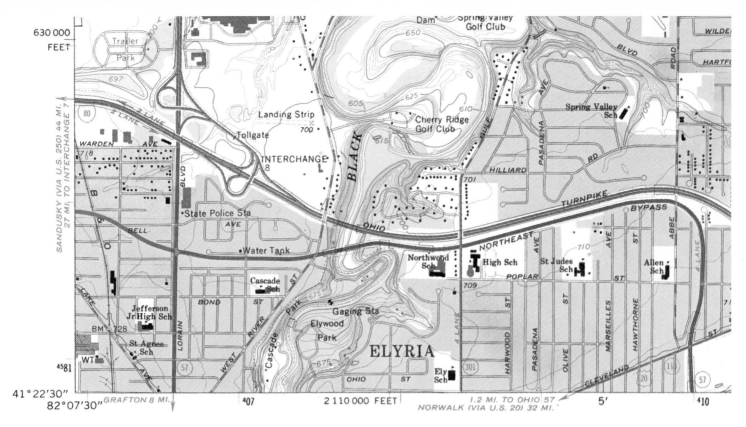

FIGURE 39. Turnpike named; overedge mileages given to next interchange and to major city; tollgate indicated by bar and label. (Avon, Ohio, quadrangle.)

used as either the immediate or the important destinations, particularly for Federal and State routes.

Road destination mileages of more than 5 miles are shown to the nearest mile; those of 5 miles or less, to the nearest 0.1 mile. In determining the mileage to a large town or city closer than 15 miles, a landmark in the center of town, such as the post office, courthouse, or civic center, is specified. If a route bypasses a town given as a destination, the mileage is measured to the town, not to the bypass junction.

As the principal function of limited-access highways is to provide high-speed routes between major cities and to bypass smaller places, the immediate destination is the next interchange or junction with a Federal or State route. The important destination is one of the major cities connected by the highway. The name or number of the exit or interchange is made a part of the destination data (fig. 39). If the exit for a major city is not within the city, the number of the Federal or State route connecting the city to the limited-access highway is added to the destination data. Other examples of over-edge destination data are:

(where interchange is within city)

(where exit is not within city)

Trails, Special Roads, and Related Features

In rugged mountainous and other remote areas and in recreational areas, trails are important map features as they not only provide access routes but also serve as means of orientation (fig. 40A). Foot, jeep, bridle, pack, ski, and historic trails are usually mapped; for example:

Δ Trails leading to mapped features, such as mines, cabins, lakes, and mountaintops, where they do not parallel roads.

Δ Trails providing access to hunting grounds, fishing waters, and other features of interest in recreational areas, regardless of roads that may exist.

Δ Trails developed for forest-fire protection.

Δ Trails that provide the only means of access to remote, isolated areas.

Minor or short connecting trails, those that are poorly maintained, and those intended only for private use generally are not shown.

Names are shown for major trails. Trails that are passable with a 4-wheel-drive vehicle are labeled "Jeep Trail" (fig. 40B). Major bridle, pack, and ski trails are also labeled.

Natural and Cultural Features on Topographic Maps

48

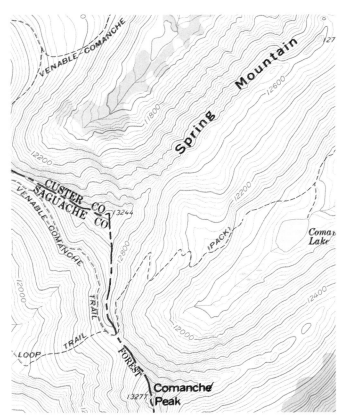

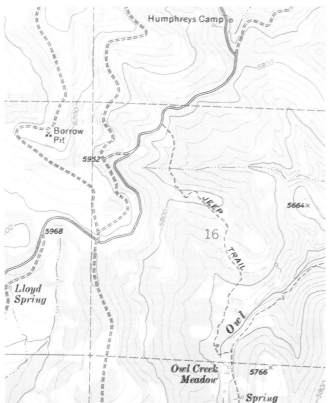

FIGURE 40A. Pack trails in mountainous area. (Horn Peak, Colo., quadrangle.)

FIGURE 40B. Trail passable with 4-wheel-drive vehicle. (Wolf Mountain, Oreg., quadrangle.)

All streets within the urban-tint area of a city, except principal arterial and secondary routes, are shown by the solid-line casing without red fill, regardless of the street condition. In populated places outside urban-tint areas, streets are classified and symbolized according to their physical condition.

In new suburban developments that represent the normal growth of a city, where curbs have been constructed or house foundations have been poured, the streets are shown with solid-line casings even though their physical condition at the time of mapping may not warrant it. In new, isolated developments some distance from a city and whose future status is uncertain, the streets are shown as they appear at the time of the mapping.

All streets up to 40 feet wide are plotted (on 1:24,000-scale maps) with the standard 0.020-inch symbol. Wider streets are mapped to scale in increments of 0.005 inch. All streets are shown regardless of length.

Named alleys having characteristics similar to those of a street and providing the only access to residential or business buildings are mapped as any other street, except that they are shown (on 1:24,000-scale maps) with the 0.015-inch symbol. Alleys in the middle of blocks that provide access only to the rear of buildings are not mapped.

In urban-tint areas the following types of highways are shown as class 1 or 2: Interstate, Federal, and State highways, including alternate routes; streets designated by traffic officials as alternate routes for through traffic but not identified by route numbers; and streets serving as main connections between through routes.

Main connecting streets between through routes may be parkways, wide or multiple-lane streets, or two parallel streets limited to one-way traffic in opposite directions. These unnumbered routes are shown as continuous class 1 or 2 routes between their junctions with other class 1 or 2 routes. Figure 41 illustrates the mapping of principal arterial and secondary routes in an urban-tint area.

Highways restricted to one-way traffic through congested areas are indicated by direction arrows. One-way streets without red fill are not marked with arrows.

Roads providing access to cemeteries, parks, other special-purpose areas, and private property are shown if they are at least 500 feet (150 m) long. Access roads are classified and symbolized the same as other roads. Within cemeteries and other special-purpose areas, only the main interconnecting roads are shown.

All private roads 500 feet long or longer are mapped according to their classification. In addition, class 3 private roads are labeled "Private" if they are through roads connecting to public roads (fig. 42). Class 4 private roads are not labeled.

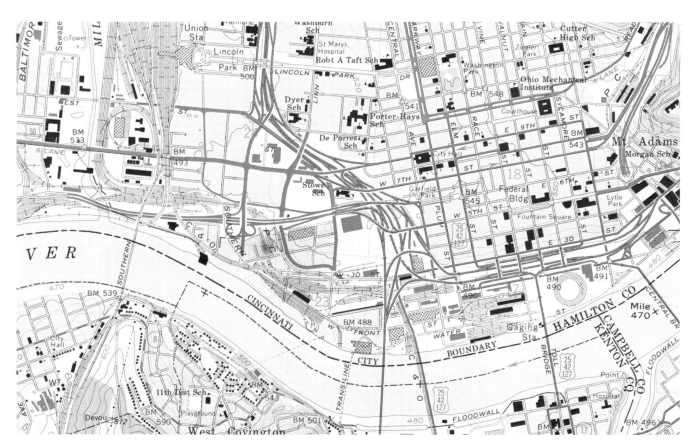

FIGURE 41. Principal arterial routes in urban-tint area. Arrows indicate direction of one-way traffic. Features added between 1961 and 1969 shown in purple. (Covington, Ky.-Ohio, quadrangle.)

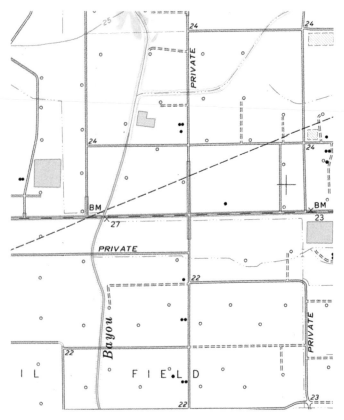

FIGURE 42. Labels indicate private roads that connect to public roads. (Monroe City, Tex., quadrangle.)

Private roads vary in degree of restricted use. Roads on suburban estates and in industrial plants may be completely closed to the public. In sparsely settled country, ranch or farm roads and logging roads are sometimes the only means of access to large areas. These may or may not be restricted for public use. Class 3 roads that could be misinterpreted as being part of the public road system but have locked gates or posted entrances are labeled "Private" or "Restricted."

In national parks, forests, and military reservations, certain roads may be closed to general use either permanently or temporarily. Regardless of classification, roads that are locked and not for general use are labeled "Restricted," and the point where the restriction begins is indicated by a tick or a gate symbol and label. Examples of restricted roads include roads to lookout towers and remote trail camps, firefighting roads, and other roads for official use only. On military reservations, roads closed periodically for firing are indicated as restricted. Public roads that are closed seasonally because of snow are not shown as restricted.

Any road for which a toll is charged is labeled "Toll Road." Each tollgate along a toll road is shown and labeled. Tollgates consisting of buildings that exceed the minimum symbol size are mapped to scale.

Facilities designed to serve users of limited-access highways, such as service or comfort stations and restaurants whose location and operation are controlled by the highway authority, are shown and labeled as posted; for example, "Service Area," "Service Facility," "Service Plaza." Officially designated rest areas, usually consisting of comfort stations and a surfaced parking area, are mapped and labeled "Rest Area."

To provide the map user with the latest available information about primary highways, class 1 roads planned or started but not finished at the time of field completion are shown if the State highway department furnishes detailed plans from which the roads can be plotted on the map manuscript and recommends that the information be published.

A road well along in construction, with substantial evidence that it will be open to traffic by the time the map is published or soon thereafter, is shown as a completed road.

A road well along in construction, with all legal and technical details of location and configuration clearly established but without evidence that it will be open to traffic by the time the map is published, is shown by a dashed black casing with solid red fill labeled "Under Construction" (fig. 43).

A road on which construction has been started but for which the location and configuration of some part or parts remain uncertain is symbolized according to the construction status of the parts. The parts for which the legal and technical details have been settled are shown and labeled "Under Construction." The parts for which the location or configuration is uncertain are shown and labeled "Proposed Location."

Bridges, Tunnels, and Other Connections

Bridges and viaducts are shown by the wing tick symbol if they are at least 300 feet (90 m) long. Bridges are also symbolized regardless of length if they are drawbridges (fig. 44), important historically, of conspicuous shape or design, or outstanding for any other reason. Names are shown for important and well-known bridges. Important footbridges are shown regardless of length. Pedestrian overpasses and the underpassing highways are also shown.

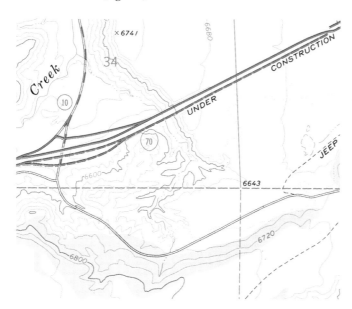

FIGURE 43. Road under construction, with exact aline-ment and configuration established. (Walker Flat, Utah, quadrangle.)

FIGURE 44. Drawbridges symbolized with circles and wing ticks. (Milwaukee, Wis., quadrangle.)

A road for which construction has been planned is shown as a proposed road if the State highway department supplies detailed route and construction plans together with a statement recommending that the proposed road be shown on the map. A proposed road is symbolized by a solid red line without casing and labeled "Proposed Location."

Fords, ferries, and tunnels are shown by dashed lines connecting the interrupted route symbols—single dashed lines for ferries and double dashed lines for road fords and tunnels. Tunnel entrances are shown by wing ticks, and the red highway fill is dropped. Trail fords are shown by single dashed lines. At single-line streams, fords for trails and class 4 roads are not symbolized or labeled. All other fords and ferries are labeled, and names are shown for important fords, ferries, and tunnels (fig. 45).

FIGURE 45. Ferries and tunnels shown by dashed lines connecting interrupted route symbols;   tunnel entrances by wing ticks. (Jersey City, N.J.-N.Y., quadrangle.)

Railroad Symbolization

Railroads are shown as map features by a line-and-crosstie symbol insofar as their roadbeds and tracks constitute physical ground features; the kind of motive power (electric, diesel, or steam) and the type of traffic (passenger or freight) are not considered. Railroads as travel routes provide a specific type of transportation and are generally uniform in width and surfacing. Consequently, railroads are not grouped into classes. Map symbols for railroads refer to operating status, gage, and number of tracks.

A railroad is symbolized according to the physical condition of its roadbed, trackage, and other facilities, as follows:

△ **A mainline railroad** is one that maintains regular or intermittent operating schedules between designated stations. This definition excludes sidings, yards, or spur tracks. Mainline railroads are shown by a solid-line railroad symbol, depending on the number of tracks. The names shown for railroads are those of the operating companies.

△ **An abandoned railroad** is one no longer in use but with ballast, tracks, and bridges substantially intact, which could be put into limited use with a reasonable amount of repair work. Abandoned railroads are labeled "Abandoned" and are shown by a dashed symbol with crossties. The beginning and end of each abandoned section are indicated by a double crosstie symbol.

ABANDONED

△ **A dismantled railroad** is one that has had most of its rails and bridges removed and is mapped only when the roadbed is a landmark or provides access to isolated areas. The roadbed is shown by the dashed trail symbol and labeled "Old Railroad Grade" (fig. 46).   *OLD RAILROAD GRADE*

△ **A railroad under construction** is illustrated by the dashed track symbols and labeled "Under Construction."

UNDER CONSTRUCTION

Natural and Cultural Features on Topographic Maps

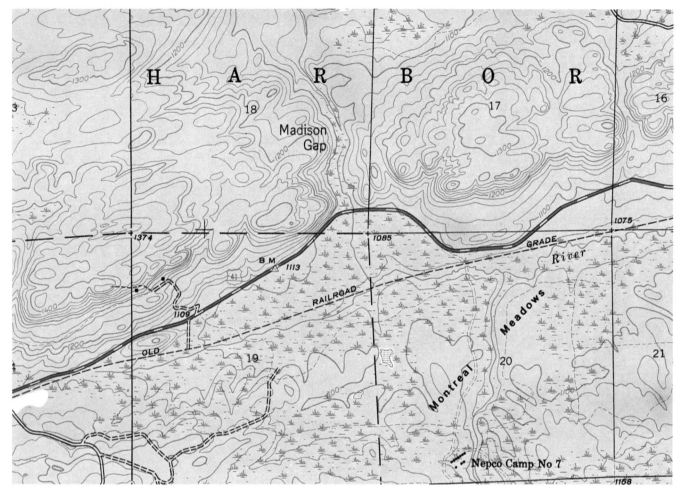

FIGURE 46. Alinement of dismantled railroad shown as landmark. (Eagle Harbor, Mich., quadrangle.)

Railroad gage is the distance between the rails of a track. In the United States, there are two:

Δ   **Standard gage.** A rail separation of 4 feet 8-1/2 inches. All mainline railroads are standard gage.

Δ   **Narrow gage.** Any rail separation less than 4 feet 8-1/2 inches, used mostly on private freight railroads.

Narrow-gage railroads are shown by line-and-half-tie symbols. If a narrow-gage railroad occupies the same roadbed as a standard-gage railroad, only the standard-gage railroad is symbolized, and the label "Narrow-Gage Railroad on Same Roadbed" is added.

The mainlines of all standard-gage railroads which have two or more tracks are shown by the multiple mainline track symbol. If there are more than two tracks, the number of tracks is shown by label, and points of change are indicated by double-tie symbols. The labels are placed parallel to the tracks on both sides of the double-tie symbol and are repeated wherever the number of tracks changes.   *3 TRACKS*

Tracks of separate operating companies that occupy the same roadbed in juxtaposition are symbolized separately. To distinguish the tracks of the two systems, the crosstie symbols of one system are staggered with respect to those of the other system.

A railroad located in a street is indicated by showing only the crossties within the road casing.

Sidings, spur tracks to such mapped features as mines or factories, or tracks used for storage of railroad cars are mapped accurately in length but may be adjusted in position at right angles to the alinement if the map scale and the adjacent detail require it. In congested or urban areas, minor industrial sidings may be omitted, but in sparsely settled areas, sidings or short sections of double track are usually landmarks, often have names, and are always shown.

Railroad yards are mapped in outline as defined by the outer tracks (fig. 47). Within the yard mainline tracks are shown in true position. Other tracks are generalized, but the distinctive pattern of the yard is portrayed to the extent feasible. The crossties are spaced in staggered rows to give a balanced, orderly appearance, with the longest crossties touching no more than six tracks.

Roads and Railroads

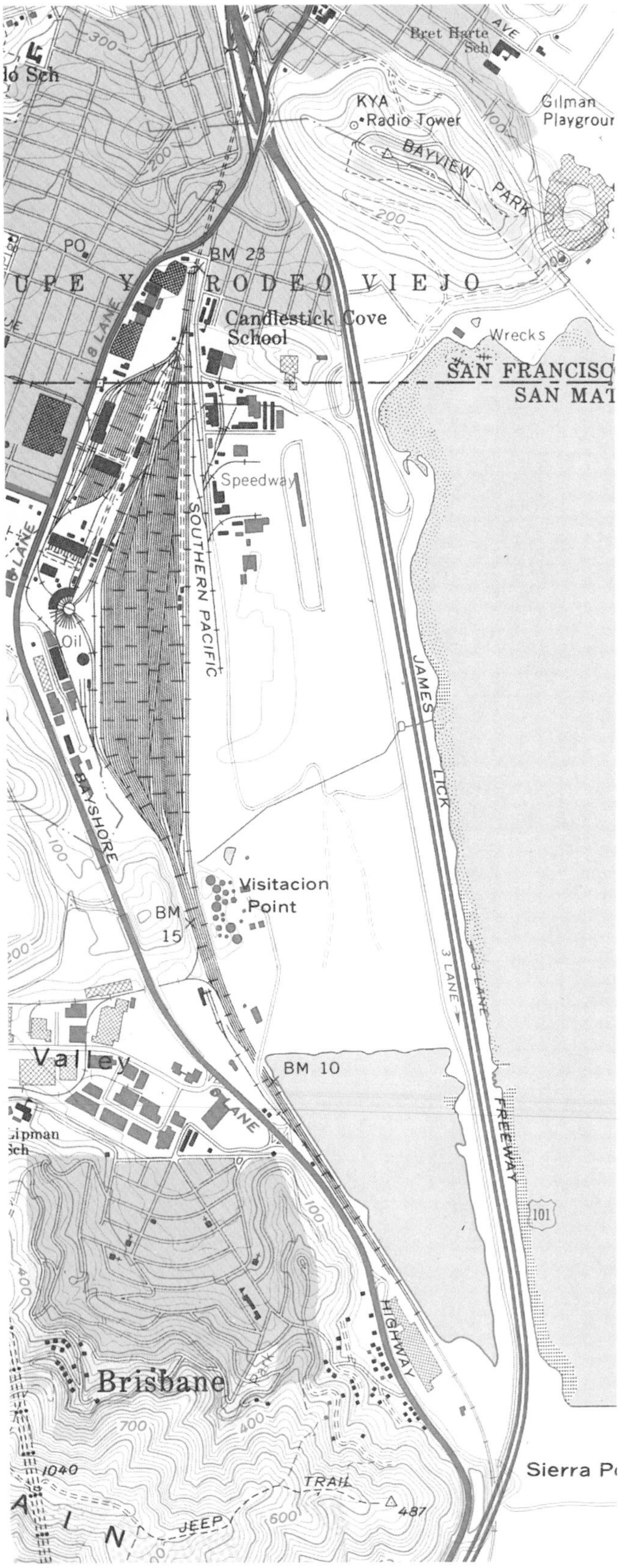

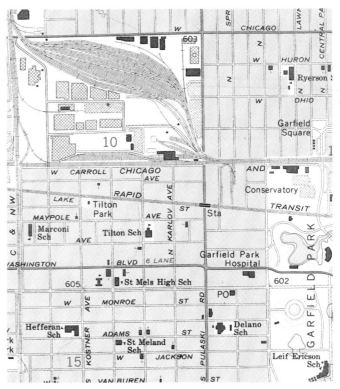

FIGURE 47. Treatment of complex railroad installations. (San Francisco South, Calif., quadrangle.)

A. Underground railroad shown by dashed double lines.

B. Railroad yard, turntable, roundhouse, and shops. Main-line tracks (*far right*) correctly alined, and inner tracks portrayed by representative pattern. Roundhouse, other buildings, and turntable plotted to scale.

C. Grade-separation crossing of road over railroad.

Roundhouses are shown in outline true to scale. Turntables are plotted as a circle with a straight line across the diameter but not connecting any tracks.

A railroad station is shown as a class 1 building; it is outlined to scale (on 1:24,000-scale maps) if larger than 40 by 40 feet. In a small city or village where the station building may be difficult to identify, it may be shown across the track. If no permanent building exists, the flag stop is shown only by name if its location on the map is apparent from an intersecting road or a siding. If the location is not evident, the double crosstie symbol is used to show the point where the name applies.

Grade crossings of two railroads or of a railroad and a road are shown by continuous symbols of the crossing features. At grade-separation crossings, the symbol of the underpassing feature is broken 0.020 inch from the symbol of the overpassing feature.

Subway systems are not shown. For mainline railroads underground, the alinement of the tunnel is shown by dashed double lines, and the railroad symbol is terminated at the headwalls of the tunnel. In congested areas the tunnel alinement may be omitted if it cannot be shown legibly.

Rapid-transit lines are mapped like conventional railroads with the standard track symbolization and labeled "Rapid Transit" (fig. 48). Stations are symbolized and labeled "Sta." The operating company name is not shown.

FIGURE 48. Rapid-transit line elevated over street. (Chicago Loop, Ill., quadrangle.)

Natural and Cultural Features on Topographic Maps

Inclined railways, cableways, belt conveyors, ski lifts, and similar features of sufficient size and importance to be mapped are shown by the dashed landmark line and labeled. Railroad snowsheds are mapped as class 2 buildings and labeled (fig. 49).

FIGURE 49. Ski lifts and tramways. Snowsheds mapped as large class 2 buildings. (Norden, Calif., quadrangle.)

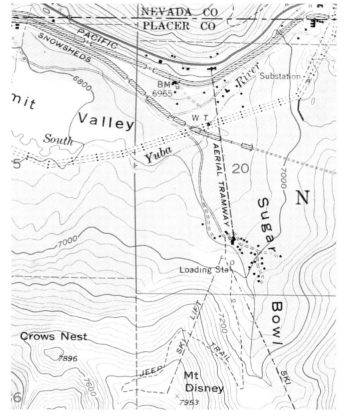

In mapping railroads, the contour crossings, always at right angles to the alinement, are carefully located (the elevations of the ties are used, not those of the tops of the rails). The spaces between contour crossings are made to represent the grade as accurately as feasible within the limitations of the contour interval.

Buildings and Urban Features

Aside from roads, buildings and groups of buildings are by far the most common manmade features shown on 7.5- and 15-minute topographic maps. As all buildings cannot be shown legibly, various means must be used to simplify the map presentation. Some kinds of buildings are omitted, some buildings are shown larger than their actual size, and in congested areas only landmark buildings are mapped.

Building Classification and Selection

All buildings shown on published maps are symbolized as either class 1 or class 2 according to the following definitions:

Δ **Class 1 buildings** are those structures intended primarily for housing human activities; this class includes residences, hotels, churches, schools, shops, factories, service stations, most public buildings, and others of a similar character.

Δ **Class 2 buildings** are those structures not intended primarily for housing human activities; this class includes barns, sheds, warehouses, greenhouses, storage garages, and others constructed to house machinery or animals, or for storage.

In applying the class definitions, the intended function of the building is the basic criterion. Factories, stores, and similar structures are class 1 because their primary function is to house human activities. Barns and warehouses are class 2 because they do not serve this function. But there are many buildings which are partly for housing human activities and partly for other purposes, and therefore can be considered either class 1 or 2. In borderline cases, the building is classified according to its predominant characteristic; for example, a small office in a large storage building does not affect the class 2 character of the building.

The term "landmark building" is used in two senses with respect to map presentation. On maps showing built-up areas covered with a tint, landmark buildings are those of importance because of their public function, historical associations, or conspicuous size or appearance relative to others in the area. Within the urban-tint areas, only landmark buildings are shown.

In the second sense, outside of urban areas, a landmark building is any building which is conspicuous because of size, height, or location, or distinctive in relation to its surroundings and therefore worthy of being mapped. In rural areas of sparse culture, even buildings such as abandoned cabins or isolated barns acquire relative importance as reference points and are shown as landmarks.

Depending on the map publication scale and the building classification, buildings are shown or omitted as follows:

Δ Class 1 buildings are shown on both 7.5- and 15-minute maps, except in urban areas covered by a tint.

Δ Class 2 buildings smaller than the average local dwelling are not shown. Examples of such buildings are sheds, private garages, and small chickenhouses.

Δ Class 2 buildings are not shown on 15-minute maps, except when they are of a landmark character. Landmark class 2 buildings for this purpose are those in a prominent location, those larger than 100 × 100 feet in any location, and those of any size in areas where cultural features are few.

An exception to these general rules applies in small towns, not covered by an urban-area tint, where space is limited by the street pattern. Most class 2 buildings are omitted in these areas; only those that are outstanding and those that can be plotted without congestion or displacement are shown.

SYMBOLIZATION. Class 1 buildings are depicted by a solid or crosshatch symbol, and class 2 buildings by an open outline or single-hatch symbol, with the hatching running in a northeast-southwest direction. For legibility a minimum limit on the size of building symbols is required. The minimum sizes specified for different types of buildings on 1:24,000-scale manuscripts are given in table 2. Regardless of the actual size of a building, its symbol is never drawn smaller than the specified minimum size.

TABLE 2. Minimum dimensions, in customary units, of buildings and symbols used on 1:24,000-scale maps

Type of building	Feet on ground	Inches on map	Symbol
		Dimensions	
Class 1	40 × 40	0.02 × 0.02	.
Class 2	50 × 50	.025 × .025	▫
School	50 × 50	.025 × .025	⌀
Flag		.02 × .03	
School (congested area)	40 × 40	.02 × .02	⌀
Flag		.017 × .025	
Church	50 × 50	.025 × .025	⌀
Cross		.04 × .025	
Church (congested area)	40 × 40	.02 × .02	⌀
Cross		.033 × .02	
Cliff dwelling	35 × 60	.017 × .03	▫
Base		.05	

In open areas, buildings larger than minimum symbol size are plotted to scale (fig. 50). In general, buildings up to 60 feet in a major dimension may be plotted with minimum-size symbols. Thus, a building measuring 60 by 40 feet would be shown as 40 by 40 feet on a 1:24,000-scale map.

FIGURE 50. Large buildings mapped to scale. Buildings hatched or crosshatched when larger than specified size. (Akron West, Ohio, quadrangle.)

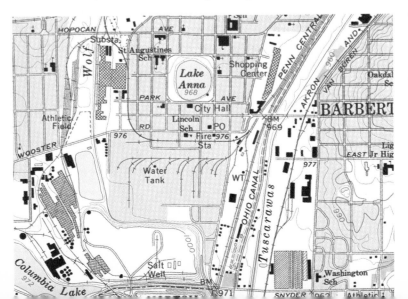

In congested areas where the street pattern or other map features leave insufficient space for all the buildings, all class 1 buildings of approximately the same size may be plotted with the minimum size symbol if necessary to avoid omitting some buildings. However, if space is limited in a block containing one or more relatively large buildings and several smaller ones, the large buildings are plotted to scale and the smaller buildings omitted if necessary (fig. 51).

FIGURE 51. Building omission in congested areas. *A*, actual ground condition; *B*, map representation at 1:24,000 scale.

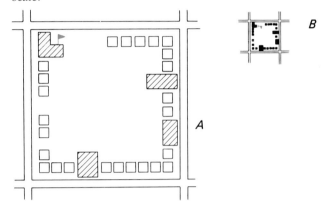

In showing buildings of irregular shape, small wings, bays, and projections usually are disregarded, but the generalized outline is presented correctly. Particular care is taken to preserve the correct orientation with respect to nearby streets and other buildings.

Accuracy standards for 7.5- and 15-minute maps require that well-defined points be shown within 0.02 inch of their true position. The center of any building drawn to symbol size and the corners of large buildings drawn to scale are considered well-defined points; they are therefore shown with standard accuracy.

Building symbols plotted in correct position sometimes touch or overlap other plotted features. For legibility it is therefore necessary to sacrifice true horizontal accuracy and displace one of the interfering symbols. When interference occurs between a building and a linear feature of regular alinement such as a road, railroad, or canal, the linear feature is held in position and the building symbol is displaced. The displacement is in the direction normal to the alinement of the linear feature and is the smallest amount necessary for legibility.

If the interfering linear feature has an irregular course like a stream or trail, the building is held fixed and the linear feature displaced. Boundary and section lines, which do not represent physical structures, and powerlines and underground pipelines, which are not on the same level as buildings, are allowed to intersect on the map with building symbols.

Natural and Cultural Features on Topographic Maps

Buildings located near boundaries are carefully checked for position in relation to the boundary and plotted on the correct side of the boundary. If buildings of symbol size or smaller fall on the edge of a quadrangle, the building symbol is displaced enough to clear the projection line. Buildings large enough to plot to scale are not displaced; they are divided along the projection line and parts are plotted in each quadrangle.

The triangular symbol for a traverse or triangulation station is always plotted in correct position. Small buildings that fall within or overlap a triangle are not shown. When the omitted building is of landmark value, however, it may be labeled even though it is not shown. A building overlapping a triangle only slightly may be shifted enough to clear the triangle. When the triangular symbol interferes with a large building, the building outline and fill are broken to permit both features to be shown in true position.

SPECIAL BUILDINGS AND RELATED STRUC-TURES. A group of attached rowhouses and abutting business buildings that form a continuous structure are shown as a single building.

A covered driveway into a building, courtyard, or parking area is not treated as a break; however, other open spaces between groups of attached buildings are shown to scale.

Rows of detached buildings, such as residences in suburban areas, are symbolized by the actual number of buildings in correct position if space permits; otherwise some buildings must be omitted. In blocks that are almost completely filled, vacant lots and open spaces are the features to be preserved. Building symbols are spaced to show the open features in correct relative position (fig. 52).

FIGURE 52. Buildings in congested area shown with minimum-size symbol; location of open areas is preserved. (Terre Haute, Ind., quadrangle.)

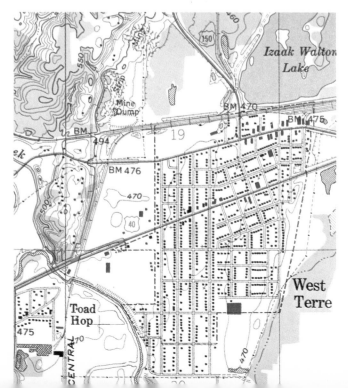

If space permits, each building is shown for hospitals, schools, colleges, or religious institutions that consist of a group of buildings (fig. 53). After the limits of the outer buildings have been correctly shown, it may be necessary to omit some of the smaller inner buildings and place the more important ones in relatively correct position.

FIGURE 53. Group of buildings plotted in true position when scale permits. Stadium mapped as class 2 building. (Princeton, N.J., quadrangle.)

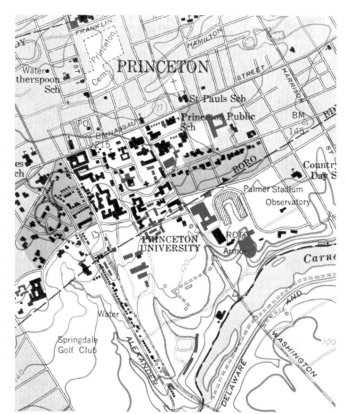

When it is necessary to displace one or more buildings of a group, the positions of the other buildings are proportionally adjusted so that the pattern of the buildings in the group approximates the true pattern on the ground. If possible, the adjustment is made so that the buildings most distant from the road or street can be shown in their true positions.

Churches and schools are distinguished from other buildings by symbolization. Each church is identified by the cross symbol and each school by the flag symbol; a building serving as both church and school is symbolized as a school. Normally, only churches and schools that are easily identifiable and occupy a separate building with some open grounds are shown with the characteristic symbol.

Universities, colleges, and public schools are always identified by the flag symbol. This category includes public and privately supported universities and colleges, schools within the public school system, and industrial schools operated by a public authority. A school that is an extension of a university or college, generally located in a metropolitan area, is identified as a school if it occupies an entire separate building or group of buildings.

Other private schools of a public character that have a physical plant similar to public schools and are well known locally are shown with the flag symbol. This group may include parochial, preparatory, boarding, and other similar schools.

Schools normally not identified with the flag symbol include extension schools occupying part of a building, private schools held in a private dwelling, commercially sponsored industrial schools, business or trade schools, dancing schools, temporary schools, and other schools of this general type.

Religious institutions identified with the cross symbol include churches, cathedrals, mosques, temples, synagogues, convents, monasteries, and other similar institutions. Buildings used for church services, on either a temporary or permanent basis, that were not designed as churches are not shown as churches.

If a school consists of a group of buildings, the flag symbol is shown only on the administration building, if identifiable, or on the most prominent building. Similarly, for religious institutions, the cross symbol is attached preferably to the building used for religious services or to the most prominent building.

Names of all schools and churches in nonurban areas and all schools and the more prominent churches in urban areas are published if space permits. Closed schools and churches are symbolized and their names supplied if they are still available for their intended use. The characteristic symbol is not used for churches or schools converted to other uses, but their names may appear on the map if still used as place names.

Tourist courts and motels vary widely in general plan and in the size and density of units. If the units are of substantial size and spaced far enough apart, they are symbolized individually, but if the units are small and congested, some are omitted. In extreme cases, the feature may be shown by a single building symbol representing the office. A row of attached units is symbolized as a single building.

Some modern trailer parks are elaborate installations with paved driveways, permanent laundry and restrooms, and swimming pools. The paved driveways and permanent buildings are shown and the features are labeled "Trailer Park." However, trailer homes are not shown even if they are temporarily immovable (fig. 54).

The wall or fence enclosing a drive-in theater is shown by a dashed line in true position; the screen is represented by a solid line and the projector housing or other structures by class 1 building symbols. The access roads to the structure are shown if they are more than 500 feet (150 m) long, and the complex is labeled "Drive-in Theater" (fig. 54).

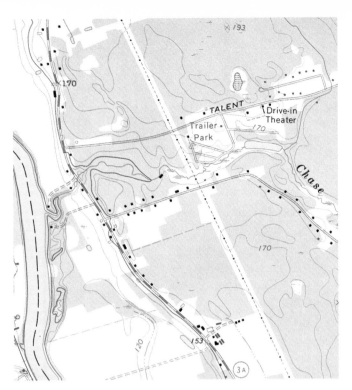

FIGURE 54. Permanent trailer park mapped to include the road system, buildings, and label. Fence, screen, and structures are shown for drive-in theater. (Nashua North, N.H., quadrangle.)

Grandstands or stadiums, covered or open, are shown as class 2 buildings, even if space beneath them is used for dressing rooms, classrooms, or other human activities. Racetracks, regardless of surface, are shown with dashed double lines, as nearly as possible to scale. Playing fields or other enclosed areas of importance (which are not a part of a larger recreational area) are shown by dashed outlines; athletic tracks are shown by the dashed single-line symbol. Names or labels are shown where they are needed for clarity or where space permits (fig. 55).

FIGURE 55. Grandstand shown as class 2 building; racetrack by dashed outline. (Louisville West, Ky.-Ind., quadrangle.)

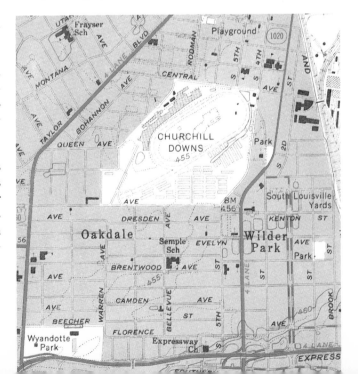

Ruins are defined for map presentation as structures of historical significance in such a state of decay that they can no longer be used for their original purposes. If they are landmarks in areas of sparse culture or if they are preserved as a local feature of interest, they are shown. Ruins smaller than 100 by 100 feet are shown with solid open outline; larger ruins are shown with a dashed outline. Ruins are identified by name, or the label "Ruins" (fig. 56).

FIGURE 56. Ruins shown by label and solid or dashed outline when of landmark or historical nature. (Cochiti Dam, N.M., quadrangle.)

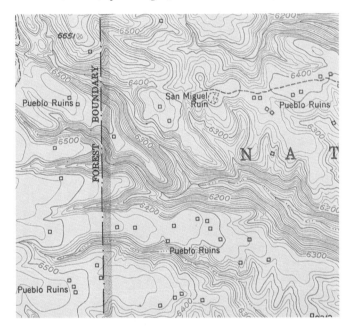

Towers that are outstanding for their height or location are shown as landmark features. Because they are visible from a distance, towers are useful for map orientation. Towers are shown by the located-object symbol and labeled appropriately.

Towers that support any type of radio antenna are labeled "Radio Tower." Radio communication embraces many types of systems, including radiotelegraphy, radiotelephone, AM, FM, TV broadcasting, and radio navigation aids. For the purpose of labeling, the towers associated with these systems are all treated as part of a radio communication installation, without regard to specific type. Such terms as relay, radar, repeater, TV, antenna, microwave, or range are not used as descriptive labels.

If the towers are part of a larger installation, they are labeled in preference to the installation. If antennas are mounted directly on buildings and there are no towers, the installation is shown as a landmark building and labeled "Radio Facility." Towers are not shown if they are located on structures used predominantly for pur-

poses other than radio communication, as on large office buildings.

Broadcasting towers of commercial stations are further distinguished by labeling them with the station call letters. If the broadcasting station and transmitting towers are in the same location, only the towers are labeled; if they are at different locations, the broadcasting station is labeled "Radio Station" with appropriate call letters.

Unusual radio facilities such as radio telescope, tracking, and detection stations are shown only if they appear as prominent landmark features. They are shown with a label appropriate to the installation; for example, "Radio Telescope."

Towers used for observation and for spotting forest fires are shown with the located-object symbol and labeled "Lookout Tower." Observation buildings not mounted on towers, or platforms located on roofs of buildings, which serve the same purpose as lookout towers, are plotted as buildings and labeled "Lookout."

Urban Areas

The term "urban area," as defined for mapping purposes, does not refer to political boundaries or legal designations, but rather denotes a congested built-up area where all buildings cannot be shown in their true position because of the limitations of map scale. If all buildings were mapped, other more valuable map information such as landmark buildings, street names, and contour lines would be obscured.

Urban areas are mapped with a tint overprint. Within the tinted area only those buildings that are landmarks are shown (fig. 57). This treatment allows landmark buildings to be accentuated and names and other detail to be shown legibly.

Urban-area treatment is not ordinarily used on areas smaller than 0.75 mi² (2 km²), except on isolated "islands" adjacent to larger urban areas (fig. 58). Such islands may carry the urban-area tint when they are as small as 0.25 mi² (0.65 km²).

Urban-area tint is always omitted from parks and cemeteries, regardless of size, and from open-water features such as lakes, ponds, reservoirs, and double-line streams.

The urban-area tint is also omitted over features that have well-defined boundaries and open grounds the size of an average city block or larger. The grounds may be occupied by a college, hospital, large shopping center, church, school, factory, or similar feature. The open areas, which need not coincide with city streets, are outlined as clearings, the tint is omitted, and detail within the opening is shown as if it were outside the urban area. Woodland is not shown in the urban-area tint.

Also excluded from the urban-area tint are certain industrial complexes consisting of large factory buildings, mills, powerplants, warehouses, refineries, stock-

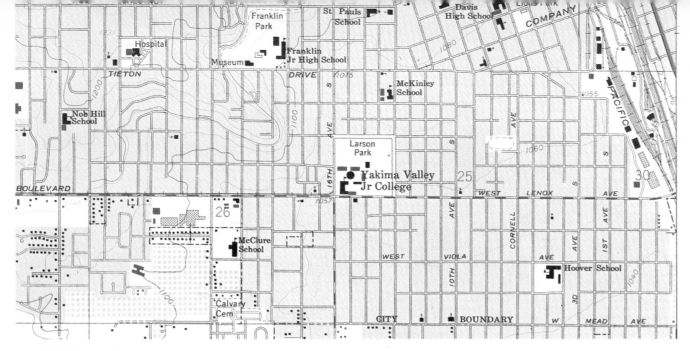

FIGURE 57. Urban-tint outline is drawn to a reasonably regular shape, without necked attachments or narrow fingers. Where practical, the limits may coincide with cultural features and boundaries. Tint is omitted from large open areas. (Yakima West, Wash., quadrangle.)

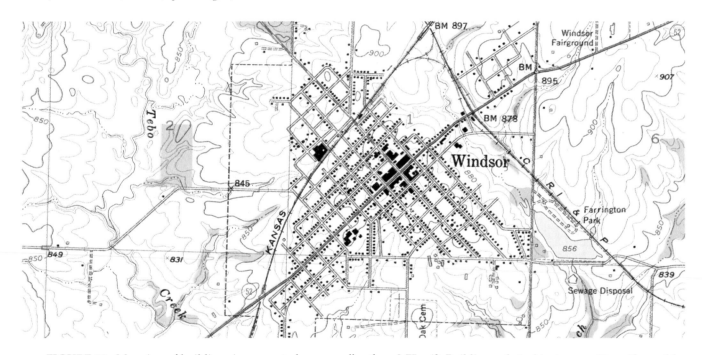

FIGURE 58. Mapping of buildings in congested area smaller than 0.75 mi². Buildings plotted in true position, if possible; otherwise displaced to allow for linear features. Small class 2 buildings omitted. (Windsor, Mo., quadrangle.)

yards, or other structures of the same general character. Interspersed with the large buildings are such features as parking lots, storage yards, tanks, miscellaneous small buildings, and railroad yards and sidings. If there is considerable open space in such areas, the tint is omitted from the entire area, and the detail is shown. Industrial complexes that are congested by numerous small structures, leaving little open space, are included within the urban-area tint, and only landmark buildings are shown.

Openings are also made for parking areas when they are larger than an average city block. If the limits of parking areas do not coincide with streets or other linear features, they are shown with black outline. However,

parking areas in conjunction with industrial plants or shopping centers are not labeled or outlined since their presence can be inferred by the open space or by the tint omission.

Within urban areas, schools, churches, hospitals, government, and other important public-use buildings are shown. Buildings of historic importance and buildings that are conspicuous because of size or appearance are also shown, as well as large groups of buildings that constitute a major manufacturing plant or an isolated, unified shopping center. Branch post offices are shown only when they occupy a separate building. Motels and hotels are not normally shown in urban areas. Only those churches and schools that would normally be identified with their characteristic symbol are shown within urban-tint areas.

Examples of public-use buildings that are shown in urban-tint areas are:

Auditoriums	Medical centers
Armories	Memorials
Bus terminals	Mosques
Capitols	Museums
Churches	Post offices
City and town halls	Private schools
Community centers	Public schools
Courthouses	Stadiums
Hospitals	Synagogues
Libraries	Universities

Corporate, locality, and boundary names are always shown within urban areas. If space permits, park and cemetery names, linear and hydrographic feature names, and public-use building names are shown for these mapped features. The names of all universities, colleges, public schools, and large private schools are shown, provided space is available. Numbered public schools are shown with their numerical designation. The names of only the historic, landmark, and unusually important churches are shown in urban-tint areas. Shopping centers are labeled, and also named if space is available. Wherever space permits, other landmark buildings are identified by name.

The names of the main streets are shown along with as many secondary street names as can be accommodated in the urban-tint area.

The use of the urban-tint treatment makes topographic information more legible. This is especially important because there are many map-use problems in urban areas that require accurate elevation information.

The contours represent the ground surface as if no buildings were present, and are drawn across building symbols to represent the natural, undisturbed terrain. All contours cross the streets at right angles. Numerous checked spot elevations are shown, usually with at least two elevations per square mile.

Miscellaneous Features

Linear Features

Linear features such as fence lines, pipelines, power transmission lines, and telephone lines are shown on topographic maps primarily because of their landmark character, not because they are transportation or communication routes. They are mapped when they are prominent in relation to their surroundings. Lines may be shown in open country and dropped as they approach congested areas where they lose their value as landmarks and where they could not be shown without overcrowding the map. Lines also may be dropped in open country if their routes coincide with, or parallel closely, more important linear features, such as roads or railroads.

FENCE LINES. Selected fence lines, except those coincident with or closely paralleling section, township, or civil boundaries, are shown on 7.5-minute maps by fine red dashed lines. The purpose in mapping fence lines is to aid the map user by showing more well-defined features in areas where cultural features are not congested. Figure 59 shows mapped fence lines in a public-land State at an appropriate density. In sectionized areas, fence lines on regular subdivision lines take precedence in publication.

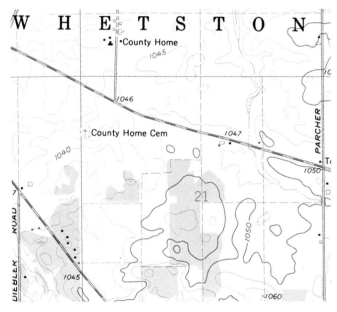

FIGURE 59. Fence lines in areas with public-land subdivisions. Lines coincident with or closely paralleling section lines, boundaries, or other linear features are omitted. (Bucyrus, Ohio, quadrangle.)

PIPELINES. In the Western States, major cross-country pipelines carrying oil or gas are important landmarks. The routes are marked by surface scars, telephone lines, clearings, or fragments of roads, although the actual pipes are underground. Except in congested areas, these pipelines are usually shown in their entirety within a quadrangle.

In the Middle Western and Eastern States, oil and gas pipelines tend to lose their landmark character because the surface scars disappear in agricultural areas and the density of other cultural features is greater. In these circumstances pipelines generally are not shown. In timbered areas the cleared right-of-way for a pipeline is shown as a landmark feature by breaking the woodland overprint, as for a firebreak.

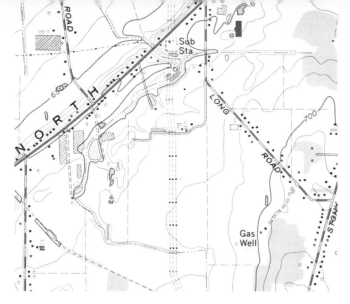

FIGURE 60A. Power transmission lines mapped in open country. Selected metal towers are plotted in true position and symbolized. Substation shown by dashed outline and label. (Avon, Ohio, quadrangle.)

POWER TRANSMISSION LINES. Major cross-country power transmission lines that are supported by steel towers or double wooden poles are shown as landmark lines if they can be plotted without displacement.

Single-pole lines may also be mapped if they cross areas devoid of other well-defined features and therefore constitute landmark features in themselves. In wooded areas the landmark value of a minor power transmission line may be preserved by showing the break in woodland, omitting the power transmission line itself. Low-grade service roads along powerlines are not shown unless they provide the only access into an area and therefore constitute important travel routes.

Metal powerline towers that can be plotted in true position are symbolized by small squares. The conventional dash-and-dot transmission line symbol is shown between the plotted towers, except that no dots are shown if plotted towers are less than 0.5 inch (1.3 cm) apart at map scale. Figure 60A shows power transmission lines with individual towers symbolized. Long spans over water are shown by dashed lines (fig. 60B).

FIGURE 60B. Transmission lines over water are shown as dashed lines unless supports actually exist. (Gig Harbor, Wash., quadrangle.)

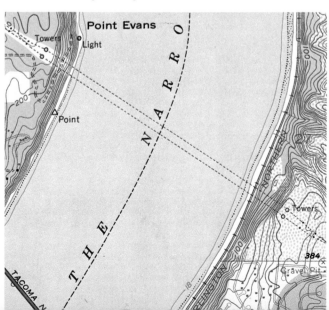

In urban-tint areas substations are not shown. In other areas landmark substations adjacent to mapped transmission lines are shown if they can be plotted to scale without displacement of other features. If they are unhoused, they are shown with a dashed outline and labeled; housed substations are represented as class 2 buildings.

TELEPHONE LINES. Telephone lines, shown with a dashed line, are mapped on the same principles as power transmission lines, except the supporting poles are not shown. Telephone lines prominent enough to be considered landmarks are shown only if other cultural features are sparse and the line of poles is conspicuous. Underground telephone cables are not shown.

Special-Purpose Areas

Ground areas used for industrial, commercial, or other special purposes are frequently difficult to show clearly on the map because the structures within the areas may not be suited to standard map symbols or the structures may be too numerous to be plotted legibly. The objective in mapping these areas is to show their boundaries and to represent the typical or most prominent characteristics without congesting the map unnecessarily.

The presentation of a railroad yard (see p. 54) is a typical example of the map treatment of industrial areas. The mainline tracks, yard limits, and principal buildings are plotted in true position, but the other tracks are simplified, preserving, as much as possible, the characteristic pattern of the yard. Other special-purpose areas are mapped according to the same principle, with the treatment modified to fit particular conditions.

AIRWAY FACILITIES. Airway facilities that are mapped include airports, airfields, landing areas, landing strips, seaplane bases, and heliports. The map representation generally shows the boundaries of the facility, runways, taxiways, aprons, and important buildings.

For mapping purposes, common airway terms are defined as follows:

△ **Airport.** An extensive body of land or water used for landing of aircraft, with appurtenant areas used for airport buildings or right-of-way. An airport has facilities for refueling, extensive repairs, and shelter for passengers and cargo (fig. 61).

△ **Airfield.** An airway installation having limited facilities, refueling services for light traffic, and facilities for limited repairs.

△ **Landing area (or field).** An area designated for the landing of aircraft, generally with limited or no facilities for refueling, repairs, or shelter for passengers and cargo and usually without hard-surfaced runways; in some cases, runways are not defined.

△ **Landing strip.** A landing area consisting of a single runway, improved or unimproved, with limited or no refueling facilities.

Natural and Cultural Features on Topographic Maps

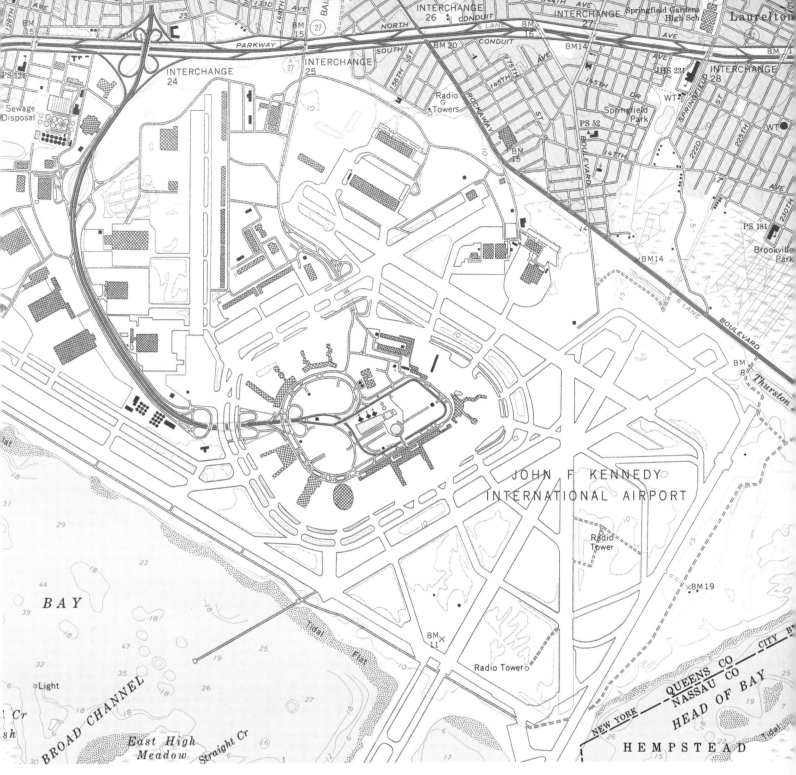

FIGURE 61. Large airport with paved runways, taxiways, and aprons shown with solid outline. Hangars, terminals, and other buildings shown with standard building symbols. (Jamaica, N.Y., quadrangle.)

Airway facilities are labeled, or labeled and named, according to the above definitions. However, the official name applied by the controlling organization is used in preference to any other designation.

The boundaries of airway facilities are shown with a dashed line, except where they coincide with other linear features. Runways, taxiways, and aprons adjoining a hangar or terminal are shown with a solid outline if they are of hard-surfaced construction. Loose-surfaced or turf runways and unimproved runways with clearly defined limits are plotted with a dashed outline (fig. 62). Unimproved or unimportant aprons and taxiways are not shown.

Hangars, terminals, and other buildings are classified and mapped with standard building symbols. Air navigation towers along the principal airway routes are shown with the located-object symbol and labeled. Runway lights, radar approach equipment, obstruction lights, and other minor facilities are not shown. In most instances a spot elevation on the highest point of the runway is published.

Miscellaneous Features

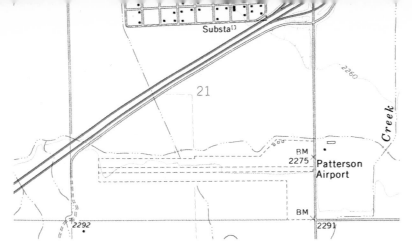

FIGURE 62. Small airport with loose-surfaced runway shown with dashed outlines. (Terry, Mont., quadrangle.)

The buildings, ramps, and hangars of seaplane bases are mapped, and the feature is named or labeled; but the limits of the water area used as a runway are usually not shown. If the information is available from hydrographic charts, the limits may be shown with a dashed blue outline, but buoys or other marks are not shown.

Landing areas for helicopters are shown by a dashed outline, or by the located-object symbol, depending on the size. They are labeled "Heliport." Heliports on buildings are not shown.

OIL AND GAS FIELDS. Oil or gas fields usually have complex systems of wells, tanks, sump pits, and buildings interconnected by pipes and roads of various kinds. In showing such an area, considerable elimination and generalization are necessary.

The main roads, principal buildings, and most conspicuous tanks are shown in correct position, insofar as symbol sizes permit. As many wells as possible are shown, preferably in correct position but displaced if necessary for clearance of other cultural features. All wells can be mapped in new fields in many States, where the minimum legal spacing is 1 well in each 10 acres; but all cannot be shown for older fields with wells spaced more closely. The minimum practical spacing between well centers is about 200 feet (61 m) for mapping at 1:24,000 scale. If wells must be omitted, the characteristic pattern of the field is preserved by showing the wells on the perimeter of the field in correct position and keeping the relative position and density of groups as accurate as possible. The individual pumphouses and the piping of the field are not shown; only the oil sumps or sludge pits that are outstanding landmarks are shown.

Exploratory "dry" wells away from developed fields are significant map features to those interested in the geology of the area. Such wells are shown, when they can be located with reasonable facility, and labeled "Drill hole."

INDUSTRIAL PLANT AREAS. Chemical plants, refineries, and similar installations are special-purpose areas that present problems of generalization. Many small features often must be omitted, but the portrayal

reflects the relative density of structures and permanent plant equipment in the area. The principal roads, railroads, tanks, and class 1 and 2 buildings are plotted to scale or to the specified minimum symbol sizes. Composite open-air structures, such as batteries of small tanks and dense clusters of stills, cracking towers, and other tanklike objects, often interconnected by pipes and catwalks, are symbolized by groups of closely spaced 0.02-inch dots arranged to depict the general shape of the batteries and clusters. Fire-protection levees associated with tank farms are shown by the levee symbol (fig. 63).

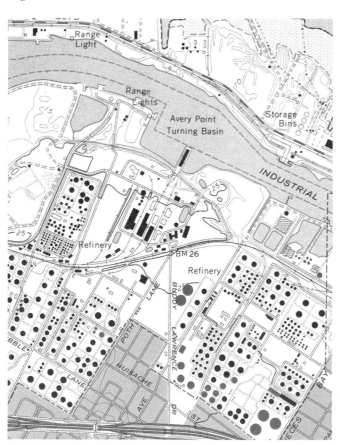

FIGURE 63. Map representation of refineries. (Corpus Christi, Tex., quadrangle.)

CEMETERIES AND GRAVES. In addition to their importance as cultural features, cemeteries are critical items of map content because they frequently present serious obstacles to land development. Cemeteries readily identifiable as such are shown, irrespective of size or whether public or private (fig. 64*A*).

Small cemeteries (less than 50 feet—15 m—square) are shown with a solid outline and labeled. Larger cemeteries are plotted to scale with a dashed outline, except where the boundaries are coincident with other linear features (fig. 64*B*). Only the main roads and important buildings are shown within cemetery limits.

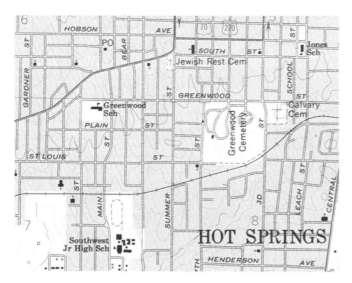

FIGURE 64A. Cemeteries with names outside or inside boundaries, depending on the size. (Hot Springs South, Ark., quadrangle.)

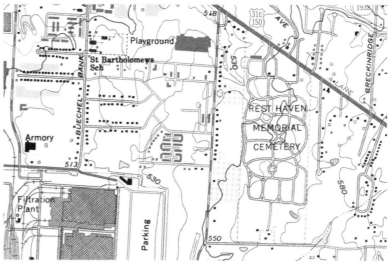

FIGURE 64B. Large cemetery with road pattern and buildings. Boundary dropped with other linear features. (Louisville East, Ky., quadrangle.)

Lone graves are sometimes landmark features and in many cases have some historical importance. They are shown with a small cross symbol and labeled "Grave." A group of several graves is considered a small cemetery.

RECREATIONAL AREAS. Although the features shown on maps of recreational areas are essentially the same as those shown on maps of other areas, emphasis is given to items that are of special interest to vacationers. Trails paralleling main roads, campsites, and viewpoints are important features on maps of recreational areas, although these same features might be omitted on maps of areas not set aside as recreational areas.

Campgrounds, campsites, and small roadside parks are shown when they are of landmark value, are operated by a public organization, are reasonably substantial and permanent, and do not conflict with more important map detail. Campgrounds or campsites along roads or trails are areas designated and developed for overnight or extended camping. These areas are shown with the tepee symbol and labeled. Permanent buildings and roads within the campground are shown, but the limits of the area are not indicated.

Permanent roadside parks and picnic grounds are shown with the table symbol, without boundaries, when they include a parking area, fireplaces, tables, and possibly some type of shelter. A lone wooden picnic table at the side of a highway is not considered to be of sufficient value to show on a map. Figure 65 shows campgrounds and roadside parks in a recreational area.

National parks, forests, monuments, and reservations usually constitute recreational areas and are mapped with special attention to features such as trails, campgrounds, scenic points, and historical landmarks. Names and boundary lines of wilderness areas are omitted in a national forest.

State forests and parks vary in map importance because of differences in size, administration, development, and the extent of public use. Generally the boundaries are shown if these areas are integrated and of substantial size or if they are named and known to the public. Small scattered and irregular plots are not shown. Features of particular value to these areas are shown with appropriate names or labels. County parks are treated in a similar manner.

Federal game preserves and wildlife refuges are always shown. State preserves are shown only when the major part of the land is owned or controlled by the State; these areas usually are named. Small private holdings that have been designated as game preserves at the request of the owners usually are not shown.

FIGURE 65. Recreational area showing complete road and trail system, permanent buildings, springs, outdoor theater, and camping and picnic areas. (Big Meadows, Va., quadrangle.)

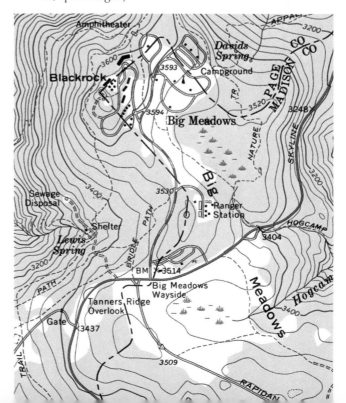

Miscellaneous Features

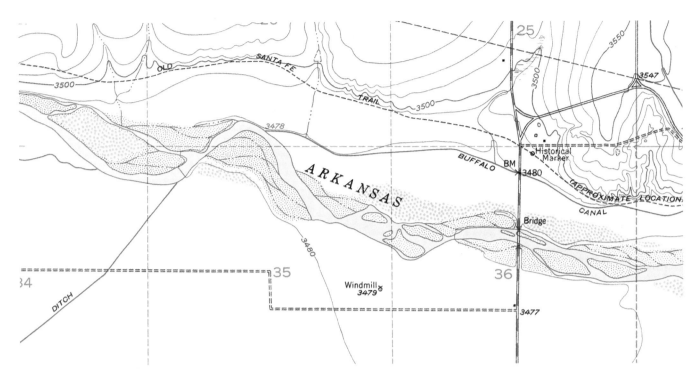

FIGURE 66. Old Santa Fe Trail shown in approximate location as determined by field evidence. Historical marker along trail plotted as located object. (Granada, Colo., quadrangle.)

HISTORICAL LANDMARKS. Historical landmarks are mapped if they are physically evident and if the persons or events commemorated interest the general public. Features classifiable as historical landmarks are so varied that there is wide latitude for judgment by the mapmakers. The first principle, however, is that there must be some substantial permanent object to portray. Signs or small monuments marking the sites of historical events ordinarily are not mapped even though the events were of great importance.

The following features are usually shown because of their historical interest:

Δ Houses, identified by name, as either birthplaces or dwellings of famous persons who were nationally prominent and are not living.
Δ Battlefields, if maintained as parks or memorials.
Δ Memorial monuments, if landmarks in themselves because of size, height, design, or location.
Δ Pioneer trails, if they are named and well known (such as the Old Santa Fe Trail), and if indisputable evidence on the ground marks the routes (fig. 66).
Δ Graves of famous persons or those that are landmarks because they are isolated and are well known locally.

Depending on the circumstances, other objects, such as rocks, ruins, and old forts, may also be shown. The usual historical markers along highways are not mapped because they are not in themselves landmarks and they do not ordinarily commemorate a specific historical event.

Historical landmarks are labeled and are shown by the located-object symbol if other standard symbolization is not appropriate.

CAVES AND ARCHEOLOGICAL SITES. Certain caves and archeological sites are shown on Geological Survey topographic maps, but there is a longstanding controversy over the propriety of showing these features. Those who advocate omission of such sites from the maps are, for the most part, certain speleologists or archeologists (by no means all) who contend that showing them can lead to their damage or destruction by curiosity seekers or vandals. The view that these features should be shown as fully as practical is held by others who believe that the maps should be as complete, accurate, and informative as possible, or who have a specific need for the location information.

Geological Survey practice is to show only those caves and archeological sites that are well known and that are protected and controlled by a Federal, State, or local organization for educational purposes, and those that are exceptionally prominent and have marked physical landmark value (fig. 67). The existence of less important caves or archeological sites is not investigated. If a cave or archeological site of apparent significant interest is discovered by chance in the course of field surveys, it is reported to a cognizant public agency or scientific society for a recommendation on whether or not the feature should be shown on the map.

Natural and Cultural Features on
Topographic Maps

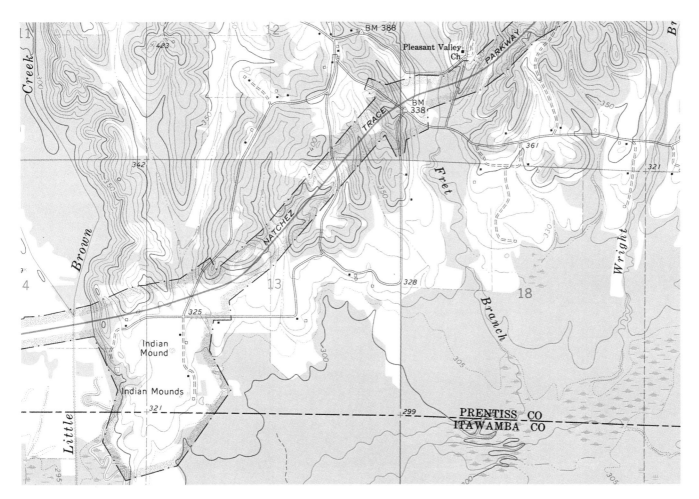

FIGURE 67. The Indian mounds shown here are archeological sites included in a national monument, the Natchez Trace. (Kirkville, Miss., quadrangle.)

Mines and Related Features

OPEN-PIT MINES AND QUARRIES. Usually open-pit mines and quarries are depressions, but they may be sidehill benches. They range in size from small borrow pits to large iron or copper mines a mile or more across. Except for very small excavations, all open pits are shown.

If small open pits or quarries are too closely spaced to show individually, the extent of the operations and the general pattern of excavations are shown by a selection of pits, and the area is labeled. Excavations in unconsolidated material—sand, gravel, clay, or borrow pits—are shown by the crossed-shovel symbol and labeled according to the type of material; for example, "Gravel Pit" or "Sand Pit" (fig. 68). ⚒ Gravel Pit

Quarries, defined for mapping purposes as excavations in solid rock for the removal of building stone, are indicated by the crossed-pick symbol and labeled "Quarry" without regard to the kind of material obtained. ⚒ Quarry

Miscellaneous Features

67

FIGURE 68. Small contoured gravel pits with symbol and label. (State line, N.Y.-Mass., quadrangle.)

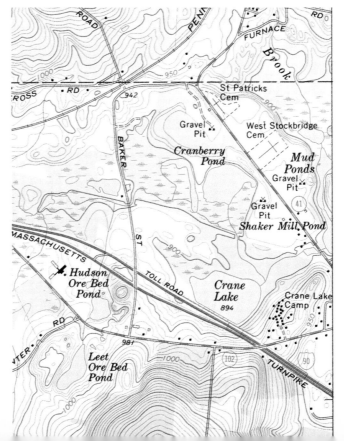

Open pits or quarries that are larger than symbol size, but not large enough to contour, are shown by a hachure outline enclosing the appropriate symbol. The largest size suitable for this symbolization depends on the map contour interval; contouring is the preferred treatment when the interval is small enough to portray the shape of the opening clearly.

In large contoured open pits, permanent water areas, roads, railroads, and other cultural features are shown to the extent permitted by the map scale (fig. 69). Where possible, a spot elevation is published at the lowest point in the depression.

FIGURE 69. Large contoured open-pit mines showing cultural features and permanent water area within the pit. (Santa Rita, N. Mex., quadrangle.)

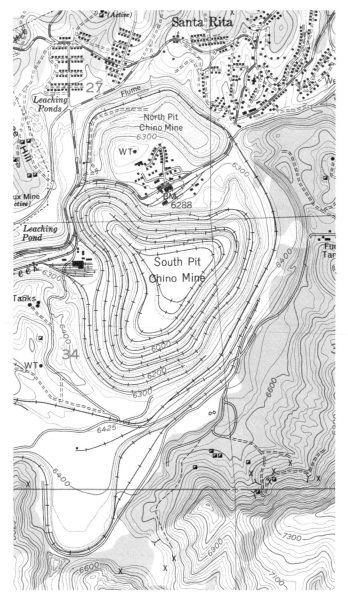

STRIP MINES AND DREDGE TAILINGS. Strip mines and some large gravel pits are characterized by a generally shallow disturbed area from which the overburden has been removed to extract the desired min-

eral, leaving the waste material piled in random heaps or, in some cases, in fairly regular ridges and furrows.

On some maps these disturbed areas are contoured as accurately as practicable. More generalization is usually required than for normal undisturbed terrain. On other maps, especially more recent ones, only very general contours are shown and the area is overprinted with the intricate-surface pattern.

Roads, buildings, and permanent water areas within large strip mines are shown in correct position. Extremes of relief are indicated by spot elevations. The stripped area is overprinted with the intricate-surface pattern (fig. 70).

FIGURE 70. Strip mines contoured and overprinted with intricate-surface pattern. (Canton East, Ohio, quadrangle.)

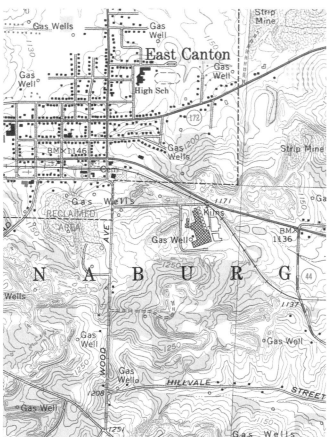

Inactive strip mines that have been regraded or that have returned to nature without regrading are contoured and mapped as a normal part of the terrain and are not identified as strip mines.

Dredging operations in some western gold-mining areas produce similar patterns of ridges and furrows of waste rock. These areas are also mapped with generalized contours, overprinted with the intricate-surface pattern, and labeled ''Dredge tailings.''

Natural and Cultural Features on Topographic Maps

UNDERGROUND MINES. Underground mines frequently present difficult mapping problems because of the complex interrelated features to be shown in a limited space. Shafts, tunnels, buildings, roads, cableways, dumps, and other details may be crowded into a narrow valley or canyon where the topography is also steep. Some displacement is usually necessary, and selective presentation of the more important surface features is almost always required. Figure 71 shows a typical complex mining area.

FIGURE 71. Complex mining area. Where prospects are too numerous to map individually, the outstanding ones are shown, maintaining the pattern and extent of the prospected area. (Handies Peak, Colo., quadrangle.)

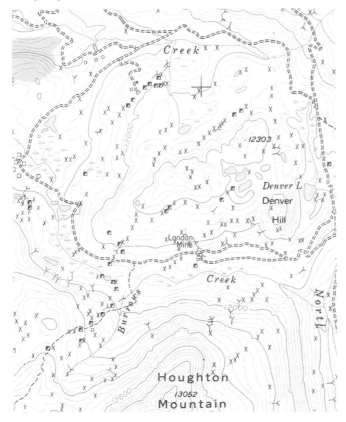

Mining terms are commonly defined on an economic basis, and these terms are not always clearly related to physical features. Therefore, for map presentation purposes only, the following terms are defined arbitrarily without regard to their economic significance:

Δ **Adit.** The entrance to a horizontal mine tunnel more than 50 feet (15 m) long and level enough for walking.

Δ **Shaft.** A more or less vertical opening, too steep for walking and more than 50 feet (15 m) deep.

Δ **Prospect.** An opening for the purpose of mineral exploration, smaller than a mine tunnel or shaft but more than 10 feet (3 m) long or deep.

A mine tunnel or adit is shown by the ⊤ symbol and labeled "Mine." The stem of the symbol is alined in the direction of the tunnel, and the junction of the arms positioned at the point of entry.

A shaft is shown by the mine-shaft symbol (square, half white, half black, on diagonal) centered on the opening. If mine shafts are coincident or very close to buildings or other structures, the position of the shaft is usually held and the buildings are displaced or omitted. Air shafts for mine ventilation are shown on 7.5-minute maps but omitted on 15-minute maps.

Prospects are shown by a sawbuck symbol oriented north-south. If there are too many prospects to be shown individually, the outstanding ones are mapped to show the pattern and extent of the prospected area.

In congested mining areas, only a few mine names can be shown. Those shown are limited to well-known and commonly used names and to names of historical interest. The mineral mined is not necessarily included in the name information, and mines are not labeled "Active," "Inactive," or "Abandoned," as they are in less congested areas.

MILL TAILINGS AND MINE DUMPS. Mill tailings are the discarded material from ore treatment processes. Where they are piled in random heaps, they are shown by a formline pattern approximating the ground appearance but preserving the correct outline. The contours are dropped at the edge of the feature, and it is labeled "Tailings."

In some cases, mill wastes are in the form of finely divided particles suspended in water and disposed of in tailings ponds. Tailings ponds are outlined with a brown dashed line, filled with a pattern of horizontal dashes, and labeled (fig. 72A).

FIGURE 72A. Map of ore-extraction-and-treatment area shows mine, tunnels, processing mill, and tailings ponds. (Telluride, Colo., quadrangle.)

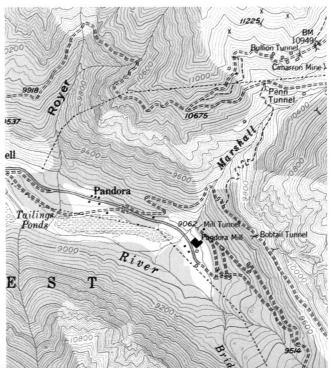

Mine dumps are piles of waste rock removed from the mine and discarded. Small dumps are depicted by hachures compiled to represent their approximate shapes, with the upper limits of the hachure symbols representing the rim or top of the dump slope. Usually only those small dumps that can be mapped to scale are shown, but isolated dumps that are landmarks are shown even though it is necessary to exaggerate their size.

Large mine dumps having a regular hill-like shape are shown by contours only and labeled (fig. 72B). Large dumps of an irregular shape, covering a considerable area in proportion to their height so that the extent is not evident from the contours, are overprinted with the intricate-surface pattern.

FIGURE 72B. Large mine dumps shown with contours and labels. (Bridgeville, Pa., quadrangle.)

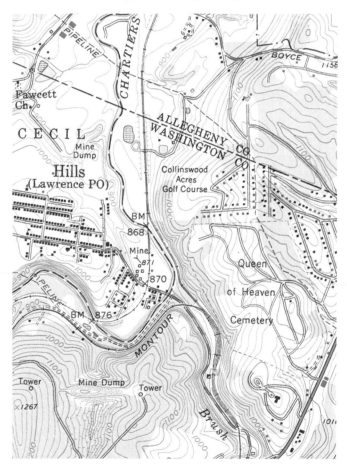

STORAGE PILES. Coal piles, ore dumps, sand and gravel piles, and other open-air storage areas of loose materials that form prominent landmarks but are subject to frequent change are not shown. Sulfur blocks formed from the hydraulic process of obtaining sulfur are also omitted. Permanent roads and buildings associated with these areas are shown. Contours are projected under the feature on the assumption that the surface was undisturbed, in the same way that the ground surface under buildings is contoured.

Vegetation

Woodland and other vegetation as represented on standard topographic maps is a feature of primary interest to map users engaged in a variety of activities. Military authorities consider woodland to be important as cover for troops or as a possible impediment to troop movement. Information on the types and distribution of vegetation is useful to managers of forests, rangelands, and wildlife, to scientists concerned with water resources, soil conservation, and land utilization, to engineers planning highways, electrical transmission lines, and recreational facilities, and to individuals interested in hunting, hiking, and camping.

Many of the intricate vegetation patterns existing in nature cannot be depicted exactly by line drawings. It is therefore necessary in some places to omit less important scattered growth and to generalize complex outlines.

Types

The term "woodland" is generally used loosely to designate all vegetation represented on topographic maps. For mapping purposes, vegetation is divided into six types, symbolized as shown, and defined as follows:

Δ **Woodland (woods-brushwood).** An area of normally dry land containing tree cover or brush that is potential tree cover. The growth must be at least 6 feet (2 m) tall and dense enough to afford cover for troops.

Δ **Scrub.** An area covered with low-growing or stunted perennial vegetation, such as cactus, mesquite, or sagebrush, common to arid regions and usually not mixed with trees.

Δ **Orchard.** A planting of evenly spaced trees or tall bushes that bear fruit or nuts. Plantings of citrus and nut trees, commonly called groves, are included in this type.

Δ **Vineyard.** A planting of grapevines, usually supported and arranged in evenly-spaced rows. Other kinds of cultivated climbing plants, such as berry vines and hops, are typed as vineyards for mapping purposes.

Δ **Mangrove.** A dense, almost impenetrable growth of tropical maritime trees with aerial roots. Mangrove thrives where the movement of tidewater is minimal—in shallow bays and deltas, and along riverbanks.

Δ **Wooded marsh.** An area of normally wet land with tree cover or brush that is potential tree cover.

Density

Woods, brushwood, and scrub are mapped if the growth is thick enough to provide cover for troops or to impede foot travel. This condition is considered to exist if density of the vegetative cover is 20 percent or more.

Growth that meets the minimum density requirement is estimated as follows: if the average open-space distance between the crowns is equal to the average crown diameter, the density of the vegetative cover is 20 percent (a of fig. 73).

This criterion is not a hard-and-fast rule, however, because 20 percent crown density cannot be determined accurately if there are irregularly scattered trees and gradual transitions from the wooded to the cleared areas. Therefore, where such growth occurs, the minimum density requirement varies between 20 and 35 percent, and the woodland boundary is drawn where there is a noticeable change in density. A crown density of 35 percent exists if the average open space between the crowns is equal to one-half the average crown diameter (b of fig. 73).

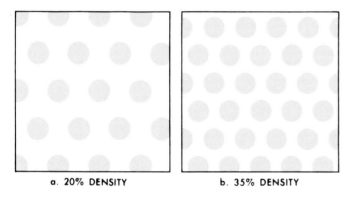

a. 20% DENSITY   b. 35% DENSITY

FIGURE 73. Patterns for estimating crown density.

Orchards and vineyards are shown regardless of crown density. Mangrove, by definition, is dense, almost impenetrable growth; crown density is not a factor in mapping mangrove boundaries.

Areas

On 7.5- and 15-minute maps, woodland areas covering 1 acre (0.4 ha) or more are shown regardless of shape. This area requirement applies both to individual tracts of vegetation and to areas of one type within or adjoining another type. Narrow strips of vegetation and isolated tracts covering areas smaller than the specified minimum are shown only if they are considered to be landmarks. Accordingly, shelterbelts and small patches of trees in arid or semiarid regions are shown, whereas single rows of trees or bushes along fences, roads, or perennial streams are not mapped.

Clearings

The minimum area specified for woodland cover on 7.5- and 15-minute maps—1 acre (0.4 ha)—also applies to clearings within woodland. Isolated clearings smaller than the specified minimum are shown if they are considered to be landmarks.

Clearings along mapped linear features, such as power transmission lines, telephone lines, pipelines, roads, and railroads, are shown if the break in woodland cover is 100 feet (30 m) or more wide (fig. 74). The minimum symbol width for a clearing in which a linear feature is shown is 100 feet at map scale. Clearings wider than 100 feet are mapped to scale.

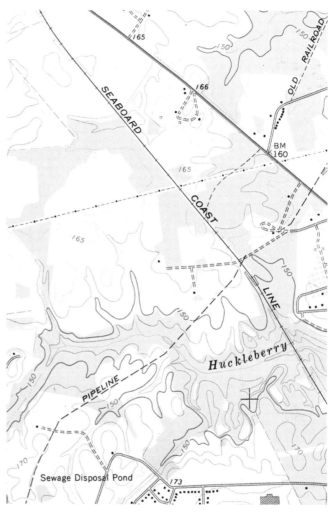

FIGURE 74. Woodland symbol registered with road casing and railroad symbol. Clearings shown along power transmission line. (Cheraw, S.C., quadrangle.)

Landmark linear clearings 40 feet (12 m) or more wide, in which no feature is mapped, are shown to scale. Firebreaks are shown and labeled if they are 20 feet (6 m) or more wide and do not adjoin or coincide with other cultural features. The minimum symbol width for a firebreak clearing is 40 feet at map scale; firebreaks wider than 40 feet are shown to scale.

Woodland Boundary Accuracy

Clearly defined woodland boundaries are plotted with standard accuracy, the same as any other well-defined planimetric feature. If there are gradual changes from wooded to cleared areas, the outlines are plotted to indicate the limits of growth meeting the minimum density requirement. If the growth occurs in intricate patterns, the outlines show the general shapes of the wooded areas. Outlines representing these ill-defined or irregular limits of vegetative cover are considered to be approximate because they do not necessarily represent lines that can be accurately identified on the ground. The outline of a tract of tall, dense timber represents the centerline of the bounding row of trees rather than the outside limits of the branches or the shadow line.

In large tracts of dense evergreen timber, sharp dividing lines between different tree heights may be shown with the fence- and field-line symbol. Published maps containing fence-line symbols that represent fences and other landmark lines in wooded areas bear the following statement in the tailored legend: "Fine red dashed lines indicate selected fence, field, or landmark lines where generally visible on aerial photographs. This information is unchecked."

Woodland is not shown in urban-tint areas, but it is shown where appropriate in areas surrounded by urban tint if such areas are equivalent to or larger than the average city block (fig. 75).

FIGURE 75. Woodland shown in openings within urban-tint areas. (Edmonds East, Wash., quadrangle.)

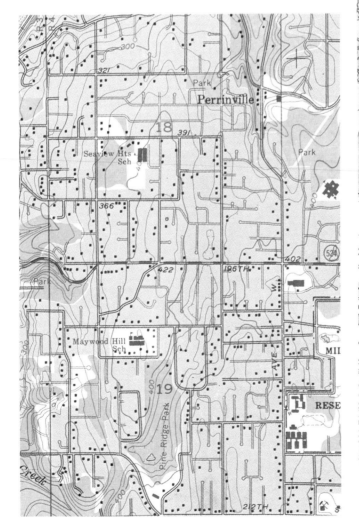

Mangrove is shown on the published map with the standard mangrove pattern and the green woodland tint (fig. 76). Breaks in the mangrove cover usually indicate water channels that provide routes for penetrating the dense growth.

FIGURE 76. Mangrove pattern overprinted on woodland tint; edge of mangrove defines shoreline. (Card Sound, Fla., quadrangle.)

Natural and Cultural Features on Topographic Maps

5:

Boundaries, Names, and Marginalia

Original boundary surveys executed by the appropriate organization provide the definitive evidence for settling boundary questions, so the source documents, not the Survey's topographic maps, have primary legal significance with respect to land ownership or jurisdictional limits.

Civil Boundaries

Civil boundaries are the limiting lines of jurisdictional authority for the various levels of government. These boundaries are shown on topographic quadrangle maps of the Geological Survey, but they are invariably derived from another source. The Survey does not make original boundary surveys, and the boundaries shown on the maps are not intended as conclusive evidence of land ownership or jurisdictional limits. Original boundary surveys executed by the appropriate organization provide the definitive evidence for settling boundary questions. Nevertheless, the boundaries shown on Survey quadrangle maps are often regarded by the general public and local authorities as representing authoritative locations. For this reason, boundaries are delineated on these maps as carefully as possible from available source documents; but the fact remains that the source documents, not the topographic maps, have primary legal significance with respect to boundaries. A notable exception is that the State of West Virginia has enacted legislation which establishes the boundaries of the State and its counties to be those shown on USGS topographic quadrangle maps.

Boundary Classification and Selection

The international boundaries of the United States were established through treaties made by the nations concerned (Van Zandt, 1976). The land portions of such boundaries have been surveyed and monumented, and are recoverable as well-defined lines. Those portions following water features are fixed by reference monuments.

State boundaries have been defined by Congress and can be changed only by agreement of the legislatures of the concerned States with the consent of Congress (Van Zandt, 1976). (As a possible exception, there is a body of opinion holding that, under the terms of the Congressional resolution consenting to the erection of Texas into a State, Texas can unilaterally divide into as many as five States.) Most of the land portions of State boundaries have been surveyed and monumented. Where the monuments exist, the boundaries are recoverable as well-defined lines; however, durable monument material was not always used, and in some localities the monuments may have partially or wholly disintegrated and disappeared over considerable lengths of the boundary.

Boundaries of civil subdivisions within a State are usually fixed by legislative action, but in some cases authority may be delegated to counties for local determination of their respective subdivisions. The boundaries of counties (including parishes in Louisiana and municipios in Puerto Rico) are reasonably stable but locations may not always be readily identifiable on the ground.

In the 50 States, the Virgin Islands, and Puerto Rico, counties or equivalent units are divided into minor civil subdivisions for governmental, administrative, educational, and other public purposes. The stability of these subdivision boundaries and the accuracy with which they have been described or marked may vary from State to State. Boundaries that are unstable or were not precisely established are difficult to recover and plot on the map. Therefore, quadrangle maps show only those minor civil subdivision boundaries that have been reasonably stable.

Records showing locations and changes of boundaries of incorporated places are kept by local or county offices, or both, and are examined before locating such boundaries on the map. Incorporated places include cities, towns, villages, and special-purpose tracts of land. These incorporated places may be subdivisions of the county, town, or township wherein they are located, or may be coextensive with them, or independent.

The international boundaries of the United States and the boundaries of each State are usually well established, can be plotted accurately, and are shown as well-defined map features (fig. 77). Boundaries of counties or equivalent units, national and State parks, forests, monuments, and reservations, cemeteries, city and county parks, and airports are shown whenever they can be located and plotted with sufficient accuracy. The boundaries of privately owned recreational areas, such as golf courses, clubs, resorts, or amusement parks, are not shown.

In most States the incorporated places form subdivisions of the minor civil divisions in which they are located. In other States, however, all or some of the incorporated places are also minor civil divisions.

Corporate boundaries are described in the articles of incorporation and amendments thereto, and are reasonably stable. Therefore they are shown even though the boundaries of the surrounding county subdivision may be omitted. Boundaries of certain other units of civil government are shown as indicated below.

Land-grant and public-land survey lines are shown in accordance with principles given in the section on public-land subdivision (see p. 80-86). The 30 public-land States were created out of the public domain, which once included a large portion of the land in the United States, especially in the West. The public lands in these States have been surveyed and subdivided according to a basic plan monitored by the Bureau of Land Management (formerly the General Land Office).

FIGURE 77. International boundary between the United States and Mexico. Officially accepted boundary monuments (like the one above) that can be located are shown by symbol with monument designation. (Midway Well, Calif., quadrangle.)

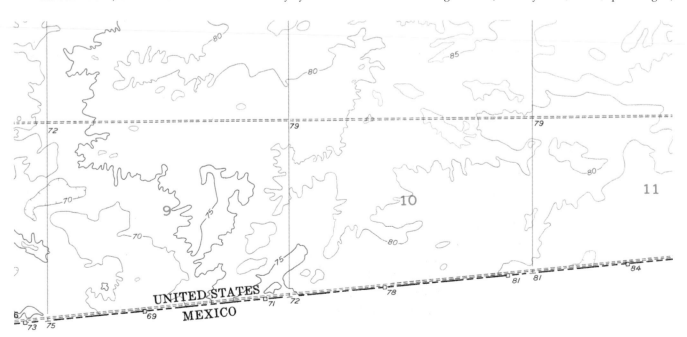

*BOUNDARIES OF STATE AND LOCAL SUBDI-
VISIONS.* The boundaries listed in the following tabulation are shown on the maps unless the text specifically states which boundaries are omitted.

Alabama is a public-land State, divided into counties that are subdivided into election precincts, except the city of Mobile. Precinct boundaries are omitted.

Alaska, a public-land State, is subdivided into boroughs. Judicial district boundaries and temporary election districts are omitted.

Arizona is a public-land State, divided into counties that are subdivided into supervisorial districts. Supervisorial district boundaries are omitted.

Arkansas is a public-land State, divided into counties that are subdivided into civil townships.

California is a public-land State, divided into counties. San Francisco is incorporated as the city and county of San Francisco. The other counties are subdivided into judicial townships. Judicial township boundaries are omitted.

Colorado is a public-land State, divided into counties. Denver is incorporated as the city and county of Denver. The other counties are subdivided into election precincts, except the consolidated Ute Indian Reservation in Montezuma County and cities that are independent of precinct organization. Election precinct boundaries are omitted.

Connecticut, not a public-land State, is divided into counties which are subdivided into towns. Incorporated cities and boroughs in some cases are subdivisions of the towns in which they are located, and in other cases are coextensive with them. (The counties are chiefly judicial districts having only minor executive functions.)

Delaware, not a public-land State, is divided into counties that are in turn subdivided into representative districts.

District of Columbia, coextensive with the city of Washington, is divided into police precincts. Police precinct boundaries are omitted.

Florida is a public-land State, divided into counties that are subdivided into election precincts. Election precinct boundaries are omitted.

Georgia, not a public-land State, is divided into counties that are subdivided into militia districts, except the city of Atlanta, which is independent of militia organization and forms a primary division of each of the two counties in which it is located. Militia district boundaries are omitted.

Hawaii, not a public-land State, is divided into five counties. Four of the counties are subdivided into districts, but the remaining area, a part of the Island of Molokai, is a county and single district, both having the name, Kalawao. The county of Honolulu includes the Island of Oahu and all of the islands and reefs west of Kauai County to and including Kure Island, but excluding Palmyra, Kingman Reef, and Midway. Districts are subdivided into smaller areas called ahupuaas, and these are subdivided into small land divisions called ilis and leles. The boundaries of ilis and leles are omitted.

Idaho is a public-land State divided into counties and the Idaho portion of Yellowstone National Park. The counties are divided into election precincts, except 15 unorganized townships in Fremont County. Election precinct boundaries are omitted.

Illinois is a public-land State divided into counties, some of which are subdivided into civil townships, except the city of Chicago, which is independent of township organization. The remaining counties are subdivided into election precincts. Election precinct boundaries are omitted.

Indiana is a public-land State divided into counties that are subdivided into civil townships.

Iowa is a public-land State divided into counties that are subdivided into civil townships, except Sioux City, which is independent of township organization and is a subdivision of Woodbury County.

Kansas is a public-land State divided into counties that are subdivided into civil townships and cities.

Kentucky, not a public-land State, is divided into counties that are subdivided into magisterial districts. Magisterial district boundaries are omitted.

Louisiana is a public-land State divided into parishes that are subdivided into police-jury wards, except the city of New Orleans, which is coextensive with Orleans Parish. Police-jury ward boundaries are omitted.

Maine, not a public-land State, is divided into counties. Primary divisions of the counties include gores, grants, islands, cities, a patent, plantations, points, strips, surpluses, towns, tracts, an Indian reservation, and unorganized townships.

Maryland, not a public-land State, is divided into the independent city of Baltimore and into counties that are subdivided into election precincts. Election precinct boundaries are omitted.

Massachusetts, not a public-land State, is divided into counties that are subdivided into cities and towns. Some towns embrace large unincorporated villages with no official boundaries.

Michigan is a public-land State divided into counties that are subdivided into incorporated cities, civil townships, and unorganized townships.

Minnesota is a public-land State divided into counties. Primary subdivision of the counties includes civil townships, unorganized townships, a borough, and most of the incorporated places. All cities except Wabasha, the one borough, and 579 of the villages are independent of township organization and constitute primary subdivisions of the counties.

Mississippi is a public-land State divided into counties that are subdivided into beats. Beat boundaries are omitted.

Missouri is a public-land State divided into counties and the independent city of St. Louis. Counties are subdivided into civil townships.

Montana is a public-land State divided into counties and the Montana portion of the Yellowstone National Park. Counties are subdivided into school districts, election precincts, civil townships in Beaverhead, Flathead, Lake, Madison, Mineral, Powell, and Ravalli Counties, and unorganized areas in Park and Carbon Counties. School district, election precinct, civil township, and unorganized area boundaries are omitted.

Nebraska is a public-land State divided into counties, which are subdivided into civil townships, one unorganized township, cities, the villages of Burwell and Elyria, and precincts. Precincts have equal status with townships.

Nevada is a public-land State divided into counties. Esmeralda County is divided into judicial districts which have replaced the former election precincts. The remaining counties are subdivided into civil townships. Boundaries of civil townships and judicial districts are omitted.

New Hampshire, not a public-land State, is divided into counties. The more densely populated counties are divided into towns and cities; Carroll and Coos Counties are subdivided into grants, locations, purchases, and unorganized towns.

New Jersey, not a public-land State, is divided into counties, which are subdivided into boroughs, cities, towns, villages, and townships. Three villages, South Orange, Ridgefield Park, and Ridgewood, are coextensive with the townships in which they are located.

New Mexico is a public-land State divided into counties, which are subdivided into election precincts and two Indian reservations (located in Rio Arriba and San Juan Counties) in which there are no precincts. Election precinct boundaries are omitted.

New York, not a public-land State, is divided into counties, which are subdivided into towns, cities, and Indian reservations. Five counties (Bronx, Kings, Queens, New York, and Richmond) are included in New York City, and are coextensive with city boroughs.

North Carolina, not a public-land State, is divided into counties that are subdivided into civil townships.

North Dakota is a public-land State divided into counties, which are subdivided into civil townships, unorganized townships, all of its incorporated places (cities, villages, and the town of Forman), and the Fort Berthold Indian Reservation.

Ohio has been largely but not entirely subdivided by public-land surveys. Its area is divided into counties which are subdivided into civil townships.

Oklahoma is a public-land State divided into counties, which are subdivided into civil townships, cities, towns, the Fort Sill Military Reservation, and the Platt National Park. The cities of Muskogee and Vinita are coextensive with the township in which each is located.

Oregon is a public-land State divided into counties, which are subdivided into election precincts, and the Fort Stevens Military Reservation in Clatsop County. Election precinct boundaries are omitted.

Pennsylvania, not a public-land State, is divided into counties, which are subdivided into civil townships, boroughs, cities, the town of Bloomsburg, and the Cornplanter Indian Reservation in Warren County. The city of Philadelphia is coextensive with Philadelphia County.

Puerto Rico, together with the islands of Vieques, Culebra, Mona, and other small adjacent islands, comprise a Commonwealth that has not been subdivided by public-land surveys. For the purpose of government, its area is divided into municipios. Culebra and Vieques each are municipios. The other islands form parts of municipios. Municipios are the smallest governmental units, but they are subdivided for other purposes into smaller areas called barrios. The city of San Juan is coextensive with the municipio of San Juan. The cities of Ponce and Mayaguez occupy only minor portions of the municipios of the same names. The places in which the governments of the remaining municipios are located are designated as towns by the Bureau of the Census. In all cases except one (Dewey in the municipio of Culebra) each town bears the same name as the municipio in which it is located. In addition to the barrios, there are military and naval reservations in several municipios and the Culebra Island lighthouse station in the municipio of Culebra.

Rhode Island, not a public-land State, is divided into counties that are subdivided into cities and towns. Some of the towns include large unincorporated villages having no official established boundaries.

South Carolina, not a public-land State, is divided into counties, which are subdivided into civil townships, the city of Charleston, and school districts in the counties of Darlington, Marlborough, Pickens, and Richland. Civil township and school district boundaries are omitted.

South Dakota is a public-land State divided into counties. Three counties are unorganized and are attached to adjoining counties for judicial purposes. The primary subdivisions of the organized counties are townships, unorganized townships, cities, towns, and Fort Meade Military Reservation, and Wind Cave National Park.

Tennessee, not a public-land State, is divided into counties that are subdivided into civil districts. Civil district boundaries are omitted.

Texas, not a public-land State, is divided into counties, that are subdivided into commissioner's precincts, justice precincts, and one unorganized area. Precinct boundaries are omitted.

Utah is a public-land State divided into counties. Daggett County is subdivided into election districts. The remaining counties are subdivided into election precincts and unorganized areas. Election precinct and district boundaries are omitted.

Vermont, not a public-land State, is divided into counties, which are subdivided into towns (two of which are unorganized), cities, gores, and a grant.

Virgin Islands of the United States, an unincorporated territory, comprises about 50 islands. The largest islands are St. Thomas, St. John, and St. Croix. The islands are divided into two municipalities (Municipality of St. Croix, Municipality of St. Thomas and St. John). Municipalities are subdivided into quarters and three cities (Christiansted, Fredericksted, and Charlotte Amalie). The islands are also divided into judicial divisions. Judicial division boundaries are shown on St. Croix maps, but omitted on St. Thomas and St. John maps.

Virginia, not a public-land State, is subdivided into counties and cities that have the status of counties. Counties are subdivided into magisterial districts. Magisterial district boundaries are omitted.

Washington is a public-land State divided into counties, which contain cities and towns. Election precincts are established but are subject to change with population changes; election-precinct boundaries are omitted. Boundaries of certain Federal installations and Indian reservations are shown.

West Virginia, not a public-land State, is divided into counties that are in turn subdivided into magisterial districts.

Wisconsin is a public-land State divided into counties, that are subdivided into towns, cities, villages, and the Menomonee Indian Reservation in Oconto and Shawano Counties.

Wyoming is a public-land State and includes most of Yellowstone National Park which is independent of county organization. The remaining area of the State is divided into counties that are subdivided into election districts. Election district boundaries are omitted.

BOUNDARY PRECEDENCE. If boundaries of two or more civil units of different rank coincide, the symbol for only the higher ranking unit boundary is shown on the map (fig. 78). The various governmental and other units are ranked in the following order:

1. National.
2. State, Commonwealth, and territory.
3. County. This includes parish in Louisiana, borough in Alaska, and municipio in Puerto Rico.
4. Specified primary county subdivisions or their equivalents, such as civil townships or towns.
5. Incorporated places that do not have the status of counties or primary subdivisions thereof.
6. National or State parks, reservations and monuments.
7. Cemeteries, parks, and airports.
8. Land grants.
9. Public land subdivisions.

FIGURE 78. State, county, and civil township boundaries shown by appropriate symbol. Boundary of incorporated borough of Wellersburg also shown. (Frostburg, Md.-W. Va.-Pa., 1:62,500-scale 15-minute quadrangle.) Shown above is a boundary monument on the Mason and Dixon line.

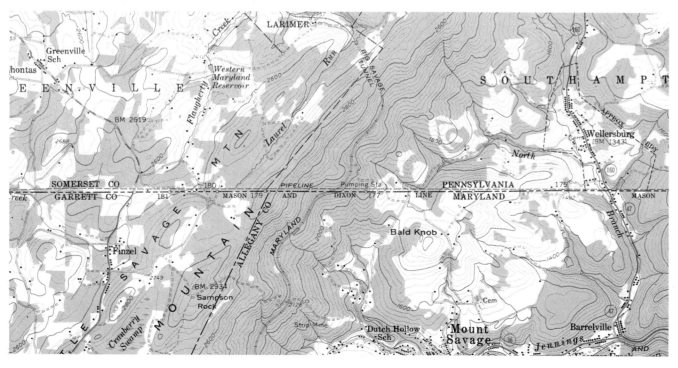

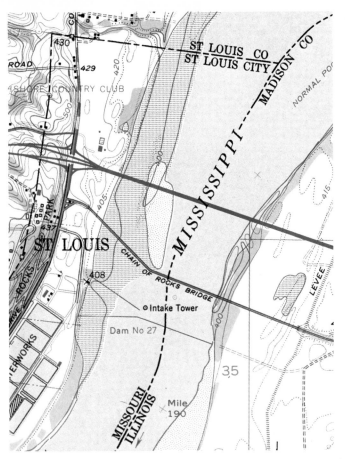

FIGURE 79. Boundary precedence for independent city of St. Louis, bounded by St. Louis County and State boundary. (Columbia Bottom, Mo.-Ill., quadrangle.)

FIGURE 80. County boundary mapped as indefinite where its accuracy of location does not meet position requirement for well-defined features. Indefinite boundaries shown at one-half specified line weight. (Indian Gap, Tex., quadrangle.)

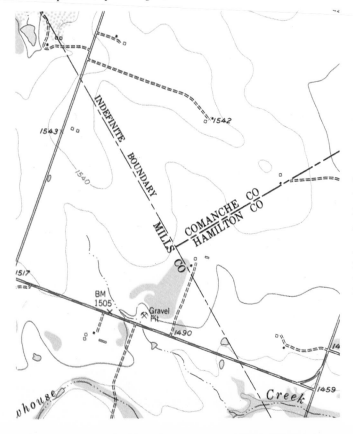

The following are some representative examples of boundary symbol precedence:

△ The State boundary-line symbol is used to outline Washington, D.C., a district and a city entirely surrounded by States.

△ Buffalo, N.Y., a primary subdivision of Erie County, is bounded on three sides by other primary subdivisions known as towns, and on the fourth side (west) by Lake Erie and the Niagara River. Therefore, its limits are shown by a national boundary symbol on the west and by a town (civil township) boundary symbol on the other three sides.

△ St. Louis, Mo., is incorporated as an independent city, bounded on the east by the Missouri-Illinois boundary, and on its remaining limits by St. Louis County. The State boundary symbol is used on the east, following the channel of the Mississippi River. The remainder of its limits, where county and city boundaries are coincident, are shown by the higher ranking county boundary symbol (fig. 79).

INDEFINITE, UNDETERMINED, OR DISPUTED BOUNDARIES. Boundaries shown on quadrangle maps are symbolized to indicate the relative certainty with which their locations have been identified and mapped. Boundary lines plotted with the accuracy of other well-defined features are shown with appropriate standard symbols.

If the accuracy of location does not meet the position requirements for well-defined features, the boundary is classed and shown as indefinite. On the published maps all indefinite boundaries are shown with the standard symbolization but reduced to one-half the specified line weight and labeled "Indefinite Boundary" (fig. 80).

If any part of a boundary is unmarked and cannot be located on the ground from other substantial evidence, if the location is in dispute, or if the recorded description cannot be reconciled with local conditions, such part may be omitted from the map. However, State and county boundaries in dispute are shown, maintaining a neutral position until the dispute is settled. Under these conditions, the disputed lines are labeled as an indefinite boundary with an appropriate marginal note. If there are two monumented locations of the same boundary, each boundary is shown and appropriately labeled.

BOUNDARY MARKS AND DESCRIPTIONS. Only officially accepted monuments or survey marks on national, State, and other required boundaries that can be recovered and located by a reasonable amount of effort and diligence are shown on Survey quadrangle maps.

Boundaries are sometimes described in the establishing statutes as following, wholly or in part, natural land features. These descriptions often contain indefinite phrases such as "following a ridge," "along a height of land," "a watershed," and "thence with the mountain." Legal interpretation of such phrases may differ from local usage, may be contradictory to survey data, or may not agree with the map representation of the feature involved. Therefore, specific inquiry is usually made to ascertain if there has been a court decision that would affect the location of such boundaries. When it is ascertained that a boundary follows the natural feature, such as height of land, it is drawn following the curve of the ridge line or other feature as shown on the plat of the survey (fig. 81), and not as a series of tangents.

Boundaries that are described as following in or along bodies of water are located on one of several possible courses—the centerline of the waterway, the thread of the stream, the center of the main channel, the right or left bank (fig. 82), or the line of low or high water on either bank. Some boundaries enter or cross bodies of water on prescribed courses between marked or unmarked points. The wording of these statutory descriptions is important in plotting boundaries on maps.

Changing watercourses often present special problems. Boundaries that are described as following a running stream or its main channel may shift in position with the stream when the location of the watercourse is changed by the natural and gradual processes of erosion or accretion. When a watercourse suddenly changes by natural avulsion or the flow is diverted to a new channel by man, the boundary generally retains its original location relative to the old channel as fixed by statute.

A boundary described as following cultural features, such as roads or railways, is carefully investigated to determine whether it is located on the centerline or along either border of the right-of-way. The investigation also determines whether all or part of the feature has been relocated since the date the boundary was established. The position on the map is then delineated in accordance with ascertained facts (fig. 83).

SPECIAL AREAS. Boundaries of national parks, forests, monuments, game preserves, and wildlife refuges are shown with the reservation-boundary symbol (fig. 84).

Δ **National parks and monuments.** Parks and monuments differ only in the way in which they are established; national monuments are established by Presidential proclamations, whereas national parks are created by acts of Congress.

Δ **National forests.** National forests are established by Presidential proclamation. Boundaries defined in the proclamation are shown. Purchase boundaries are not shown.

Δ **Federal game preserves.** The boundaries of U.S. Fish and Wildlife reservations are shown, along with the official name of the preserve.

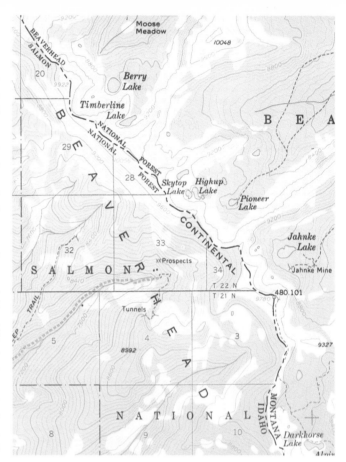

FIGURE 81. State boundary following Continental Divide is plotted along the curve of the ridge line and not as a series of tangents. Forest boundary coincident with State boundary indicated by label. (Goldstone Mountain, Idaho-Mont., 1:62,500-scale 15-minute quadrangle.)

FIGURE 82. State boundary located on right bank of stream. (Frostburg, Md.-W. Va.-Pa., 1:62,500-scale 15-minute quadrangle.)

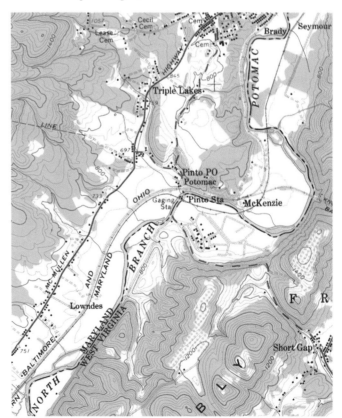

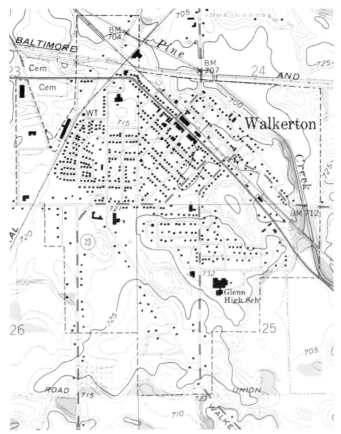

FIGURE 83. Boundary of incorporated place described as following roads or railroads is closely checked to ascertain whether its location is on the centerline or the right-of-way. (Walkerton, Ind., quadrangle.)

FIGURE 84. National monument boundary shown by appropriate symbol. A band of tint is used to accentuate the boundary. (Devils Postpile, Calif., 1:62,500-scale 15-minute quadrangle.)

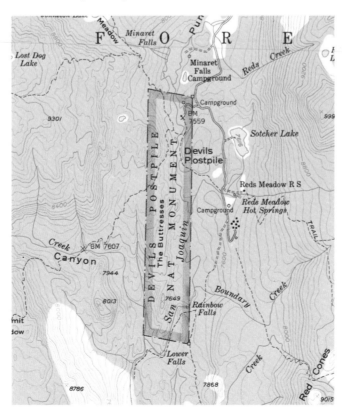

The boundaries of State forests and parks are shown if these areas comprise a unit of substantial size, or if they are named and well known to the public. Small, scattered, and irregular plots that are not well known are omitted. State game preserves are shown only when the major part of the land is owned or controlled by the State. Boundaries are shown with the reservation-boundary symbol, with the same accuracy requirements and classification specified for other civil boundaries.

Indian reservations vary widely in their status and forms of administration, and the procedure for showing reservation boundaries also varies. The Bureau of Indian Affairs, Department of the Interior, divides Indian reservations into four categories:

1. **Tribal lands.** Reservations that are owned by the entire tribe, subject to tribal laws, and are intact.
2. **Allotted in part.** Reservations made up of both tribal lands and tracts of land allotted to individual Indians.
3. **Allotted and open.** Reservations containing tracts of land allotted to individual Indians; other tracts open to the public; and any remaining tribal lands.
4. **Former Indian reservations.**

The boundaries of reservations in category 1 are shown with the reservation boundary symbol, and the name of the reservation is placed across the bounded area (fig. 85).

For reservations in categories 2 and 3, the treatment depends on the location of the boundaries and on the amount of remaining tribal lands. Boundaries that coincide with civil boundaries of higher precedence, public-land subdivision lines, or natural features, such as a stream course, are indicated by labeling with the name of the reservation. Boundaries not coincident with such features are shown with a red line of section-line weight, and labeled (fig. 86).

Reservations in category 4 are omitted unless their boundaries are reflected in the public-land subdivision net, or in the local land system in non-public-land States. When boundaries of reservations in this category are included, they are shown in their entirety and labeled "Old Indian Treaty Boundary." When such boundaries do not coincide with other boundaries or streams, they are shown by a red line of section-line weight.

Indian agency headquarters, whether inside or outside the reservations, are identified by name, such as "Warm Springs Indian Agency."

Public-Land Subdivisions

In 1785 Congress drew up the basic plan for surveying the public lands. According to the plan, as finally modified and adopted, land was to be divided into

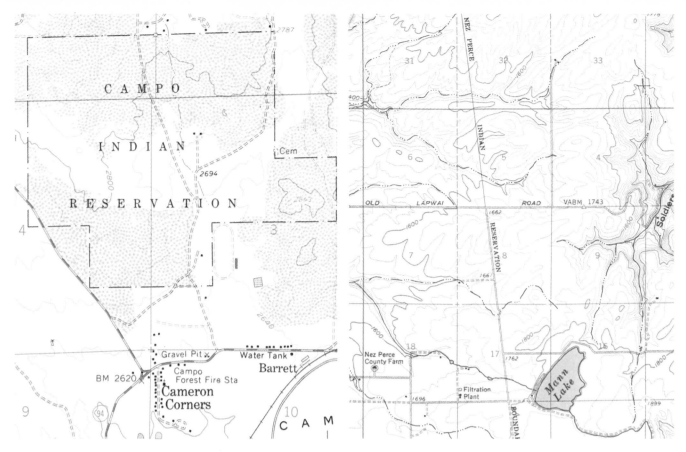

FIGURE 85. Indian reservation (category 1) shown by reservation-boundary symbol with name across the bounded area. (Cameron Corners, Calif., quadrangle.)

FIGURE 86. Indian reservation boundary (category 3), not coincident with other mappable feature, shown by red line and labeled. Boundary, coincident with road, shown by label only. (Lewiston Orchards, Idaho, 1:62,500-scale 15-minute quadrangle.)

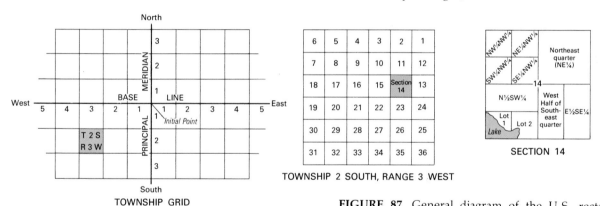

TOWNSHIP GRID

TOWNSHIP 2 SOUTH, RANGE 3 WEST

SECTION 14

FIGURE 87. General diagram of the U.S. rectangular system of surveys.

townships 6 miles square with boundaries running due north, south, east, and west, and townships were to be subdivided into 36 sections 1 mile square (fig. 87). Principal meridians and base lines were established as a reference system for the township surveys (fig. 88). The Bureau of Land Management (BLM) is responsible for subdividing public lands and maintaining records of all related surveys. The Geological Survey does not make these original surveys but records selected BLM data on quadrangle maps.

Public-land lines and corners that have been approved and accepted by BLM are fixed in position and unchangeable. Hence, the ground positions of original township corners, section corners, and quarter-section corners remain the true positions, even though directions and lengths of lines on the land plats indicate positions different from the ground positions.

Clearly marked subdivison lines and corners are well-defined features that are shown on Survey quadrangle maps, and therefore they are mapped to meet National Map Accuracy Standards. Subdivision corners are mapped (1) to form a framework for positioning land lines and (2) to indicate which corners were recovered during field surveys.

PRINCIPAL MERIDIANS AND BASE LINES
GOVERNING THE UNITED STATES PUBLIC LAND SURVEYS

Adapted from U.S. Dept. of the Interior, Bureau of Land Management,
*Principal Meridians and Base Lines; governing the United
States Public Land Surveys*, map, Washington, 1968

Dates indicate establishment of initial points
or first survey

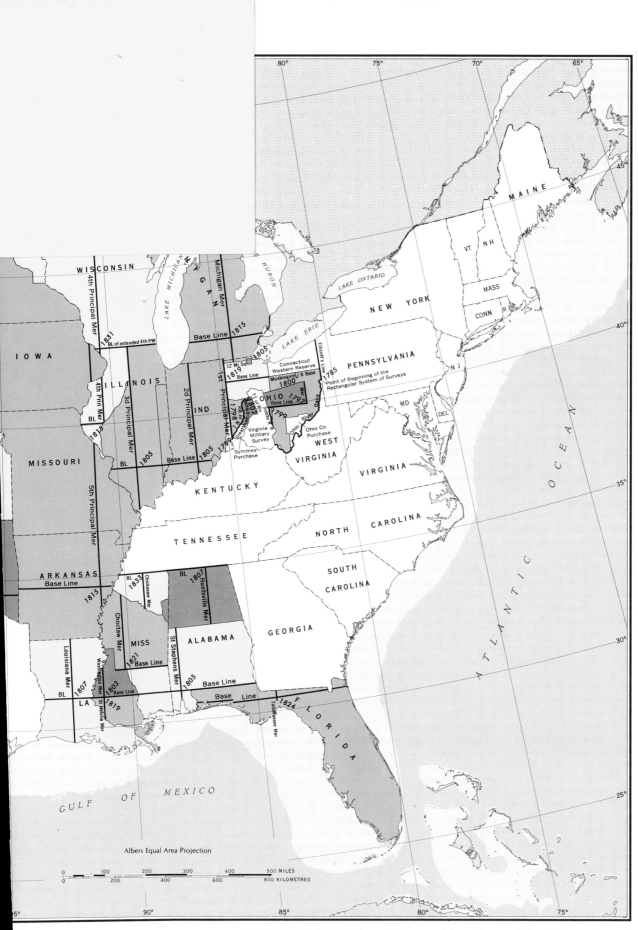

FIGURE 88. Principal meridians and base lines of the U.S. system of rectangular surveys. Each colored area represents the extent of public-land surveys based on the principal meridian and base line indicated in that area. Areas shown in white are not included in the public-land system.

In order to position the land net accurately, the Geological Survey field party tries to identify and plot on the map manuscript as many corners and other clearly marked ground evidence as possible. The land lines plotted on Survey topographic maps are not intended to show conclusive evidence of land ownership or to substitute for boundary surveys, yet these maps are sometimes used as evidence of boundaries between adjacent properties. This does not alter the fact that the original survey, not the lines shown on the topographic map, constitutes the only legal basis for determining land boundaries.

REPRESENTATION OF SUBDIVISION CORNERS. Public-land corners and the accessory monuments that are shown on Geological Survey maps are defined as follows:

Δ   **Standard corner.** A corner on a standard parallel or base line, serving as a starting point for surveys to the north.

Δ   **Township corner.** A corner at an extremity of a township boundary.

Δ   **Section corner.** A corner at an extremity of a section boundary.

Δ   **Quarter-section corner.** A corner at an extremity of a quarter-section boundary, theoretically located 40 chains north or west of the southeast corner of a section. (Quarter-section corners in the middle of the section are not official.)

Δ   **Witness corner.** A monumented point usually on a section line within 10 chains of the true corner location. Witness corners are established if the true corner cannot be occupied or monumented because of difficult terrain or an obstruction at the corner site. If no suitable monument site is on the line within 10 chains of the true corner, a witness corner may be set any place within 5 chains of the true corner.

Δ   **Meander corner.** A corner established at the intersection of a township, range, or section line with the banks of a navigable stream or a meanderable body of water.

Δ   **Closing corner.** A corner at the intersection of a surveyed line with a previously established public-land line, grant line, reservation boundary, or the like.

Δ   **Angle point.** A monument marking a change in azimuth on an irregular boundary line, reservation line, boundary of a private claim, or re-established nonriparian meander line.

All corners defined above are classified as "found," "indicated," or "theoretical" by the field party.

1.   **Found corners.** Found corners are those (1) whose original or restored monuments or marks are recovered or (2) whose positions are definitely established by one or more witness corners or reference monuments.

    For privately owned land formerly in the public domain, restored corners regarded as authentic by local landowners and courts may be shown on maps by the found-corner symbols. If the land is part of the public domain, the only corners shown are those

established by BLM or other government agency surveys which are platted and approved by BLM.

    Recovered corners may be shown on maps in areas where subdivision lines are omitted due to insufficient data.

2.   **Indicated corners.** These corners have definite positions locally accepted as correct, but their official marks or monuments cannot be recovered or identified. The corners are identified by unofficial marks, such as stakes, pipes, piles of rocks, fence corners, road intersections, and intersecting roads and fence lines.

3.   **Theoretical corners.** The official marks or monuments of these corners were not recovered or identified, and their positions are therefore determined by adjusting the land lines.

4.   **Closing corners along decreed boundaries.** In mapping closing corners and land lines closing on surveyed boundaries that follow physical features (as the crest of a divide, a curving ridge, a watershed) (1) found closing corners are shown at their ground locations, and (2) the land lines are closed on the decreed feature, not on the tangents of the traverse run to establish the boundary. It may be necessary, therefore, to lengthen or shorten the land lines so that they terminate at the decreed boundary.

SUMMARY OF CORNER SYMBOLIZATION. Section corners are symbolized on published Geological Survey maps as follows:

Δ   Found section corners and quarter-corners are shown with double-weight red crosses.

Δ   Indicated and theoretical corners are shown by the intersections of subdivision lines.

Δ   Found meander, witness, and closing corners are shown with double-weight red T's; the crossbars are alined with the meandered line or the line closed upon.

SYMBOLIZATION OF PUBLIC-LAND LINES. Public-land lines are shown on published maps by symbols indicating the relative accuracy of their mapped positions. If the lines are not mapped, an appropriate note must be shown in the map margin.

The symbols for public-land lines and the criteria for using them are:

Δ   **Solid-line symbol.** Land lines are shown by the solid-line symbol (1) if they connect found or indicated corners, (2) if the number of found or indicated corners is adequate to control a standard-accuracy adjustment of the land lines, and (3) if on-the-ground evidence (such as fences, crop lines, cleared or blazed lines, and roads) agrees with the land plat, and the lines are accepted locally.

Δ   **Dashed-line symbol.** Land lines are shown by the dashed-line symbol if there is not enough evidence to ascertain that their positions are within the horizontal accuracy tolerance of the National Map Accuracy Standards. There must be sufficient evidence, however, to show that the map positions in relation to the positions indicated by the plat data are within 0.1 inch at map scale (200 feet—61 m—for a 1:24,000-scale map).

Δ **Dotted-line symbol.** Subdivision lines are shown by dotted-line symbolization if the surveys and plats (1) were done by private surveyors or government agencies other than BLM and (2) are accepted by local landowners and courts but not by BLM. If the dotted-line symbol is used, the following note is added in the map legend: "Dotted land lines established by private survey."

Δ **Omitted lines.** Land lines are omitted if none of the above conditions apply. A note is added in the map legend to explain the omission.

Land lines are also omitted if they coincide with features of higher order symbolization, such as civil boundaries, land grants, roads, levees, and canals, but it is not necessary to explain these omissions.

Surveys by metes and bounds of mineral claims, small holding claims, private-land claims, disposal tracts, and forest-entry claims do not conform to legal subdivisions of the rectangular system of surveys. The boundaries of these irregular parcels of land are generally not shown on topographic maps. However, they may be shown by the grant boundary symbol, if they are needed to show the limits of the land net, if they are important boundaries, or if section lines do not penetrate the area.

Land-grant boundaries are shown on published maps by a long-dash-and-two-dots symbol. Township and range lines inside grants are shown with continuous lines (fig. 89A), but if these lines coincide with grant boundaries, the land-grant symbol takes precedence over the land-line symbol. If township or range lines divide grants, different identifying numbers for the same grant may appear on adjacent plats (fig. 89B).

FIGURE 89A. Township and range lines shown within grants. (Dalies, N. Mex., quadrangle.)

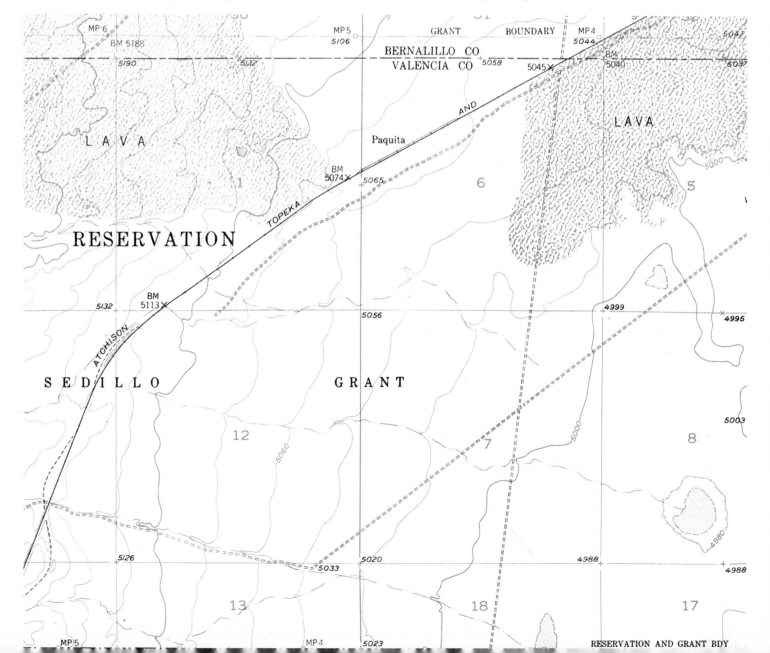

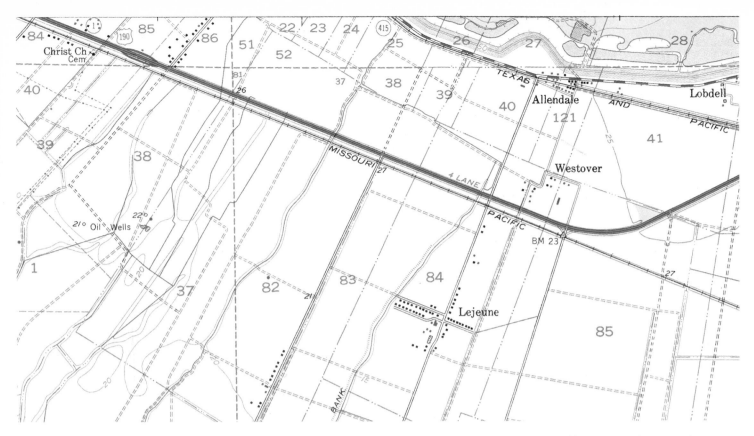

FIGURE 89*B*. Exterior township lines dividing grants. Parts of the same grant are given different identifying numbers, as shown on the plats. (Lobdell, La., quadrangle.)

BLM independent resurveys containing large areas of tracts are treated as follows: Tract boundaries are not shown, and resurveyed public-land lines are not shown within tract areas but are terminated where they intersect tract boundaries.

The section-line symbol is used to show townsite boundaries that break the land net. If BLM plats do not show section lines through a townsite, these lines are dropped at the intersection of the townsite boundary.

Location (or mineral) monuments are fixed reference points supplementing regular public-land survey monuments. Location monuments are established during the official patent survey of a mining claim in areas not covered by public-land surveys or not having adequate monumentation; for example, in areas not having a public-land survey corner within 2 miles (3.4 km) of the mineral claim. The survey of the mineral claim is tied to the location monument, which is later tied to the public-land surveys when they are extended over the area. These monuments formerly were designated mineral monuments. Most of them are marked stones with rock cairns nearby. However, some monuments have metal tablets stamped either "USLM" or "USMM" (U.S. location monument or mineral monument) and a serial number.

These monuments are accurately located on the map regardless of the status of public-land surveys in the area at the time of mapping. They are shown on the map with the USLM and USMM symbol and identifying letters and numbers.

ADJUSTMENT ON THE MAP. Adjustment, as used here, means determining theoretical map positions of unrecovered corners and subdivision lines by referring to land-plat data, field evidence, photoimages, and overedge map data. In this connection, the following general rules, established by Congress in 1805, are taken into account:

Δ Boundaries and subdivisions of public lands, as surveyed and approved, are unchangeable after the passing of title by the United States.

Δ Physical evidence of the original monument must stand as the true subdivision corner it was intended to represent and must be given controlling preference over recorded directions and lengths of lines.

Several factors—the date of the original survey, the type of terrain, and the number and distribution of the recovered corners and lines—influence the method of adjustment. BLM surveys made since 1910 are generally considered sufficiently accurate to permit using the minimum number of found corners to control the plotting of subdivision lines and corners with standard accuracy. After the land net has been plotted from the plat data, the lines are adjusted so that their positions in relation to the topographic and planimetric features on the map agree with the corresponding positions on the plats.

Boundaries, Names, and Marginalia

LAND-LINE PROTRACTIONS. BLM has prepared protraction diagrams of all areas of Alaska not yet subdivided by ground surveys. The unsurveyed land lines are protracted to represent theoretically perfect public-land subdivisions. Protracted land lines are shown with solid gray lines on all new Geological Survey Alaska maps and on revisions and reprints. Township, range, and section lines are shown on 1:24,000- and 1:63,360-scale maps; only township and range lines are shown on 1:250,000-scale maps. (Subdivision lines and corners established by BLM ground surveys are shown with standard red symbols.)

BLM has also prepared protraction diagrams of suspended and unsurveyed townships in the conterminous United States. The land lines are protracted from positions in adjoining surveyed townships, and the protracted townships are made to fit between the valid townships. These protracted land lines are not shown on topographic maps. However, they may be useful in locating civil boundaries because their positions are accepted until ground surveys are made.

Place and Feature Names

The names shown on quadrangle maps are those in local usage, as nearly as can be ascertained from officials and residents of the area and from other sources, such as previously published maps, historical records, and reference publications. In selecting the names that are to be published, the mapmakers make sure that the most important ones are included and that the overall density of names and descriptive labels is appropriate for the scale of the map. Names that disagree with other government publications or are controversial in local usage are referred to the U.S. Board on Geographic Names, an interdepartmental board that is the legal authority on names used on Federal Government maps and in other Federal Government publications. Although the Board's decisions are widely followed in non-Federal publications, there is no legal requirement to do so. The quadrangle name itself is usually that of the most prominent city, town, or other feature appearing within the mapped area.

The legal spelling for place names is usually followed; however, if the legal names differ from local and official usage, the local usage is given preference. Unless the names differ only in being contracted forms (as "boro" for "borough"), the differing name is shown underneath, in parentheses, in type smaller than the place name (see example printed below). If the name of

a post office differs from the name of the railroad station, or if either differs from the locally used place name, the place name is given preference and the differing name is shown underneath, in parentheses.

In addition to towns and localities designated by their post office or railroad station names, all other well-known localities are designated by local names established through recognized usage. Well-established locality names within cities and their environs are shown. Generally, within metropolitan areas, branch post offices are named for the localities in which they are located. When housed in their own buildings, branch post offices are shown as landmark buildings and labeled "Post Office" or "PO." The main post office is labeled "Main Post Office" or "Main PO."

Regional and Area Names

Names for extensive areas such as Rocky Mountains, Great Smoky Mountains, Shenandoah Valley, and Allegheny Mountains are omitted from standard quadrangle maps. However, if the limits of an important feature are well defined, as exemplified by the escarpment of the Cumberland Plateau or the face of the Front Range in Colorado, the name is shown.

Names of long linear features with a definite main ridge such as Blue Ridge and Continental Divide may be selected for publication. Occasionally, to indicate the continuity of a linear feature, the name may be applied to the slope if the main ridge is located along the edge of the adjoining map.

Reservation Names

The names of national parks, forests, and monuments, Indian reservations, private land grants, game preserves, State parks, military and naval reservations, and similar areas are published on quadrangle maps. These names are usually ascertained from publications of the appropriate agencies or consultation with local officials of these areas.

Church and School Names

The names of all churches and schools in rural areas are shown on published maps. Normally church and school names are omitted in small communities. In urban areas selected names are published according to the historical or landmark value of the church and the space available for names. The denomination is not ordinarily published as part of the name, except when it is a part of a numerical designation, as "First Baptist Church."

The names of schools, colleges, and universities generally are given preference over church names and are selected for publication in order of their importance;

for example, the name of a university takes precedence over the name of a high school. Names of private schools are shown in urban areas if the buildings are of landmark value. The names of public schools may sometimes consist of numbers.

Railroad Names

The selection of the correct names to apply to railroads requires good judgment and sometimes considerable research. When a railroad has lost its identity as a separate road through absorption or lease by a larger operating organization, the name of the larger organization is shown; however, if the affiliation does not include operation, the name of the operating entity is used.

The word "railroad" or its abbreviation "RR" is omitted except when it is a part of a descriptive label or a proper name. Government-owned railroads, such as spur lines to military installations, are labeled "US Government Railroad."

Street and Road Names

In urban areas a map shows the maximum number of street names compatible with map scale after the application of essential descriptive labels and other feature names. Preference is given to the names of the principal or through arteries. Additional names are shown at intervals to serve as ready points of orientation without unduly congesting the map.

If streets are parallel and have an orderly sequence of letters or numbers, the density of letters or numbers is reduced as shown in figure 90.

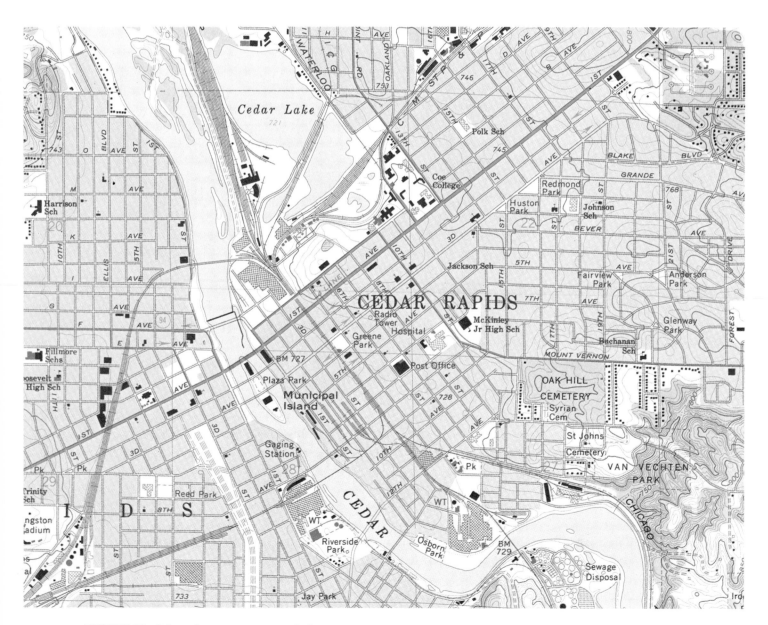

FIGURE 90. Selected street names—orderly street pattern. (Cedar Rapids South, Iowa, quadrangle.)

Boundaries, Names, and Marginalia

Many places have irregular street patterns and naming systems. In such places street names are applied as frequently as the density of map detail permits (fig. 91).

Road names that are posted or well established by local use are shown; however, a road name is omitted if the designation is uncertain or is not recognized by local residents. Posted names are published, if space is available, unless they involve some conflict with official designations or local use. Names such as "Jonesville-Smithville Road" are omitted unless posted.

In recent years the motoring public has practically ceased to refer to named highways. In recognition of this trend, the Federal Highway Administration, the American Association of State Highway Officials, the American Automobile Association, and commercial mapmakers have generally dropped highway names and use the numbering system. Highway name determination is further complicated when local civic groups propose and often adopt a new name for part or all of a route already designated by a well-established name.

Memorial and commemorative highway names such as United Spanish War Veterans Memorial Highway, Jefferson Davis Highway, Lincoln Highway, Grand Army of the Republic Highway, and Blue Star Memorial Highway on numbered Federal and State routes are omitted from all maps. However, this does not apply to historical names such as Santa Fe Trail, Wilderness Road, National Road, and Chisholm Trail where the name is needed to preserve continuity with the labeled original route that may depart from, or follow in part, the Federal or State numbered routes. Names are shown for prominent turnpikes, parkways, and toll roads such as the Pennsylvania Turnpike, New York State Thruway, and Santa Ana Freeway. The distinction between

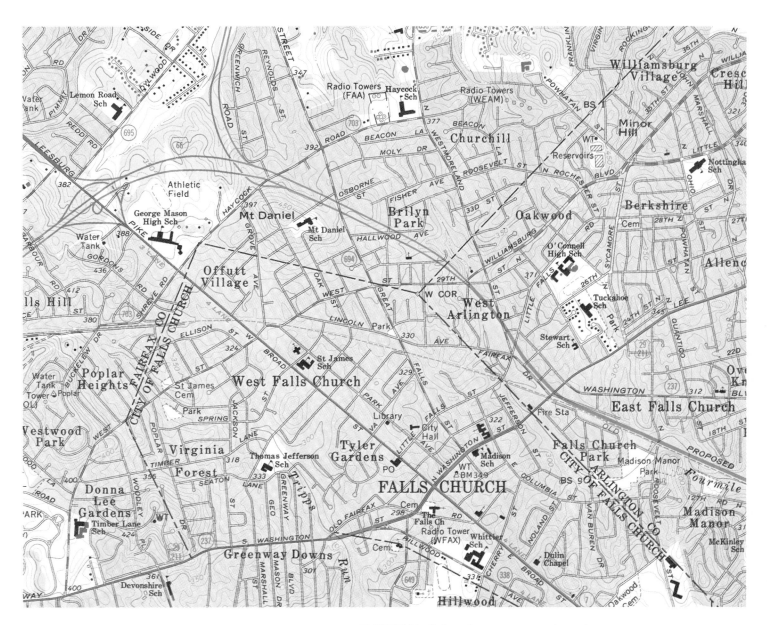

FIGURE 91. Selected street names—irregular street pattern. (Falls Church, Va.-Md., quadrangle.)

commemorative and historical names may not always be obvious; however, the decision is based on consideration of the association of the name with the history of the route—for example, Chisholm Trail rather than a purely honorary designation for a person, such as Alvin C. York Highway.

In urban areas, where named highways are frequently well established as part of the street system and are marked as such, the names may be shown as part of the street naming system.

Commercial Names

Commercial culture features such as logging railroads or large factory buildings, are identified, if necessary, by a type label, but not by company name. In selecting the name for publication the criterion is the private or public character of the organization controlling the feature. Because maps are not an advertising medium, the mapmakers must decide whether the feature is of enough public interest to publish the full name. Many colleges and universities, for example, are private organizations of a public character; factories usually are not.

Unusual or Controversial Names

Names which may be considered derogatory, obscene or vulgar, whimsical, or merely amusing or inconsequential are continually encountered. The decision as to whether to publish the name as is, or to alter, abbreviate, disguise, or delete is often subject to criticism. Names with a derogatory implication are not accepted for publication. Experience and the reactions from map users have proved that good taste is much easier to defend than vulgarity. If a solution that retains identification and yet avoids undue criticism cannot be devised, the name is omitted.

Correct decisions concerning controversial names and name changes must be reached before the maps involved are published. All names of natural features are the responsibility of the Board on Geographic Names. In addition, there are place names and other names which must be considered by the Board.

Quadrangle Names

By mutual agreement of several Federal mapping agencies, the Geological Survey is responsible for assigning names to all quadrangle maps prepared by these agencies.

Because it is sometimes impractical to select the most suitable publication name for a quadrangle in advance of mapping, provisional names are given to quadrangles when planning is begun. The provisional names are used throughout operational phases and for cost accounting even though the maps may be published with new names.

Provisional names have been assigned to 30- and 15-minute quadrangles throughout the United States. These assigned names are shown on the State administrative index maps and are used in deriving provisional names for unnamed subdivisions of the named quadrangles.

For an unnamed 15-minute quadrangle, the provisional name is derived by using the 30-minute quadrangle name together with a number indicating the proper quarter of the 30-minute area. For an unnamed 7.5-minute quadrangle, the provisional name consists of the 15-minute quadrangle name plus the abbreviation for the proper quarter of the 15-minute area. Provisional names derived from the assigned names of large quadrangles are not shown on the administrative index maps. Figure 92 illustrates the system of numbering and provisional naming for subdivisions of 30-minute and 15-minute quadrangles.

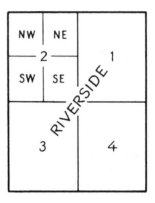 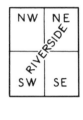

FIGURE 92. System of numbering and provisional naming for subdivisions of the Riverside 30- and 15-minute quadrangles.

The name selected for a quadrangle is intended to identify the mapped area to the greatest number of people. Usually, each quadrangle is named for its principal city or place or most prominent feature, provided that all or most of the feature lies within the quadrangle. If that name designates another quadrangle of the same series in the same State, the name of the secondary place or feature is selected. Duplication of a quadrangle name within a State is permissible only when the name is for a feature common to maps of different series; for example, Williamsburg is an appropriate name for the 30-, 15-, and 7.5-minute Williamsburg, Va., quadrangles. If a quadrangle lies in two or more States and the logical name for it has already been used in one of the States, the name of a less prominent feature is selected, provided it adequately identifies the quadrangle. If there is only one suitable feature in the area it may be used as the quadrangle name, even though it has been duplicated in one of the adjacent States. Whenever there are two or more features on the quadrangle having equal or nearly equal identification quality, the one not previously used is chosen as the quadrangle name.

Depending upon their relative importance in the area, the following features are considered for naming quadrangles: principal city, town, or village; most prominent mountain, peak, lake, or stream; rural post offices and localities; and other features such as prominent ranches, well-established country schools, railroad sidings, or minor physical features.

Sometimes a prominent feature is common to two adjacent 7.5-minute quadrangles, and the feature name may be used for both maps by adding to it the directional names north and south or east and west. For example, the Washington East quadrangle map shows the eastern part of the city of Washington, D.C., and the Washington West quadrangle map, the western part. This method of naming is not suitable for 15-minute quadrangles because directional names are often coupled with the 15-minute name to give final names for the 7.5-minute quadrangles, and the result might be such confusing names as Washington South NW or Washington North NE.

Names for partially surveyed quadrangles generally are selected as though the whole area were mapped. When two places of equal importance are within the quadrangle and one is in the unmapped area, however, the quadrangle is named for the place that is located in the mapped area.

A completely mapped quadrangle that straddles an international boundary is named for the most prominent place or feature, regardless of the nation in which the feature is located. The names of the States or provinces are shown as part of the quadrangle name.

Lettering

Much of the information on a map is shown by the lettering. Names, labels, and notes are added to make the picture shown by the topographic map complete and usable. In the body of the map, lettering includes place and feature names, descriptive labels, identification of control marks, spot elevations, and contour labels. The information shown in the margin of the map includes the quadrangle name and location, map series, scale, contour interval, authorship, mapping methods, and other pertinent data.

An important part of map composition is the positioning of lettering. Each name is placed to assure immediate and unmistakable identification of the feature with minimum interference with other map detail.

A map is read usually from the bottom or south edge. Therefore most names and labels are positioned parallel to the south projection line. Straight-line lettering on any diagonal is avoided unless it parallels a linear feature to which it refers. If lettering must be placed diagonally it is oriented to read from left to right, regardless of the angle. Names which must be placed vertically (parallel to the meridian) are oriented to read from south to north, so that they can be read from the right or east side of the map.

A very important factor in map appearance and readability is the flow or alinement of lettering. Names are placed on a straight line or a smooth curve, avoiding an angular or zigzag arrangement. Insofar as practicable the components of names for natural features are alined on broad arcs or easy curves following the general trend of the feature (fig. 93).

FIGURE 93. Placement of names for streams, mountains, and valleys. (Strasburg, Va., 1:62,500-scale 15-minute quadrangle.)

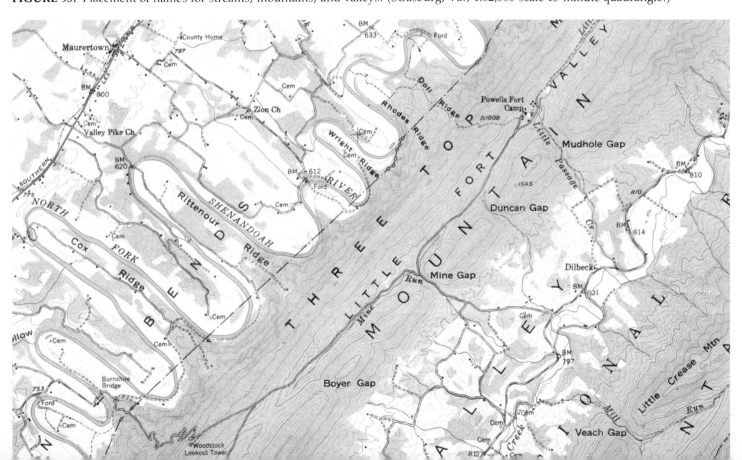

For simplicity and uniformity, and because it is not good practice to use any mark that could be mistaken for a map symbol, most punctuation marks are omitted from the body of the map. The period is not shown, and the apostrophe is never used to indicate possession. Harpers Ferry and Pikes Peak are the correct map forms, not Harper's Ferry or Pike's Peak. The apostrophe is used only where necessary to conform to legal spelling, such as O'Brien Creek. The hyphen is used only to conform to legal spelling, as in Pre-emption Road, Shut-in Cove, St. Louis-San Francisco, Geneva-on-the-Lake, or Hole-in-One-Mountain, and for separating parts of two-part names, as Hall-Mills School, Plainville-Hillytown Park, or Smith-Brown Cemetery.

Diacritical marks are used in names in Puerto Rico, where the official language is Spanish. Diacritical marks are not used on Anglicized words.

Variations in type styles help to identify and differentiate between classes of map features. For example, on conventional 7.5-minute maps, labels for hydrographic features are usually shown in *italic (slanted)* type while those for hypsographic features are shown in **gothic (vertical)** type.

Information Shown on Map Margins

The space outside the neatline on published Geological Survey maps identifies and explains the map. The marginal information corresponds somewhat to the table of contents and introduction of a book—it tells briefly how the map was made, where the quadrangle is located, what organizations are responsible for the contents, and gives other information to make the map more useful.

Map Identification

Each map is identified in the upper right margin by its quadrangle name, State or States in which it is located, series, and type, arranged as follows:

QUADRANGLE NAME. Criteria for determining the quadrangle name are discussed in the section on place names (p. 90–91).

STATE NAME. If the quadrangle includes areas of more than one State, the State names are shown in the title in the order of decreasing area, even if only the part falling in one State is mapped. If a quadrangle is over-edge to a State boundary, the adjacent State name is shown along the boundary but not in the map title. If a very small part of a State falls within a quadrangle, the State name is included in the map title even though it may not have been shown on the boundary because of insufficient space.

COUNTY NAME. The name is not shown in the title if it appears on the face of the map.

QUADRANGLE SERIES AND TYPE. Series refers to the area mapped in terms of minutes or degrees; type is either topographic or planimetric.

RELATIVE POSITION. If a new 7.5-minute map covers a part of a published 15-minute quadrangle, a note is added giving the position of the 7.5-minute quadrangle. An example of an assembled map title is:

NEW BUFFALO EAST QUADRANGLE
MICHIGAN—INDIANA
7.5 MINUTE SERIES (TOPOGRAPHIC)
SW/4 THREE OAKS 15' QUADRANGLE

The title block in the lower right margin shows the quadrangle and State name, the geographic index number, and, for a 7.5-minute map, its position in relation to the 15-minute map, if applicable. This title block also shows the year of the map. The geographic index number is the geographic position of the corner of the map nearest the Greenwich meridian and the Equator, followed by the series, such as 7.5 minute.

JACKASS BAY, LA.
SE/4 LOREAUVILLE 15' QUADRANGLE
N3000—W9130/7.5

1973

AMS 7644 II SE—SERIES V8850

Cooperative Credit

States and municipalities that cooperate in the preparation of Survey quadrangle maps by contributing funds are given appropriate credit on the published maps. An example of the heading for new mapping or remapping completed as part of a cooperative program is:

STATE OF KENTUCKY
KENTUCKY GEOLOGICAL SURVEY
UNIVERSITY OF KENTUCKY

The address line may be shown but is generally considered unnecessary. This heading appears in the center of the upper margin.

If the cooperator contributes to only a minor extent, the cooperation is shown only by the credit legend which appears in the lower left margin, for example:

Mapped, edited, and published by the Geological Survey in cooperation with State of Michigan agencies
Control by USGS, USC&GS, and City of Detroit

³58   47'30"   2 700 000 FEET   ³60   R. 40 E.   R. 41 E.   ³62   106°45'
45°07'30"

⁴⁹98

State plane
coordinate
420 000
FEET
(See p. 241–42.)

4997
UTM coordinate
4,997,000 meters
North of Equator
(See p. 240–42.)

Federal agencies that cooperate in the preparation of Survey quadrangle maps either by contributing funds or by performing mapping operations that are incorporated in the published map are listed only in the credit legend. A typical credit legend statement for such maps is:

Mapped by the Army Map Service
Edited and published by the Geological Survey
Control by USGS USC&GS, and USBR

The Department of the Interior-Geological Survey heading, in the upper left margin, is always the same in composition and placement.

UNITED STATES
DEPARTMENT OF THE INTERIOR
GEOLOGICAL SURVEY

Adjoining Quadrangle Names

4349 I NE
(ALLIE CANYON)

Adjoining quadrangle names are shown so that map users may know that topographic data are available for these adjacent areas. The following rules govern the use of these names:

Δ Names of adjoining maps that appear on the current sales indexes, have been completed for publication, or will be completed in the near future, are shown on all four sides and at all four corners.

Δ Only the quadrangle name is shown if the adjoining map is published at the same scale or is of the same series.

Δ Both the name and scale are shown if the adjoining map is of a different series, as where a 15-minute map adjoins a 7.5-minute map, or two 7.5-minute maps adjoin a 15-minute map.

Δ If there is map coverage of the same adjoining area in two series, one of which is the same as that of the map being prepared, the name of only the map of the same series is shown.

Projection and Grid Labels

Geographic coordinates are shown at all four projection corners, and along the projection lines at 2.5-minute intervals for 7.5-minute maps, and at 5-minute intervals for 15-minute maps. When a map has an over-edge area and one or more projection lines are extended, the coordinate value is positioned at the end of the extended projection lines. Coordinates for both the State and the Universal Transverse Mercator (UTM) grid systems are shown near the projection corners.

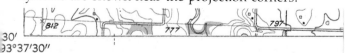

30'
93°37'30"

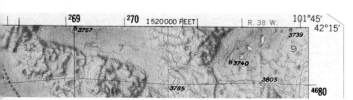

STATE ZONE GRID TICKS. If a quadrangle lies entirely within one grid zone, the numerical values of the grid lines are indicated for the x- and y-ticks nearest the southwest and northeast corners of the quadrangle. If a quadrangle lies in two or more grid zones, the second zone grid values are shown for the x- and y-ticks nearest the southeast and northwest corners; the third, at the southwest and northeast corners on the tick next to the first grid zone figures; and the fourth zone grid, in the southeast and northwest corners on the tick next to the second grid zone figures. Zone sequence is in order of decreasing area.

UTM GRID. In 1974, the Survey stated its intention to show a full fine-line UTM grid on its published maps at scale 1:1,000,000 or larger, except in special cases for which it is not appropriate or justified. As of 1978, this intention had been implemented for new 1:25,000- and 1:100,000-scale line maps and 1:24,000-scale orthophotographic maps. The UTM grid is in addition to and does not replace reference systems previously indicated.

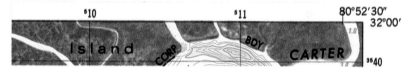

⁶10   ⁶11   80°52'30"
32°00'

Credit Legend

The credit legend is located in the lower left margin.* Because of the almost infinite number of possible combinations of data, credit legends cannot be rigid. The information is listed in the following order:

1. Name of the mapping agency.
2. Name of the editing and publishing agency. If one agency is responsible both for the mapping and for the editing and publishing, the two notes are combined.
3. Name of the agency or agencies that furnished the geodetic control.
4. Method or methods by which the mapping was performed.
5. Credit note for hydrographic information.
6. Informative and explanatory notes.

* ────────────────────────────────

Mapped, edited and published by the Geological Survey and the National Ocean Survey
Control by USGS and NOS/NOAA

Orthophotomap prepared by the Geological Survey from aerial photograph taken April 18, 1974. Topography by planetable surveys 1957; revised from aerial photographs taken 1974. Field checked 1975. Map edited 1978
Supersedes topographic map dated 1957

Bathymetry compiled by the National Ocean Survey from tide-coordinated hydrographic surveys
Soundings compiled from NOS 11512
This information is not intended for navigational purposes

Mean low water (dotted) line and mean high water (solid) line compiled by NOS from tide-coordinated photography dated 1971, 1973, 1974. Apparent shoreline (outer edge of vegetation) shown by photoimagery

Projection and 10,000-foot grid ticks: Georgia coordinate system, east zone (transverse Mercator)
1000-meter Universal Transverse Mercator grid, zone 17
1927 North American datum

There may be private inholdings within the boundaries of the National or State reservations shown on this map

Lower Margin Data

The magnetic declination for the year of field survey or revision is determined to the nearest 0.5 degree from the latest isogonic chart. It is shown by a diagram centered between the credit legend and bar scale (fig. 94).

FIGURE 94. Magnetic declination diagram.

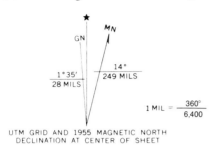

UTM GRID AND 1955 MAGNETIC NORTH
DECLINATION AT CENTER OF SHEET

The center of the lower margin contains the following information, arranged in the order indicated:

1. Publication scale expressed as a ratio.*
2. Bar scales in metric and customary units.*
3. Contour-interval statement. If the map contains supplementary contours, a statement to that effect is added.* When the maximum elevation on the quadrangle is less than the specified contour interval, the following note is used in place of the standard contour-interval statement:

ENTIRE AREA BELOW 5 FEET

When a quadrangle area is located in two countries and the contour interval is different, the following note is used:

CONTOUR INTERVAL 20 FEET IN THE UNITED STATES AND 10 METERS IN MEXICO

4. Vertical datum: The statement DATUM IS MEAN SEA LEVEL is on standard Survey topographic maps printed prior to 1975. On maps printed since, the statement is NATIONAL GEODETIC VERTICAL DATUM OF 1929

   The change was made to eliminate confusion arising from the difference between local "mean sea level" and the vertical control datum.
5. Depth-curve and soundings statement, where applicable. DATUM IS MEAN LOW WATER is used for the Atlantic and Gulf coasts, DATUM IS MEAN LOWER LOW WATER for the Pacific coast. The datum for the Great Lakes is low water to the nearest 0.1 foot as shown on the U.S. Lake Survey chart. A typical note is:

DEPTH CURVES AND SOUNDINGS IN FEET—DATUM IS LOW WATER 576.8 FEET

6. Shoreline and tide-range statements, shown on maps that include tidal shoreline.

SHORELINE SHOWN REPRESENTS THE APPROXIMATE LINE OF MEAN HIGH WATER
THE MEAN RANGE OF TIDE IS APPROXIMATELY 4 FEET

7. Map accuracy statement. The standard statement is:

THIS MAP COMPLIES WITH NATIONAL MAP ACCURACY STANDARDS

Its absence means that in some respects the map may not comply with accuracy standards. (See the section on "Map Accuracy Standards," p. 102–107.)

A legend explaining the various road symbols that are shown on the map is placed in the lower right margin. This legend is tailored for each map to include only the classes of roads and the route markers that are shown in the body of the map. Trails are not included in the legend unless there are no roads on the map.

ROAD CLASSIFICATION

Primary highway, all weather, hard surface —— Light-duty road, all weather, improved surface ——

Secondary highway, all weather, hard surface —— Unimproved road, fair or dry weather ========

Interstate Route · U. S. Route · State Route

FIGURE 95. Quadrangle location diagram.

QUADRANGLE LOCATION

The location of the quadrangle within the State is shown by a diagram centered between the road legend and the bar scale, as shown in figure 95. The small square representing the quadrangle mapped is positioned accurately. If a quadrangle falls within two or more States, the State having the largest area of quadrangle within its borders is shown.

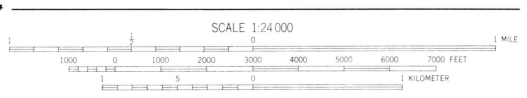

SCALE 1:24 000

CONTOUR INTERVAL 40 FEET
DOTTED LINES REPRESENT 20-FOOT CONTOURS

The year of the data shown on the map is printed beneath and as part of the title in the lower right margin. The latest date of field completion or revision is used. It remains unchanged in future reprintings but is changed when the map is revised.

ROYAL OAK, MICH.
N4222.5—W8307.5/7.5

1968
PHOTOREVISED 1973
AMS 4368 I NW—SERIES V862

If minor cartographic corrections are made for a reprint, a note in small type is added under the year:

1957
MINOR REVISIONS 1973

Federal printing and binding regulations require that there shall be a note on all maps and other publications issued by Government agencies showing the name of the Department responsible for the publication and the name and location of the printing plant. For Geological Survey publications, the year of printing is included in the plant imprint note:

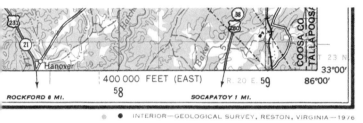

The note is placed immediately below the border or the projection line in the lower right margin and may be moved to the left if necessary, to avoid interference with other marginal data, such as road destinations, grid ticks, and grid labels.

Miscellaneous Marginal Data

Road destinations are shown in the map margin for convenience in determining the distance to the next town or important road junction beyond the map border, and to facilitate orientation of the map with respect to well-known features. (See the section on Roads, p. 47–48.)

On 7.5- and 15-minute maps range and township numbers normally are placed in pairs just outside the neatline. If one of a pair interferes with other marginal lettering, both numbers are moved to avoid the interference and maintain the equidistant spacing from the point where the range or township line intersects the projection line.

If a range or township line does not extend to the projection line, the numbers, without punctuation, are placed inside the map near the end of and straddling the line.

A statement identifying the available larger scale coverage is placed above the lower margin title and is worded as in the following example:

This area also covered by 1:24 000-scale maps of
Cumberland 1949, Frostburg 1949, Lonaconing 1950
and Cresaptown 1949, 7.5 minute quadrangles

If the area of a 15-minute map being reprinted has coverage by one or more 7.5-minute maps, a statement patterned after the following note is shown below the road classification legend:

This area is also partially covered by 1:24 000
scale maps of Olds Ferry NW, Olds Ferry, and
Olds Ferry SE 7.5 minute quadrangles

A map for which there is a shaded-relief edition carries the statement:

THIS MAP AVAILABLE WITH OR WITHOUT SHADED RELIEF OVERPRINT

The statement is placed in the center of the lower margin, directly above the map-accuracy statement.

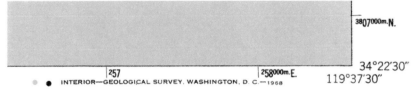

6:

Map Maintenance and Accuracy Standards

"Maintenance" means continuing to provide maps that are up-to-date, accurate, complete, and suitable for their intended use. "Accuracy" means conforming to specifications that hold errors within tolerable limits.

Map Maintenance

As more and more areas are mapped by the Geological Survey, the problem of map maintenance becomes a formidable one because of the sheer number of maps to be maintained (fig. 96). Map maintenance is the task of providing, on a current basis, maps that are up-to-date, accurate, complete, and suitable for the intended use.

The terms "map maintenance" and "map revision" are often regarded as synonymous, but they are not quite the same. Map maintenance may be accomplished by supplementing an existing map with a completely new product (such as an orthophotoquad) that is not derived from the existing map. In the majority of instances, however, the existing map is revised by determining which elements of the old data are no longer valid and then substituting correct, up-to-date data. The map maintenance program of the Survey is generally referred to loosely as "the revision program"; it should be understood that this usage includes the production of up-to-date maps that replace but are not derived from

FIGURE 96. Significant changes in map content on successive editions of this map illustrate the need for a continuing map maintenance program.

Mapped in 1949 ⟶

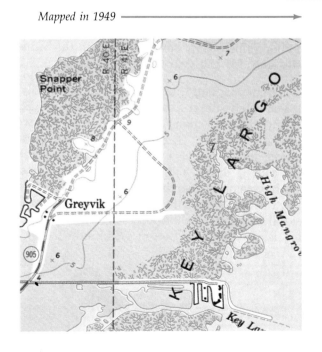

Revised in 1956 ⟶

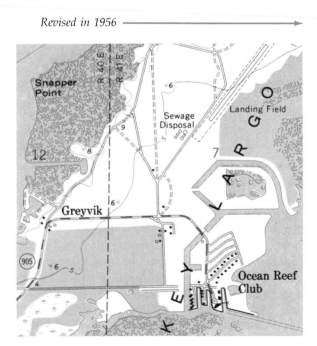

older maps, as well as those resulting from the revision of older maps.

The following definitions apply to the map maintenance program of the Survey:

Revision. Updating, improving, and correcting map content for publication in the same series.

Total revision. Correcting all deficiencies in planimetry and relief features, including improvement of accuracy, vertical and horizontal, to result in a map meeting current specifications. Formerly called "complete revision" if little or no original material was salvaged, or "standard revision" if much of the original material was salvaged.

Partial revision. Correcting specified map deficiencies. The revised data appear on the published map in conventional colors. Formerly called "limited revision."

Photorevision. Updating maps from aerial photographs and other available sources to reflect planimetric changes which have occurred since the date of the latest existing map. The revised information is not field checked and is printed in a distinctive color on the new map. Formerly called "interim revision."

Photoinspection. Comparing the latest published map to recent aerial photographs to determine both the need for revision and the extent of the changes.

Total Revision

A phased (sequential) approach is usually employed in total revision to yield this sequence of map products:

Δ **Orthophotoquad.** An orthophotoquad is prepared from high-altitude quad-centered photographs; it may be available in lithographic, photographic, or diazo form.

Δ **Advance planimetric edition.** An advance planimetric edition is prepared by direct scribing on an orthophotoquad base. In compiling this edition,

some stereoscopic compilation may be required for accurate positioning of obscure features, such as single-line drains or drains in timbered areas. Nonphotographic source materials are used when available to add boundaries, names, and other features not visible on the photographs. This product is available in black-and-white lithographic or diazo form.

Δ **Total revised map.** In the total revision process the advance planimetric edition is field checked, and additional field information is obtained for completing the map. Contours and additional planimetric features are stereocompiled as needed. The planimetric additions and corrections are then applied to the color-separation materials produced for the advance planimetric edition. Parts of the old map may be used if they are known to be of standard quality and accuracy. Content of the total revised map complies with current specifications for new maps.

Partial Revision

Procedures for partial revision vary according to the specified deficiencies to be corrected. Corrections may range from minor updating, such as the addition of a single reservoir or highway, to field checking of revised features. Aerial photographs are used in stereoscopic or monoscopic mode as appropriate. Surveys, engineering plans, and other source material are also used when available. Changes made by partial revision are shown on the published map in conventional colors.

Photorevision

Corrections, additions, and deletions of planimetric features are made by photointerpretation and transfer of detail from aerial photographs. Either monoscopic or stereoscopic procedures are used depending on terrain

Photorevised in 1969 ⟶

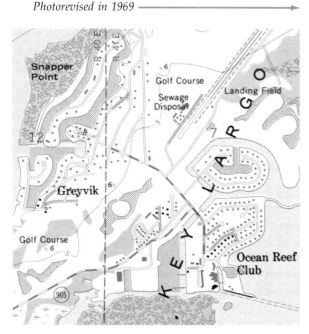

Photorevised in 1973 ⟶

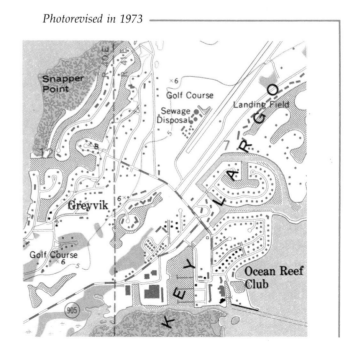

Map Maintenance

relief. Other available source materials, such as surveys, engineering plans, or local maps, are used to revise boundaries, names, or other features not visible on the photographs. The revised features are not field checked, and the new information is printed in a distinctive color on the new map (figs. 97–99).

Photoinspection

Quadrangles are selected for photoinspection in response to commitments to statewide cyclic inspection programs or other requirements. Areas of known high rate of change are generally reviewed on a 5-year cycle. Generally, maps are not reviewed more frequently than every 5 years nor less frequently than every 20 years.

Photoinspection criteria used to determine the need for revision are given in table 3. Three examples of inspection results which qualify a quadrangle for consideration for total revision are

Δ Total change of linear features exceeds 50 miles.
Δ Total change of areal features exceeds 15 mi² or 25 percent of the land area.
Δ Total change of linear features is 30 miles (60 percent) and areal features, 6 mi² (40 percent).

TABLE 3. Revision criteria for topographic quadrangle maps as determined by photoinspection

| Feature | Major changes[1] | |
	Description	Minimum change required for revision
Roads, major	Interstate and major highways of at least four lanes.	1 mile per quad (or in lesser amounts if necessary to preserve continuity of the feature through a block of several quadrangles).
Roads, minor	Double-line roads symbolized by 40-foot road width.	5 miles per quad with no segment less than 1 mile.
Drainage	Double line. Single line, perennial	1 mile per quad. 5 miles per quad with no segment less than 1 mile.
Reservoirs	Water storage, controlled outlet.	1 mile or more in length and covering at least 0.25 mi².
Airports	Major landing fields: private, commercial, or military, generally hard surfaced.	New runways, additions, or changes of at least 0.5 mile.
Strip mines	Areas of disturbed earth, active or inactive.	Extensions of mining area or reclaimed areas of at least 0.25 mi².
Urban-suburban	Areas in and surrounding metropolitan areas.	Subdivision-type pattern of streets and buildings covering at least 0.125 mi².

| Feature | Minor changes[1] | |
	Description	Minimum of three changes or more to justify revision
Ponds	Stock tanks, private ponds.	Eight per quad with average width 200–300 feet.
Airfields	Private landing fields, generally not hard surfaced.	One or more, regardless of size.
Industrial sites	Large areas, usually with rail or highway access, designated as industrial parks, manufacturing, or commercial areas.	One or more buildings totaling 100,000 ft² or more.
Woodland	Major timber areas or orchards.	Total of 2 mi² of addition or deletion with no area less than 1 mi².
Miscellany	Pipelines, major power transmission lines, ditches.	5 miles per quad with no segment less than 1 mile.

| Feature | "Total revision" criteria[2] | |
	Description	Minimum change required for total revision
Linear	All roads, railroads, drainage, coastline, and airport runways and taxiways.	50 miles.
Areal	Reservoirs, strip mines, urban-suburban, and beaches.	15 mi² or 25 percent of land area.

[1] When none of the major changes or fewer than three of the minor changes occur on a map being reviewed, the photoinspection date and note will be added to reprint editions.
[2] Features will not be double counted. For example: (1) if a double-line stream change is counted as a linear change, the open-water tint will not be counted as an areal change, or (2) if the urban-tint change is counted as an areal change, minor roads in urban-tint areas will not be counted as linear changes.

When reviewing maps, the cumulative change that would be shown in purple overprint with this anticipated revision is considered. Any map on which the summation of both categories approaches 100 percent will be considered for total revision rather than photorevision.

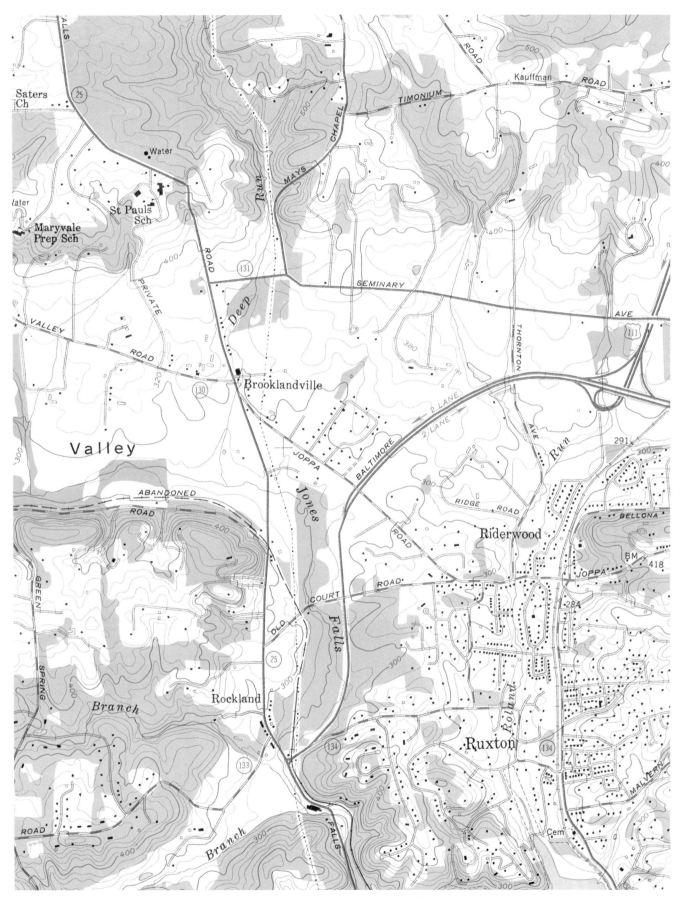

FIGURE 97. Portion of Cockeysville, Md., quadrangle mapped in 1957.

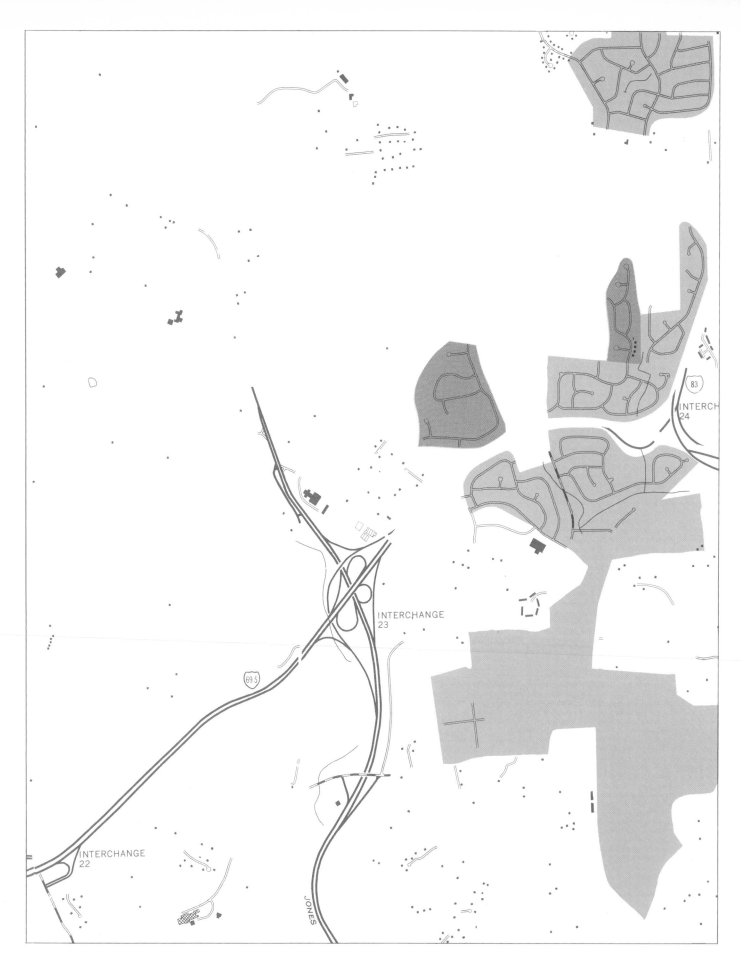

FIGURE 98. Compiled new data for 1966 and 1974 photorevisions of Cockeysville, Md., quadrangle map. Darker shade indicates 1974 photorevision.

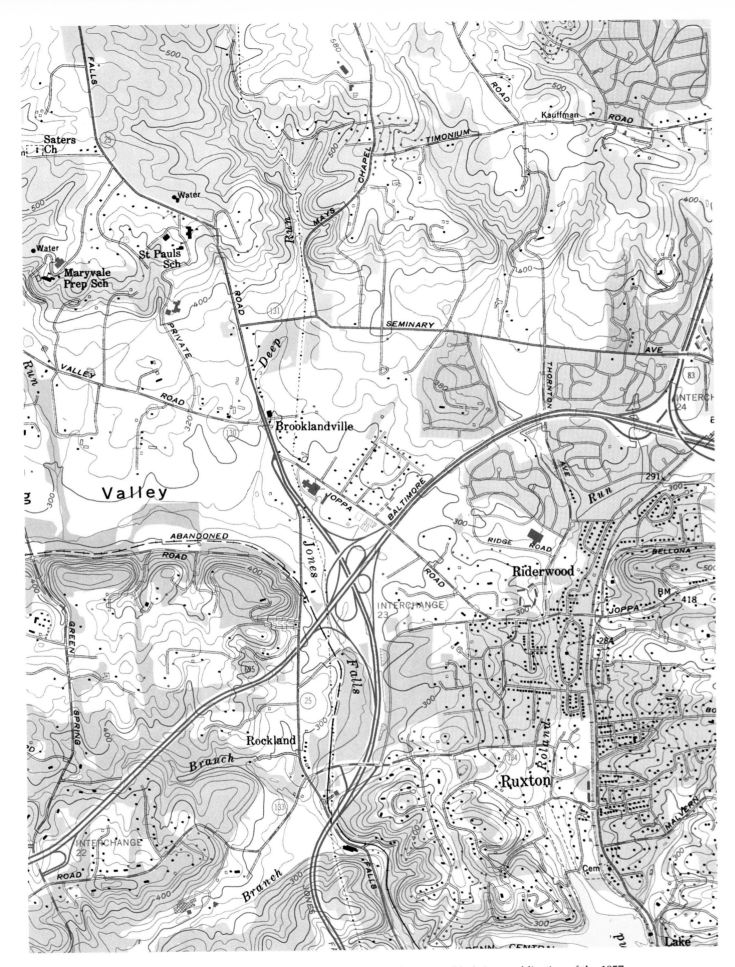

FIGURE 99. Portion of Cockeysville, Md., map, 1974 edition. All map features added since publication of the 1957 map are shown in purple.

Revision Selection

Quadrangles needing revision, by the criteria in table 3, are revised by means of total, partial, or photorevision procedures. Total revision updates maps requiring a new base, extensive contour corrections, or extensive planimetric update. Partial revision updates selected features based on special Federal requirements, requests from State cooperators, or special needs. Photorevision updates maps that have accurate bases but need moderate planimetric revision.

The following factors, along with the criteria in table 3, are considered in determining the type of revision:

Δ **Cartographic materials.** Maps for which cartographic materials (color-separation negatives or positives, or manuscripts) are nonexistent or in poor condition are candidates for total revision.

Δ **Amount of change.** Maps of good geometric quality but needing updating receive: total revision if the planimetric change is extensive; partial revision if the planimetric changes are not extensive, but the map warrants contour correction or classification verification (roads, buildings, boundaries); and photorevision if the planimetric change is moderate.

Δ **Contour interval.** Maps with an interval two or more steps larger than designated in the current interval plan are candidates for total revision.

Δ **Accuracy.** Maps which fail to meet established accuracy standards are candidates for total revision.

Δ **Survey date.** Maps can be separated into three groups of implied accuracy based on methods used during the original compilation. These methods can in turn be related to dates. Generally, (1) maps prepared prior to 1948 do not meet established horizontal accuracy standards; (2) maps surveyed between 1948 and 1957 have questionable horizontal accuracy and should be checked; and (3) maps surveyed after 1958 have acceptable horizontal accuracy and need be checked only if reasonable doubt exists.

In evaluating a map to select the appropriate revision procedure, the evaluation of adjoining maps is also considered.

The review date and an explanatory footnote are added to reprint editions of those maps which, upon comparison with recent source material, are found to require no revision. If a map has been inspected more than once and found to be adequate, only the most recent review date is added.

Dependent upon the availability of bathymetric data, all coastal quadrangles are converted to topographic-bathymetric maps at the time of revision.

Map Accuracy Standards

The idea of producing maps that conform to specified standards of accuracy has long been known, and many such maps, meeting very rigid specifications, have been prepared. Before 1900, accurate control surveys were carried out in many of our larger cities, including Washington, St. Louis, and Baltimore, and accurate, large-scale topographic maps were prepared for these areas. The accuracy of these maps was controlled by (1) specifying the methods of ground surveying, (2) specifying the density and distribution of the control network, and (3) closely inspecting the work as it progressed. The same principles were applied to the 15-minute USGS quadrangle maps up to the mid-1930's. The amount, distribution, and accuracy of the control were always specified for each mapping project, and some of the maps were sampled and checked in the field. The accuracy of the maps produced during this period was largely dependent upon the skill and integrity of the individual topographers. It became common practice to evaluate the accuracy of any given topographic map according to the professional reputation of the topographer who made it.

Mathematical standards of accuracy were used by private engineers as early as 1912 in the production of special-purpose large-scale maps for engineering works. As an example, a private firm contracted with the city of Cincinnati for the production of topographic maps and charts at the scale 1:4,800. The specifications for acceptable work included the statement that "each contour interval must not be in error more than one-half the contour interval," and also that "all horizontal distances between well-defined points must scale correctly to the smallest plottable distance"—in this case 1/80th of an inch—representing 5 feet on the ground. Provisions were also made for the testing of the work by the city of Cincinnati "at any time and place" (Marsden, 1960).

In 1934, a standard set of specifications for mapping city areas at 1:2,400 scale was adopted by the American Society of Civil Engineers. These specifications, among other things, recommended that all elevations obtained from the maps be accurate to within one-half the contour interval, and that the error in horizontal position of well-defined map points be within a tolerance of 0.01 inch.

The modern idea of standard-accuracy topographic mapping became practical because aerial photography and modern stereophotogrammetry made it possible to produce remarkably uniform results over a large variety of terrain conditions. In 1937 the American Society of Photogrammetry appointed a committee to draw up appropriate accuracy specifications. After 2 years of work, the committee published its recommended map-accuracy specifications (American Society of Photgrammetry, 1939) and invited criticism from the principal mapping agencies, societies, and individuals interested in the subject.

At that time various combinations of mapping methods were being used, and the committee realized that it might be several years before photogrammetric

PRECISE CALIBRATION. The Survey's calibration of aerial mapping cameras contributes to the maintenance of map accuracy standards.

equipment became available for use in extensive mapping programs. Photogrammetric and field methods would have to be used, both separately and combined. Hence, this group related its concept of standard accuracy to methods of production, and recommended a set of specifications that covered all the methods. Four different vertical-accuracy standards were recommended for (1) photogrammetric contouring, (2) field contouring on planimetric bases, (3) complete field mapping, and (4) substandard reconnaissance mapping.

In August 1940, the U.S. Bureau of the Budget arranged a series of conferences with representatives of the mapping industry to develop standards that would

be applicable to maps at all scales and that would be clear, concise, and free of ambiguity.

The original version of the National Map Accuracy Standards, as drawn up by the conferees, was issued by the Bureau of the Budget, June 10, 1941, as "Standards of Accuracy for a National Map Production Program." Three reference scales, 1:62,500, 1:24,000, and 1:12,000, were established with corresponding tolerances for each scale of 1/50, 1/40, and 1/30th of an inch in horizontal position. Maps with scales between the reference scales were permitted a tolerance in ground distance equal to that of the next smaller reference scale. Thus, this sliding scale of horizontal accuracy produced a peculiar anomaly when applied to the two standard military publication scales of 1:25,000 and 1:50,000; maps of both scales had the same tolerance despite the considerable difference in scales. The standards were revised in 1943 to provide the present tolerance of 1/50 inch for scales of 1:20,000 and smaller, and 1/30 inch for scales larger than 1:20,000.

The revision of June 17, 1947, which is still in effect, is called "United States National Map Accuracy Standards." Among other things, it specifies that maps which comply with the specifications should carry the statement "This map complies with the National Map Accuracy Standards."

As finally adopted, the standards provide for only one class of standard-accuracy maps. The standards also make it clear that each mapping agency is responsible for determining which of its maps should be designed to meet the standards and for labeling those that do. There is no requirement, other than that imposed by the producing agency, that all maps must meet the National Map Accuracy Standards.

Accuracy specifications for planimetric and topographic maps, as revised June 17, 1947, follow:

United States National Map Accuracy Standards

With a view to the utmost economy and expedition in producing maps which fulfill not only the broad needs for standard or principal maps, but also the reasonable particular needs of individual agencies, standards of accuracy for published maps are defined as follows:

1. **Horizontal accuracy.** For maps on publication scales larger than 1:20,000, not more than 10 percent of the points tested shall be in error by more than 1/30 inch, measured on the publication scale; for maps on publication scales of 1:20,000 or smaller, 1/50 inch. These limits of accuracy shall apply in all cases to positions of well-defined points only. Well-defined points are those that are easily visible or recoverable on the ground, such as the following: monuments or markers, such as bench marks, property boundary monuments; intersections of roads, railroads, etc.; corners of large buildings or structures (or center points of small buildings); etc. In general what is well defined will also be determined by what is plottable on the scale of the map within 1/100 inch. Thus while the intersection of two road or property lines meeting at right angles would come within a sensible interpretation, identification of the intersection of such lines meeting at an acute angle would obviously not be practicable within 1/100 inch. Similarly, features not identifiable upon the ground within close limits are not to be considered as test points within the limits quoted, even though their positions may be scaled closely upon the map. In this class would come timber lines, soil boundaries, etc.

2. **Vertical accuracy,** as applied to contour maps on all publication scales, shall be such that not more than 10 percent of the elevations tested shall be in error more than one-half the contour interval. In checking elevations taken from the map, the apparent vertical error may be decreased by assuming a horizontal displacement within the permissible horizontal error for a map of that scale.

3. **The accuracy of any map may be tested** by comparing the positions of points whose locations or elevations are shown upon it with corresponding positions as determined by surveys of a higher accuracy. Tests shall be made by the producing agency, which shall also determine which of its maps are to be tested, and the extent of such testing.

4. **Published maps meeting these accuracy requirements** shall note this fact on their legends, as follows: "This map complies with National Map Accuracy Standards."

5. **Published maps whose errors exceed those aforestated** shall omit from their legends all mention of standard accuracy.

6. **When a published map is a considerable enlargement** of a map drawing (manuscript) or of a published map, that fact shall be stated in the legend. For example, "This map is an enlargement of a 1:20,000-scale map drawing," or "This map is an enlargement of a 1:24,000-scale published map."

7. **To facilitate ready interchange and use of basic information for map construction** among all Federal mapmaking agencies, manuscript maps and published maps, wherever economically feasible and consistent with the uses to which the map is to be put, shall conform to latitude and longitude boundaries, being 15 minutes of latitude and longitude, or 7.5 minutes, or 3–3/4 minutes in size.

Issued June 10, 1941
Revised April 26, 1943
Revised June 17, 1947

U.S. BUREAU OF THE BUDGET

Evaluating Map Accuracy

Map-accuracy determination is by no means an exact science. Map accuracy specifications and testing procedures cannot be so clear and mathematically incontrovertible that they will give the exact and only answer to the problem of evaluating the accuracy of a given map. There is an area of interpretation, whose existence must be recognized to avoid rigidly applying narrow rules in a way that does not reflect the spirit or intent of the specifications.

In a sense, accuracy specifications are akin to laws in a civil community. A law can be clearly written and apparently unmistakable in meaning, yet a case involving the application of that law may go through court after court with many variations in its interpretation. In the same way, a map may pass or fail, according to how the accuracy specifications are applied or interpreted.

RELIABILITY OF TEST DATA. An important point to consider is: What credence shall be given to the data obtained from the accuracy-test survey? Every survey embodies some error. Relatively minor accidental errors are expected in a test survey of good quality, and these errors will tend to give favorable results about as often as unfavorable. Truly accidental errors are no cause for concern, nor do they call for interpretation.

Apart from accidental errors in the test survey, there is need to take account of another type of error—the blunder in applying test data. These blunders can often be detected by simple examination of test data and the application of common sense. The "signal flag" for detecting such blunders is the sudden occurrence of large errors in a series of small errors.

Regardless of the amount of detailed instruction embodied in an accuracy-testing procedure, the value of the test depends in the final analysis on the training and judgment of the man doing the job. He needs to know, for example, that he should not choose as a test point, an object that may have been shifted for clearance purposes or for exaggeration of symbolization (fig. 100). He takes due note of recent new construction, especially minor road relocations. He recognizes whether or not a checkpoint may or may not be representative of the overall accuracy of the map. For example, in figure 101, both the main road and the side road may be in perfect position and alinement, except for the jog at the intersection, which was missed by both the stereocompiler and the field completion man. If the checker measures the distance between the true intersection A and the plotted intersection B, he is indeed finding the "error" at this intersection, but this is not representative of the accuracy of the surrounding detail. This should be treated as a factual error, such as omission of a building, rather than as a quantitative error.

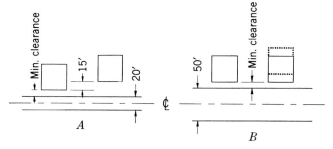

FIGURE 100. Effect of standard-width road symbolization. *A*, road and houses at true scale. *B*, roadside detail adjusted to accommodate conventional road width. Position of the right-hand house, indicated by solid-line square, is correct relative to centerline of road; dotted position is correct relative to left-hand house.

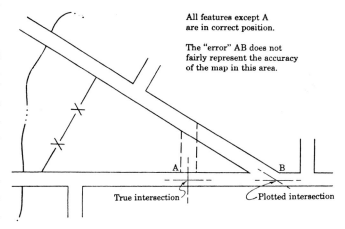

All features except A are in correct position.

The "error" AB does not fairly represent the accuracy of the map in this area.

FIGURE 101. Local error misrepresenting overall accuracy of the map.

STATISTICAL ANALYSIS. It is recognized in the field of surveying and mapping that the mathematical expression of horizontal and vertical accuracy embodied in the National Map Accuracy Standards—namely that not more than 10 percent of the points tested shall be in error by more than a certain tolerance—has certain disadvantages (Thompson, 1960). Fortunately, it is a simple matter to convert the existing standards to a mathematical equivalent in terms of root-mean-square error (RMSE), defined as follows:

$$RMSE = \sqrt{\frac{\Sigma x^2}{n}},$$

where $x_1, x_2, \ldots, x_n$ are the errors at n checkpoints.

Consider, for example, the horizontal tolerance of 40 feet on the ground (1/50 inch on the map) for 90 percent of the horizontal test points on a 1:24,000-scale map. According to statistical theory, 90 percent of the accidental errors should not be larger than 1.66 times the RMSE (assuming a normal error distribution). The equivalent allowable RMSE would then be

$$allowable\ RMSE_h = \frac{40}{1.66} = 24\ feet.$$

Likewise, the RMSE equivalent of the vertical tolerance of one-half the contour interval for 90 percent of the vertical test points would be

$$\text{equivalent RMSE}_v = \frac{0.5CI}{1.66} = 0.3CI,$$

where $\qquad$ CI = contour interval

Adding the vertical component of the allowable horizontal error, the allowable tolerance in elevation (in feet) for a 1:24,000-scale map is

$$\text{allowable RMSE}_v = 0.3CI + 24t,$$

where $\qquad$ t = tangent of angle of slope.

The Geological Survey Manual provides that, in evaluating map accuracy in statistical terms, an appropriate value of the allowable RMSE may be used.

NONQUANTITATIVE ERRORS. There is another facet of map accuracy, which is of paramount importance to many map users but which is not even mentioned in the standard specifications; that is, factual, rather than mensural accuracy. To illustrate, here is a quotation from a letter received by the Survey: "My faith in map accuracy received a jolt when I noted that on the map the borough water reservoir is shown as a sewage disposal plant."

It is likely that this particular map user would never have noticed if the waterworks had been plotted 500 feet out of position, and if he had noticed it, he probably would not have been greatly disturbed. The map could test out 100 percent metrically accurate, but as far as this man is concerned it is still unacceptable.

Here are typical complaints from map users concerning factual errors:

Δ "Your map shows the roads on my property but does not label them Private Road, and consequently we are overrun by tourists."
Δ "Your map shows a passable road up Skunk Hollow, and I tried to follow it and broke an axle."
Δ "Your map shows Pickerel Lake, which sounded like a good fishing spot, so I drove 17 miles up a winding road and when I got there a farmer was plowing on it and he told me the lake was drained twenty years ago."
Δ "Your map designates our local pond as Poison Lake. Everybody around here knows that the original Cajun settlers named it 'Lac des Poissons' because there were so many fish in it. Your map with the 'Poison' label is ruining my bait business."

Names and symbols of features and classification of roads or woodland are among the principal items that are subject to factual error. It is not possible to apply a numerical value to individual errors of fact; a given item of information is either right or it is wrong. The only known attempt to apply a yardstick to such accuracy is a statement in a British publication (Crone, 1953) to the effect that errors of fact should not exceed one or two per hundred thousand words or symbols. Although American general-purpose maps probably do not attain this high an accuracy, the thorough checking that is generally practiced by makers of precise maps, as a matter of professional integrity, tends to keep factual errors to a practical minimum.

Modification of Standards

One of the oft-debated questions concerning the National Map Accuracy Standards is whether they are too loose, too tight, or about right. Considering that the maps under consideration are general-purpose maps, the question is not an easy one to answer, for every user has a specific purpose in using the general-purpose map.

There is a body of opinion—particularly among map users whose needs are not every exacting—which holds that the progress of current topographic mapping should not be impeded by the fetters of standard-accuracy requirements. "Let us get the country mapped," they say, "as quickly as possible; the accuracy can be added later."

But there is another side to the coin. Consider, for example, the map needs for the general layout and design of a proposed engineering facility. This phase of engineering design requires every bit of the accuracy implicit in the current standards. Then, when we go a step further in the engineering design, we find that the current standards are quite inadequate for the next phase: computation of earthwork quantities for final design and payment.

There are many uses to which topographic quadrangle maps are put, in which an accuracy is presumed that was never intended: for example (these are actual cases), a long-range missile engineer pinpoints a distant target to 5-foot accuracy on the only medium at his disposal—a Geological Survey map; a property-ownership case in Alaska is adjudicated on the basis of the land net shown on a Geological Survey map (despite protestations by the Survey that the cadastral information has no legal significance), because there is no other evidence available. When topographic quadrangle maps are put to such unforeseen and demanding uses, it is imperative that sufficient standards be maintained.

In looking again at the philosophy of "Map it now; make it accurate later," one must not overlook a lurking pitfall: the problem of revision. Low-quality maps are obviously going to become obsolete sooner than high-quality maps, if, indeed, they are not obsolete when they are made. The need often arises very quickly to bring the cheap maps up to standard quality. How is a cheaply made map brought up to standard quality without spending a lot of money? The answer is that it can't be done; the users are stuck for all time and for all future revisions with a map base that is simply unsuitable as a base for standard-accuracy revision. Often the best thing to do is to get rid of the old map and start over—a procedure that is far more costly in the long run than making a standard-accuracy map to begin with.

On the other hand, it would be equally poor economy to set accuracy standards high enough to anticipate every emergency need for an extremely demanding degree of accuracy. It would seem that by maintaining the present order of accuracy, the country can be moderately well prepared for many emergency needs without spending the great sums required to meet every possible need. For this reason, the maintenance of the status quo, in general, appears to be the best alternative.

In considering how rigid the accuracy standards should be and how rigidly they should be applied, it must be remembered that under certain conditions of terrain, it may be impracticable to maintain the accuracy standards literally. In line with this, the Geological Survey Manual states: "In certain obstructed or inaccessible areas, such as densely wooded terrain, it may not be technically and economically feasible to comply fully with the standards." When such conditions prevail over an extensive portion of the area covered by a map, the standard accuracy statement is omitted.

STEEP, DENSELY WOODED TERRAIN. On such maps, strict compliance with the accuracy standards throughout the entire area is seldom needed and may not be economically justified. (Carter Dome, N.H., quadrangle.)

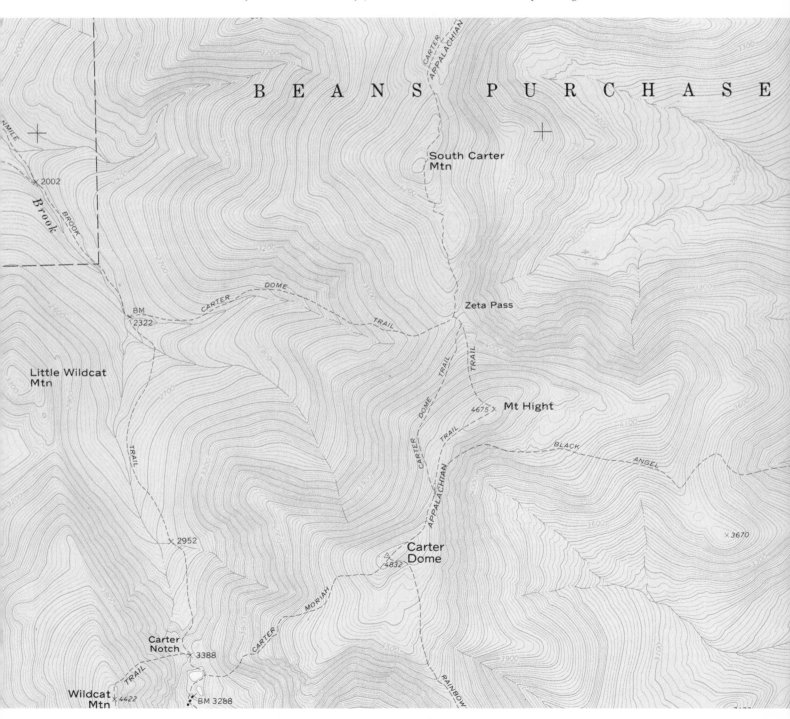

7:

Geological Survey Cartographic Products

The best known are the conventional line maps of the 7.5-minute topographic quadrangle series. Others include the 15-minute maps, the intermediate-scale maps, the 1:250,000-scale maps, the State map series, the 1:1,000,000-scale maps, and a miscellany for special uses.

Topographic Maps

7.5-Minute Maps

The best known topographic maps produced by the Geological Survey are the conventional line maps of the 7.5-minute 1:24,000-scale topographic quadrangle series (fig. 102). The completion of national topographic map coverage in this series (15-minute series in Alaska) is a prime objective of the National Mapping Program. The size of this program is reflected in the fact that it includes 53,838 separate 7.5-minute quadrangle maps covering the conterminous United States, Hawaii, and the territories. More than 70 percent of these maps have been published. Publication of the remainder by the mid-1980's is anticipated.

FIGURE 102. Portion of a 7.5-minute topographic map at a scale of 1:24,000. (San Francisco South, Calif., quadrangle.)

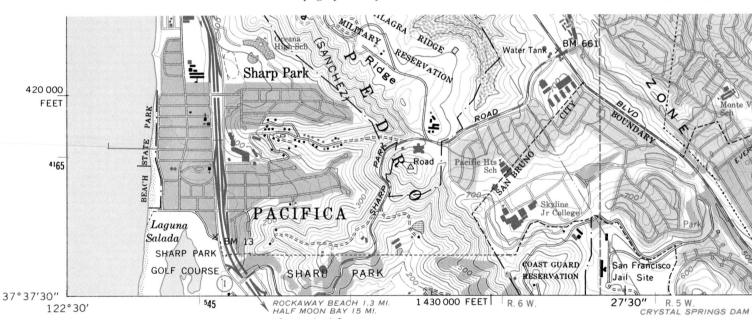

Mapped, edited, and published by the Geological Survey

Control by USGS, USC&GS, and USCE

Topography by multiplex methods from aerial photographs taken 1946. Culture and partial contour revision from aerial photographs taken 1956   Field checked 1956

Hydrography compiled from USC&GS charts 5531 and 5535 (1956)

Polyconic projection.   1927 North American datum
10,000-foot grid based on California coordinate system, zone 3

1000-meter Universal Transverse Mercator grid ticks, zone 10, shown in blue

Red tint indicates areas in which only landmark buildings are shown

Revisions shown in purple compiled from aerial photographs taken 1968 and 1973.   This information not field checked

Purple tint indicates extension of urban areas

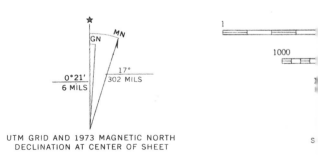

UTM GRID AND 1973 MAGNETIC NORTH
DECLINATION AT CENTER OF SHEET

TH
FOR SALE BY U. S.
A FOLDER

About 1950, the 7.5-minute quadrangle maps became the major topographic product of the Survey, superseding the 15-minute quadrangle maps as the most popular series. The 7.5-minute maps are especially suitable for densely settled areas and other areas where detailed map information is needed, because they can be used in engineering planning and for similar purposes.

Some of the earlier 7.5-minute maps were published at a scale of 1:31,680 (1 inch represents 0.5 mi). In the late 1930's there was a marked transition to the scale of 1:24,000 (1 inch represents 2,000 feet). By 1978, published 1:24,000-scale topographic maps were available for about 70 percent of the conterminous United States and Hawaii. With the general changeover to the metric system in the United States, the 7.5-minute series will eventually be produced with metric contours at a scale of 1:25,000. A few States have agreed to adopt the 1:25,000 scale before the completion of 7.5-minute mapping at 1:24,000 scale. Nevertheless, a desire to complete 7.5-minute coverage of the entire country at one uniform scale will doubtless lead to complete coverage of most States at the 1:24,000 scale in the 1980's. Map coverage in the 7.5-minute series as of September 30, 1980, is shown in figure 103.

FIGURE 103. Status of 7.5- and 15-minute topographic mapping September 30, 1980. Areas covered by published 7.5-minute maps shown in blue; 15-minute maps, in gray. Areas with revisions in progress are shown in darker blue.

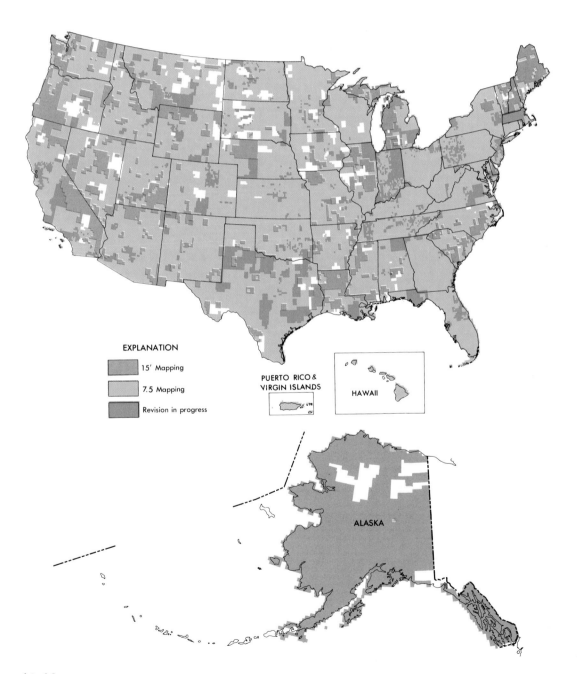

EXPLANATION

15' Mapping

7.5 Mapping

Revision in progress

PUERTO RICO & VIRGIN ISLANDS

HAWAII

ALASKA

The essential specifications for the 7.5-minute topographic quadrangle maps are as follows:

UNITED STATES 7.5-MINUTE SERIES. Maps of the United States having quadrangle dimensions of 7.5 minutes in both latitude and longitude, the bounding parallels and meridians being integral multiples of 7.5 minutes. The series includes the few maps whose boundary lines are offset or extended to cover islands, irregular coastal features, or areas needed to complete mapping to political boundaries. The scales of this series are 1:24,000 and 1:31,680; however, the 1:24,000 scale is standard and the 1:31,680 scale has been almost entirely superseded. A conversion to the scale of 1:25,000 is anticipated for use with metric measurements.

Quadrangle ground area: 64 mi² at lat. 30°.
  49 mi² at lat. 49°.
Paper size: 22 × 27 inches north of lat. 31°.
  23 × 27 inches south of lat. 31°.

PUERTO RICO 7.5-MINUTE SERIES. Maps of Puerto Rico, originally at the scale of 1:30,000, later at the scale of 1:20,000, having quadrangle dimensions of 7.5 minutes in both latitude and longitude, the bounding parallels and meridians being integral multiples of 7.5 minutes. The series includes the few maps whose boundary lines are offset or extended to include small islands or irregular coastal features. Puerto Rico has been completely mapped at the scale of 1:30,000, because it is convenient to use with the metric system, which has long been adopted for measurements in the island. The scale of 1:20,000 was adopted in the 1950's to provide more detail.

Quadrangle ground area: about 70 mi².
Paper size: 20 × 22 inches, for 1:30,000 scale.
  29-3/8 × 32-3/8 inches, for 1:20,000 scale.

VIRGIN ISLANDS 1:24,000-SCALE SERIES. Maps of the Virgin Islands of the United States published at the scale of 1:24,000. Three islands—St. Croix, St. John, and St. Thomas—have been mapped in this series. Their total land area is 133 mi².

Quadrangle size: 7.5 minutes in latitude
  by 6 minutes in longitude.
Quadrangle ground area: about 56 mi².
Paper size: 20 × 27 inches.

Maps of the 7.5-minute topographic series are constructed generally to comply with the National Map Accuracy Standards (p. 104). Each map bears the standard statement, "This map complies with National Map Accuracy Standards," except for those unusual cases in which the statement is omitted because of known deficiencies.

15-Minute Maps

During the period 1910–50 (see fig. 17), the standard Geological Survey maps for general topographic coverage were the 15-minute quadrangle maps (fig. 104) published at a scale of 1:62,500 (1 inch represents approximately 1 mile). Although most map users now prefer the 7.5-minute maps because they provide more space and more detail, there are still many applications of the 15-minute maps, particularly if greater coverage per map sheet is desired. Since the 1950's, production of 15-minute maps has generally been limited to areas where a special need for coverage at this scale has been demonstrated. The principal exception is Alaska where complete coverage is planned using a standard 15-minute map scale of 1:63,360 (1 inch represents 1 mile). The extent of map coverage in the 15-minute series for areas not having 7.5-minute maps, as of June 30, 1977, is shown in figure 103.

The essential specifications for the 15-minute topographic quadrangle maps are as follows:

UNITED STATES 15-MINUTE SERIES. Maps of the United States, at the scale of 1:62,500 (1:63,360 for Alaska), having quadrangle dimensions of 15 minutes in both latitude and longitude, the bounding parallels and meridians being integral multiples of 15 minutes, except for some Hawaiian maps. The series includes the few maps whose boundary lines are offset or extended to cover islands, irregular coastal features, or areas needed to complete mapping to political boundaries.

Quadrangle ground area for conterminous United States: Varies with latitude; about 271 mi² in the southern part of Florida (lat. 24°30′ N.), and about 196 mi² near the Canadian border (lat. 49° N.).

Except for the Island of Hawaii, the quadrangle boundaries in the State of Hawaii are designed to include each of the principal islands on one map. The Island of Hawaii is covered by quadrangle maps having dimensions of 15 minutes in both latitude and longitude, the bounding parallels and meridians being integral multiples of 15 minutes, except for those maps whose boundary lines are offset or extended to include small islands or irregular coastal features. The State of Hawaii has been completely covered by 15-minute maps at a scale of 1:62,500.

Quadrangle ground area: for the Island of Hawaii, approximately 282 mi².
Paper size: 18 × 21 inches and 19 × 21 inches.

ALASKA 1:63,360-SCALE SERIES. Maps of Alaska at the scale of 1:63,360, usually having quadrangle dimensions of 15 minutes in latitude and from 20 to 36 minutes in longitude, depending on the quadrangle location. Approximately 83 percent of the 2,920 maps covering Alaska at this scale have been published. Quadrangle ground area varies considerably within zones as can be seen in the table on the next page.

The features shown on 15-minute maps are generally the same as those shown on 7.5-minute maps. The principal difference is that, because of the smaller scale and consequent space restrictions, it is necessary to omit or generalize some of the detail.

Like the 7.5-minute maps, the 15-minute maps bear the statement of compliance with National Map Accuracy Standards unless there are known deficiencies. Omission of the accuracy statement occurs more frequently on 15-minute maps than on 7.5-minute maps, especially for Alaska, because of the less exacting survey methods used in remote or inaccessible areas.

Zone	Quad size (minutes)	Range of area (mi²)
North of 68th parallel	15×36	230–269
62d to 68th parallel	15×30	226–280
50th to 62d parallel	15×22.5	212–231
South of 59th parallel	15×20	207–249

Paper size: 17×21 inches, south of 62° N.
18×21 inches, north of 62° N.

FIGURE 104. Portion of a 15-minute topographic map at scale of 1:62,500. (Ennis, Mont., quadrangle.)

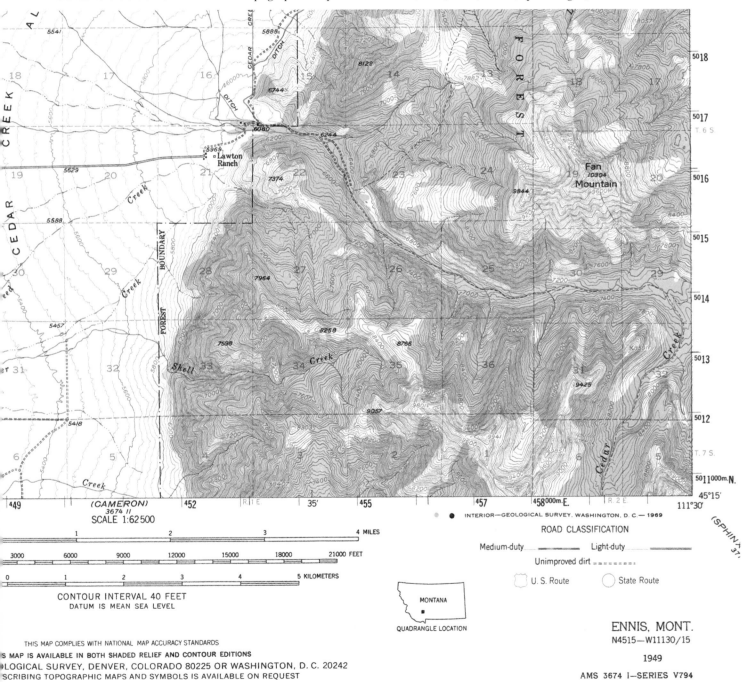

Intermediate-Scale Maps

The intermediate-scale mapping series, implemented in 1975, includes topographic base maps at scales of 1:100,000 in quadrangle, county, or regional format and 1:50,000 in county format (fig. 105).

These maps are normally derivative products of standard 1:24,000-scale maps. The 1:100,000-scale 30- by 60-minute series (fig. 106) is produced in metric units with a contour interval of 5, 10, 20, or 50 m, depending on terrain relief, and includes a full fine-line UTM grid on each map.

FIGURE 105. Portion of an intermediate-scale map in county format at 1:50,000 scale. Contour intervals are 80 feet in this portion of the map and 10 feet in flatter areas. Reference systems shown include a full State plane coordinate grid, public land net, and UTM grid ticks. (Alamosa County, Colo., quadrangle.)

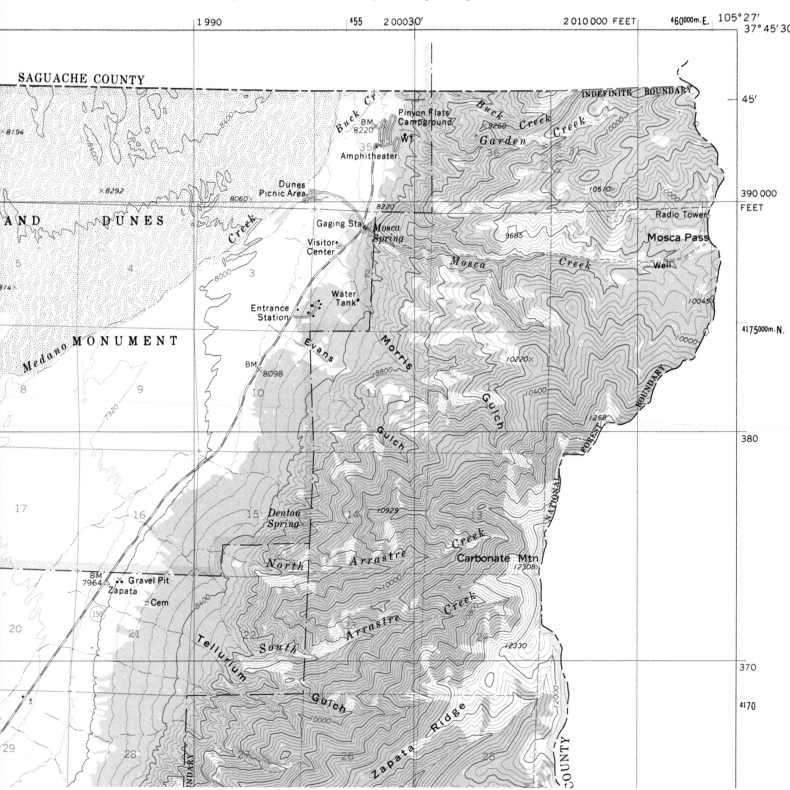

FIGURE 106. Portion of an intermediate-scale map in 30- by 60-minute series at 1:100,000 scale. Contour interval is 20 m. Reference systems shown include state plane coordinate ticks, public land net, and a full fine-line UTM grid. (Killdeer, N. Dak., quadrangle.)

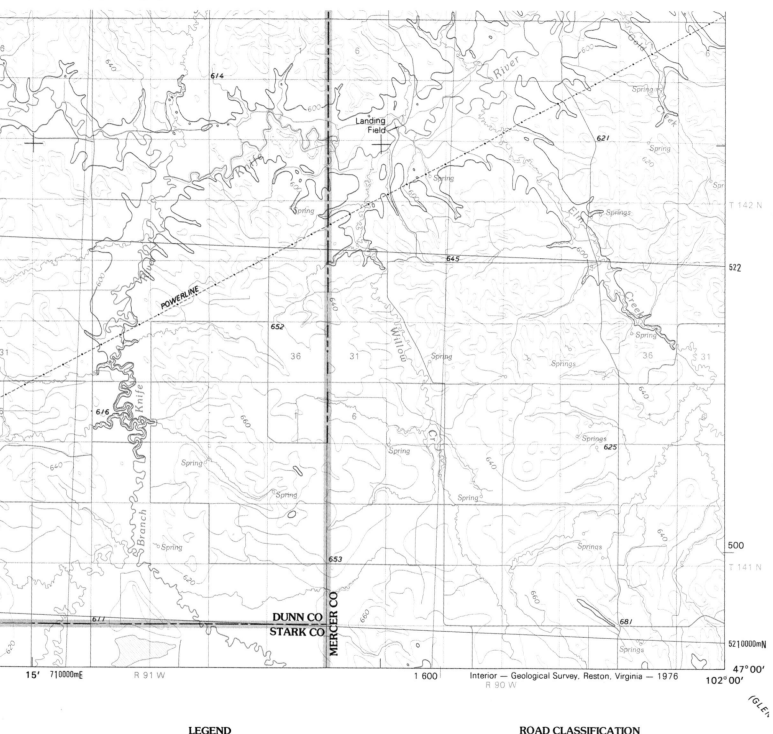

LEGEND

Village or locality . . . .   •

Landmark building . . . .

Perennial stream, lake . . . .

Intermittent stream, lake . . . . . .

Public park or recreation area . . . .

National, State forest or
gameland area . . . .

Other public area or
military or Indian Reservation . . . .

ROAD CLASSIFICATION

Primary highway, hard surface . . . .

Secondary highway, hard surface . . . .

Light duty road, hard or improved surface . . . . .

Unimproved road . . . .

Trail . . . .

⬡ Interstate route   ⬡ U.S. route   ◯ State route

KILLDEER, N. DAK.

Intermediate-scale mapping is designed to provide, in either graphic or digital form, basic map data at various levels of detail and scales. It enables map users to select the combinations of content, scale, and format that best suit their general or special needs.

The essential specifications for the intermediate-scale series are as follows:

UNITED STATES 1:100,000-SCALE SERIES. Maps of the United States at 1:100,000 scale in quadrangle, county, or regional format. The quadrangle dimensions are 30 × 60 minutes except along the coast. County or regional maps may be composed of one sheet or multiple sheets, depending on the size of the mapped area.

UNITED STATES 1:50,000-SCALE COUNTY MAP SERIES. Maps of the United States in county format at 1:50,000 scale. A county map may consist of one sheet or multiple sheets, depending on the size of the county.

The 1:50,000-scale intermediate-scale maps correspond closely in content with the 1:62,500-scale quadrangle maps. Less detail is shown on 1:100,000-scale maps because of space restrictions. Table 4 indicates differences in content for various categories of map scales ranging from 1:20,000 to 1:1,000,000. Hypsometric data are derived from 1:24,000-scale maps insofar as contours in metric intervals can be derived accurately from the contours in foot intervals shown on the 1:24,000-scale maps.

The statement of compliance with the National Map Accuracy Standards is shown on intermediate-scale maps if appropriate.

1:250,000-Scale Maps

The largest map scale at which coverage is available for the entire area of the United States is 1:250,000. The sheets of this map series were originally prepared as military editions by the U.S. Army Map Service (now Defense Mapping Agency Topographic Center) during the 1950's; they are now maintained by the Geological Survey. The Department of Defense and National Ocean Survey are the primary users (as bases for aeronautical charts), but use is also expanding for these maps as a geographic reference and as bases for regional land use, transportation, and utility system planning.

The 1:250,000-scale series (fig. 107, p. 122) has been designated by the Board on Geographic Names as the standard reference for geographic nomenclature in Government publications. Elevation data, digitized from the contours on the 1:250,000-scale maps, are available on magnetic tape from the National Cartographic Information Center. Figure 108 shows the extent of 1:250,000-scale map revision as of 1980.

The essential specifications for the 1:250,000-scale series are as follows:

UNITED STATES 1:250,000-SCALE SERIES. Maps of the United States, at 1:250,000 scale, originally prepared by the Army Map Service from existing maps and from aerial photographs and published by the Geological Survey for civil use; now maintained by the Survey. The quadrangle dimensions are 1 degree latitude by 2 degrees longitude except along the coasts, where for a few maps the quadrangle dimensions are modified.

Quadrangle ground area (conterminous United States):
  varies with latitude, 8,218 mi² at lat. 30° N.
  and, 6,222 mi² at lat. 49° N.
Paper size (conterminous United States):
  22 × 34 inches.

The quadrangle dimensions for Hawaii are 1° latitude and from 1°30′ to 1°35′ longitude.

Quadrangle ground area (Hawaii):
  varies from 6,645 to 6,990 mi².
Paper size (Hawaii): 22 × 29 inches.

ALASKA RECONNAISSANCE SERIES. Interim 1:250,000-scale maps of Alaska having quadrangle dimensions of 1 degree latitude and from 2 to 3 degrees longitude, depending on the quadrangle location.

These maps are of uncertain quality, having been compiled from many sources of information, and are being superseded by later maps at the same scale. The series is complete, comprising 153 sheets and covering all the mainland and adjacent islands of Alaska.

Quadrangle ground area:
  for 1 × 2-degree quadrangles,
    from 5,015 to 6,030 mi².
  for 1 × 3-degree quadrangles,
    from 4,580 to 7,310 mi².
Paper size: 22 × 32 inches.

ALASKA 1:250,000-SCALE SERIES. Maps of Alaska at 1:250,000 scale having quadrangle dimensions of 1 degree latitude and from 2 to 3 degrees longitude, depending on the quadrangle location. These are being compiled from more accurate source data than were the Alaska Reconnaissance series they are to replace.

The features shown on 1:250,000-scale maps correspond in general to those shown on 1:100,000-scale maps (table 4). Hypsographic data on 1:250,000-scale maps are much more generalized than the hypsographic data on 7.5- and 15-minute maps. As the contour interval is 50, 100, 200, or 500 feet, many small relief features are not indicated.

The statement of compliance with National Map Accuracy Standards is not shown on 1:250,000-scale maps.

A comparison of the size of the area covered by the various map series ranging from 1:24,000 scale to 1:250,000 scale is shown graphically in Appendix B, page 246.

TABLE 4. Features shown on topographic maps

[Variations will be found on older maps]

FEATURE	SERIES AND SCALE						
	7.5-minute 1:20,000 1:24,000 1:25,000	15-minute 1:62,500 1:63,360	County 1:50,000	30 × 60 minute 1:100,000	1° × 2° 1:250,000	State base 1:500,000	IMW 1:1,000,000
Boundaries							
Built-up area					●	●	●
City park	●	●	●	●			
Civil township	●	●	●	●			
County, parish, Alaska borough	●	●	●	●	●	●	●
Incorporated city, town, village	●	●	●				
National, international	●	●	●	●	●	●	●
National reservation, park, forest, monument, etc.	●	●	●	●	●	●	●
State	●	●	●	●	●	●	●
State forest, park, or monument	●	●	●	●	●	●	●
Culture—Miscellaneous							
Airport, airfield, landing strip	●	●	●	●	●	●	●
Archeological site	●	●	●	●			
Boardwalk	●	●	●				
Borrow pit	●						
Breakwater, pier, wharf	●	●	●	●	●		
Buildings, class 1	●	●	●	●	●		
Buildings, class 2	●	●	●				
Campground, campsite (public)	●	●	●	●			
Canal lock or sluice gate	●	●	●	●			
Cave, cavern	●	●	●	●	●		
Cemetery	●	●	●	●	●		
Cliff dwelling	●	●	●	●			
Coke oven	●	●	●				
Control, horizontal and vertical	●	●	●				
Dam masonry	●	●	●	●	●	●	●
Dam with lock	●	●	●	●	●	●	
Drive-in theater	●	●	●				
Drydock	●	●	●	●			
Fence line	●						
Filtration plant	●	●	●	●	●		
Fish hatchery	●	●	●	●	●		
Fort	●	●	●	●	●		
Gaging station	●	●	●	●			
Gravel, sand, claypit	●	●	●	●	●		

TABLE 4. Features shown on topographic maps (continued)

[Variations will be found on older maps]

FEATURE	SERIES AND SCALE						
	7.5-minute 1:20,000 1:24,000 1:25,000	15-minute 1:62,500 1:63,360	County 1:50,000	30 × 60 minute 1:100,000	1° × 2° 1:250,000	State base 1:500,000	IMW 1:1,000,000
Culture—Miscellaneous—*continued*							
Heliport	●	●	●	●	●		
Lock, shipping canal	●	●	●	●	●	●	
Mine dump	●	●	●	●	●		
Mine shaft	●	●	●	●			
Mine tunnel entrance	●	●	●	●			
Monument: boundary, reference, mineral or location	●	●	●	●			
Oil- or gasfield	●	●	●	●	●		●
Oil sump or sludge pit	●	●					
Open oil reservoir	●	●					
Open-pit mine	●	●	●	●	●		●
Picnic grounds	●	●	●	●			
Pipelines	●	●	●	●	●		●
Port of entry	●	●	●	●	●		
Power substation	●	●	●	●	●		
Power transmission line	●	●	●	●	●		●
Prospect	●	●					
Quarry	●	●	●	●	●		
Racetrack, raceway	●	●	●	●	●		
Reservoir	●	●	●	●	●	●	●
Ruins	●	●	●	●			
Seawall	●	●	●	●	●		
Sewage disposal	●	●	●	●	●		
Ski lift, tramway, incline railway	●	●	●	●			
Stadium	●	●	●	●	●		
Strip mine	●	●	●	●	●		
Tank farm	●	●	●	●	●		
Tanks, oil, gas, water	●	●	●	●	●		
Tower (radio, lookout, etc.)	●	●	●	●	●		
Watermill	●	●	●	●	●		
Windmill	●	●	●	●	●		
Culture—Transportation							
Railroads and related features:	●	●	●	●	●	●	●
Bridge	●	●	●	●	●		
Carline	●	●	●	●			

FEATURE	SERIES AND SCALE						
	7.5-minute 1:20,000 1:24,000 1:25,000	15-minute 1:62,500 1:63,360	County 1:50,000	30 × 60 minute 1:100,000	1° × 2° 1:250,000	State base 1:500,000	IMW 1:1,000,000
Culture—Transportation— *continued*							
Drawbridge	●	●	●				
Ferry	●	●	●	●	●	●	●
Roundhouse	●	●	●	●			
Sidings	●	●	●	●	●		
Snowshed	●	●	●	●	●		
Station	●	●	●	●	●		
Tracks, narrow gage:	●	●	●	●	●	●	●
Juxtaposition	●	●	●	●			
Multiple	●	●	●	●	●	●	●
Multiple, abandoned	●	●	●	●	●		
Multiple, dismantled	●	●	●	●	●		
Multiple, under construction	●	●	●	●	●	●	●
Single	●	●	●	●	●	●	●
Single, abandoned	●	●	●	●	●		
Single, dismantled	●	●	●	●	●		
Single, under construction	●	●	●	●	●	●	●
Tracks, standard gage:	●	●	●	●	●	●	●
Juxtaposition	●	●	●	●			
Multiple	●	●	●	●	●	●	●
Multiple, abandoned	●	●	●	●	●		
Multiple, dismantled	●	●	●	●	●		
Multiple, under construction	●	●	●	●	●	●	●
Single	●	●	●	●	●	●	●
Single, abandoned	●	●	●	●	●		
Single, dismantled	●	●	●	●	●		
Single, under construction	●	●	●	●	●	●	●
Tunnel	●	●	●	●	●	●	●
Turntable	●	●	●				
Underpass, overpass	●	●	●	●	●		
Yards	●	●	●	●	●		
Roads and related features:	●	●	●	●	●	●	●
Bridge	●	●	●	●	●		
Bridge (covered)	●	●	●				
Change in number of lanes	●	●					

TABLE 4. **Features shown on topographic maps** (continued)

FEATURE	SERIES AND SCALE						
	7.5-minute 1:20,000 1:24,000 1:25,000	15-minute 1:62,500 1:63,360	County 1:50,000	30 × 60 minute 1:100,000	1° × 2° 1:250,000	State base 1:500,000	IMW 1:1,000,000
Culture—Transportation— *continued*							
Class 1	●	●	●	●	●	●	●
Class 2	●	●	●	●	●	●	●
Class 3	●	●	●	●	●	●	●
Class 4	●	●	●	●	●	●	●
Class 5 (trail)	●	●	●	●	●	●	●
Cul-de-sac	●	●	●				
Dead-end road	●	●	●	●			
Destinations	●	●					
Direction arrows	●	●					
Drawbridge	●	●					
Ferry	●	●	●	●	●	●	●
Footbridge	●	●					
Ford	●	●	●				
Interchange	●	●	●	●	●		
Parking area	●	●	●	●			
Paved service and rest areas	●	●	●	●			
Private road	●	●					
Proposed road	●	●					
Route markers, Interstate, Federal, State	●	●	●	●	●	●	●
Tollgate	●	●	●				
Traffic circle	●	●	●				
Tunnel	●	●	●	●	●	●	●
Under construction, class 1	●	●	●	●	●	●	●
Under construction, class 2	●	●	●				
Underpass, overpass	●	●	●	●	●		
Drainage and Related Features							
Abandoned aqueduct, canal, flume, etc.	●	●	●				
Alkali flat	●	●	●	●	●	●	●
Aqueduct, conduit, flume (elevated)	●	●	●	●	●	●	●
Aqueduct, flume, etc. (underground)	●	●	●	●	●	●	●
Aqueduct tunnel	●	●	●	●	●	●	

TABLE 4. Features shown on topographic maps *(continued)*

[Variations will be found on older maps]

FEATURE	SERIES AND SCALE						
	7.5-minute 1:20,000 1:24,000 1:25,000	15-minute 1:62,500 1:63,360	County 1:50,000	30 × 60 minute 1:100,000	1° × 2° 1:250,000	State base 1:500,000	IMW 1:1,000,000
Drainage and Related Features— continued							
Area subject to controlled inundation	●	●	●	●	●	●	●
Area to be submerged	●	●	●	●	●	●	●
Canal, flume, aqueduct, or perennial ditch	●	●	●	●	●	●	●
Canal, intermittent	●	●	●	●	●	●	●
Canal, navigable	●	●	●	●	●	●	●
Channel in water area	●	●	●	●	●		
Cranberry bog	●	●	●	●	●		
Ditch, intermittent	●	●	●	●	●	●	●
Dry lake or pond	●	●	●	●	●	●	●
Falls	●	●	●	●	●	●	●
Flow arrow	●	●	●	●	●		
Glacial crevasses	●	●	●	●	●	●	●
Glacier or permanent snowfield	●	●	●	●	●	●	●
Lake or pond, intermittent	●	●	●	●	●	●	●
Lake or pond, perennial	●	●	●	●	●	●	●
Mangrove	●	●	●	●			
Marsh or swamp	●	●	●	●	●	●	●
Rapids	●	●	●	●	●	●	●
Salt evaporator	●	●	●	●	●		
Shoreline	●	●	●	●	●	●	●
Siphon	●	●	●	●	●		
Spring	●	●	●	●	●	●	●
Stream, braided	●	●	●	●	●	●	●
Stream, disappearing	●	●	●	●	●	●	
Stream, intermittent	●	●	●	●	●	●	●
Stream, perennial	●	●	●	●	●	●	●
Stream, unsurveyed perennial	●	●	●	●	●	●	●
Submerged marsh or swamp	●	●	●	●			
Wash	●	●	●	●	●	●	●
Water surface elevation	●	●	●	●	●	●	●
Water well	●	●	●	●	●		
Wooded marsh or swamp	●	●	●	●			

TABLE 4. Features shown on topographic maps (continued)

[Variations will be found on older maps]

FEATURE	7.5-minute 1:20,000 1:24,000 1:25,000	15-minute 1:62,500 1:63,360	County 1:50,000	30 × 60 minute 1:100,000	1° × 2° 1:250,000	State base 1:500,000	IMW 1:1,000,000
Foreshore-Offshore Features							
Foreshore flat	●	●	●	●	●		
Rock or coral reef	●	●	●	●	●		●
Rock, bare or awash	●	●	●	●	●		
Exposed wreck	●	●	●				
Mast exposed on sunken wreck	●	●	●				
Bathymetry or depth curves	●	●	●	●	●	●	●
Public-Land Survey Data							
Auxiliary meridian	●	●	●	●	●	●	
Base line	●	●	●	●	●	●	
Corners:							
Closing: found	●	●	●				
Meander	●	●	●				
Section: found	●	●	●				
Witness	●	●	●				
Exterior grant line	●	●	●	●	●	●	
Indian treaty line	●	●	●	●	●	●	
Interior grant line	●	●	●				
Land grant monument	●	●	●				
Principal meridian	●	●	●	●	●	●	
Private land survey accepted by BLM	●	●	●	●	●	●	
Range, township lines (location doubtful)	●	●	●	●	●	●	
Range, township lines (protracted)	●	●	●	●	●		
Range, township lines (surveyed)	●	●	●	●	●	●	
Section lines (location doubtful)	●	●	●	●			
Section lines (protracted)	●	●	●	●			
Section lines (surveyed)	●	●	●	●			
Tints							
Built-up area				●	●	●	●
County boundary						●	
Federal reservations						●	
House omission	●	●	●				
National, international boundary					●		

TABLE 4. Features shown on topographic maps (continued)
[Variations will be found on older maps]

FEATURE	SERIES AND SCALE						
	7.5-minute 1:20,000 1:24,000 1:25,000	15-minute 1:62,500 1:63,360	County 1:50,000	30 × 60 minute 1:100,000	1° × 2° 1:250,000	State base 1:500,000	IMW 1:1,000,000
Tints—*continued*							
State boundary						•	
State forest, park, or monument						•	
Vegetation							
Orchard	•	•	•	•	•		
Vineyard	•	•	•	•	•		
Woods, brushwood	•	•	•	•	•		
Reference Systems							
Geographic ticks and intersections	•	•	•	•	•	•	•
State grid	•	•	•	•	•		
UTM grid	•	•	•	•	•	•	•
Relief and Related Features							
Contours:	•	•	•	•	•	•	•
Approximate	•	•	•				
Depression	•	•	•	•	•	•	•
Index	•	•	•	•	•	•	•
Intermediate	•	•	•	•	•	•	•
Supplementary	•	•	•	•	•	•	•
Underwater	•	•	•	•	•		
Divide, continental	•	•	•	•	•	•	•
Dune area	•	•	•	•	•	•	•
Ephemeral drainage	•	•	•	•			
Glacial moraine	•	•	•	•	•	•	•
Intricate surface area	•	•	•	•	•		•
Lava	•	•	•	•	•	•	•
Levee	•	•	•	•	•		
Levee with road, railroad	•	•	•	•	•		
Mud	•	•	•				
Sand area	•	•	•	•	•	•	•
Sand beach	•	•	•	•	•		
Shifting sand	•	•	•	•	•	•	•
Spoil area	•	•	•	•	•		
Spoil bank	•	•	•				
Spot elevations	•	•	•	•	•	•	•
Tailings	•	•	•	•			
Tailings pond	•	•	•	•	•		

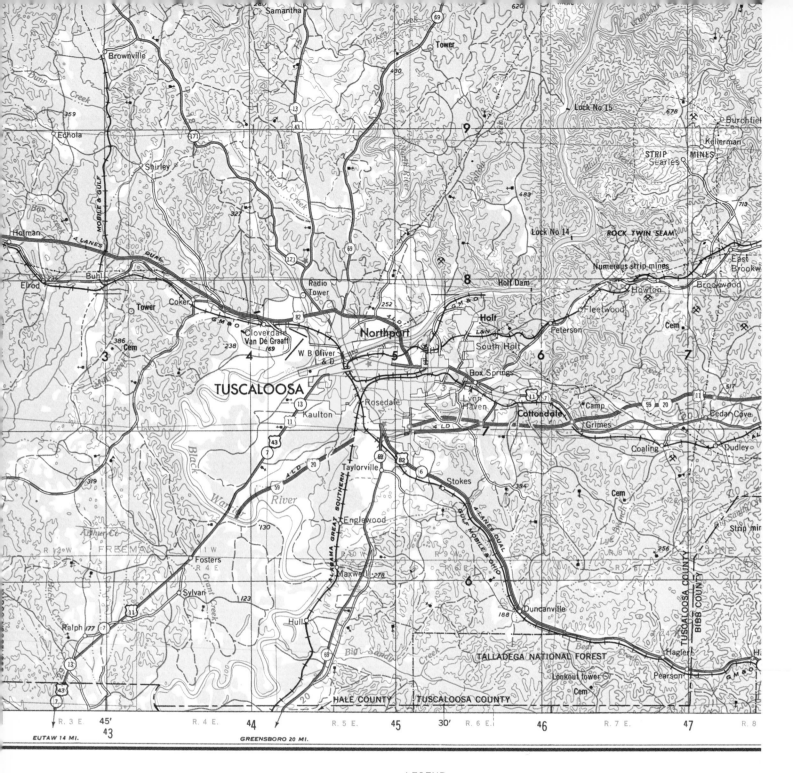

FIGURE 107. Portion of a 1:250,000-scale topographic map. (Tuscaloosa, Ala., quadrangle.)

FIGURE 108. Shaded areas represent 1:250,000-scale maps in process of revision as of September 30, 1980.

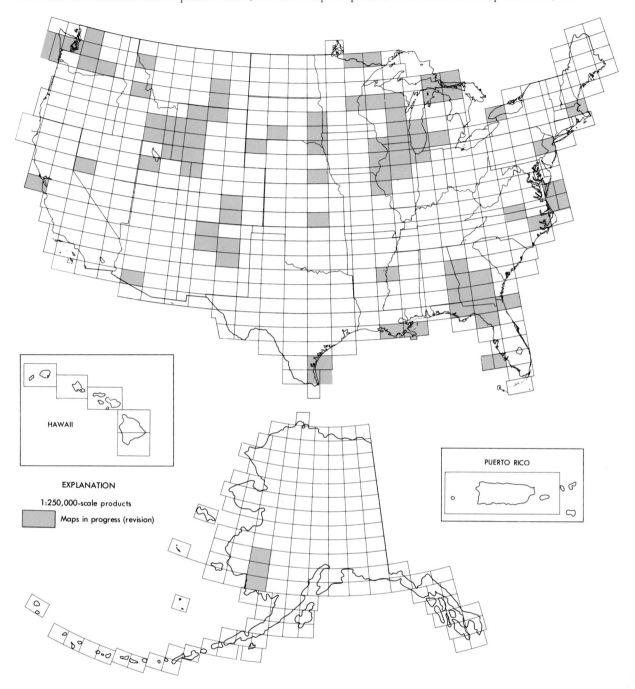

EXPLANATION

1:250,000-scale products

Maps in progress (revision)

State Map Series

The State map 1:500,000-scale series is usually published in three separate editions: base map (fig. 109), highway and contour map (fig. 110), and shaded relief map (fig. 111).

The State maps are derived from a variety of map source material, including Geological Survey 1:250,000-scale topographic maps, Survey 7.5- and 15-minute topographic quadrangle maps, Defense Mapping Agency topographic maps, National Ocean Survey maps and charts, State and county highway maps, U.S. Department of Transportation maps, photoindex maps in areas not covered by standard topographic maps, and other miscellaneous maps such as those produced by the Forest Service, Soil Conservation Service, National Park Service, Bureau of Land Management, and Bureau of Indian Affairs. Additional basic sources include commercial atlases, census reports, and the *Official Railway Guide* (Woods, 1978).

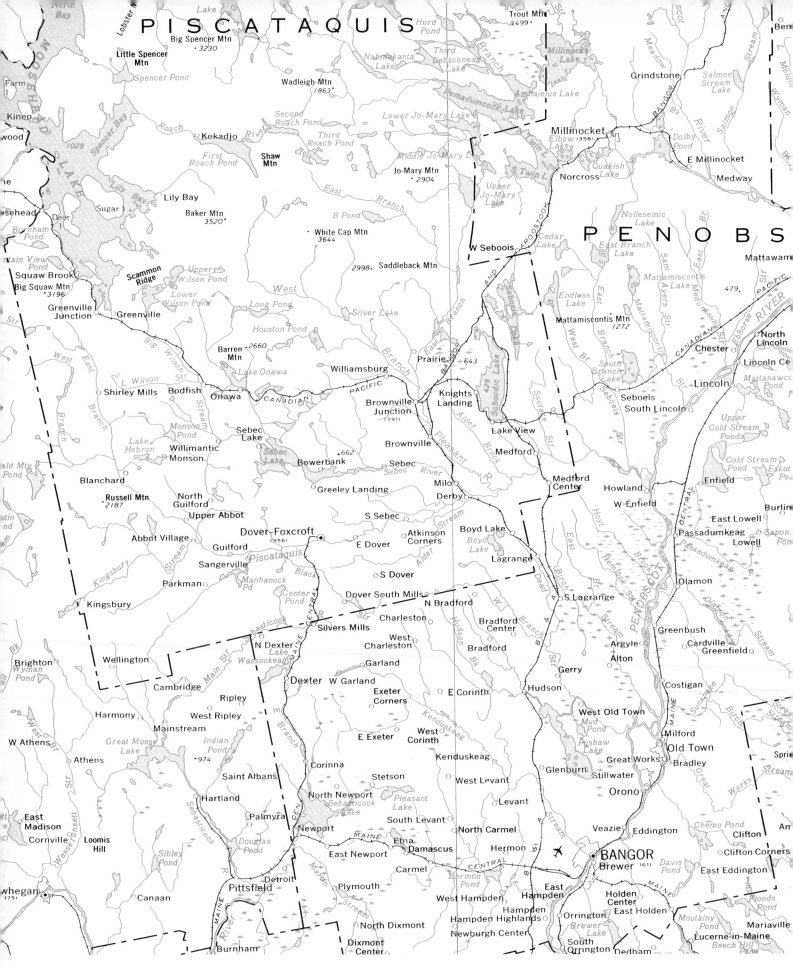

FIGURE 109. Portion of base edition of Maine State map at 1:500,000 scale.

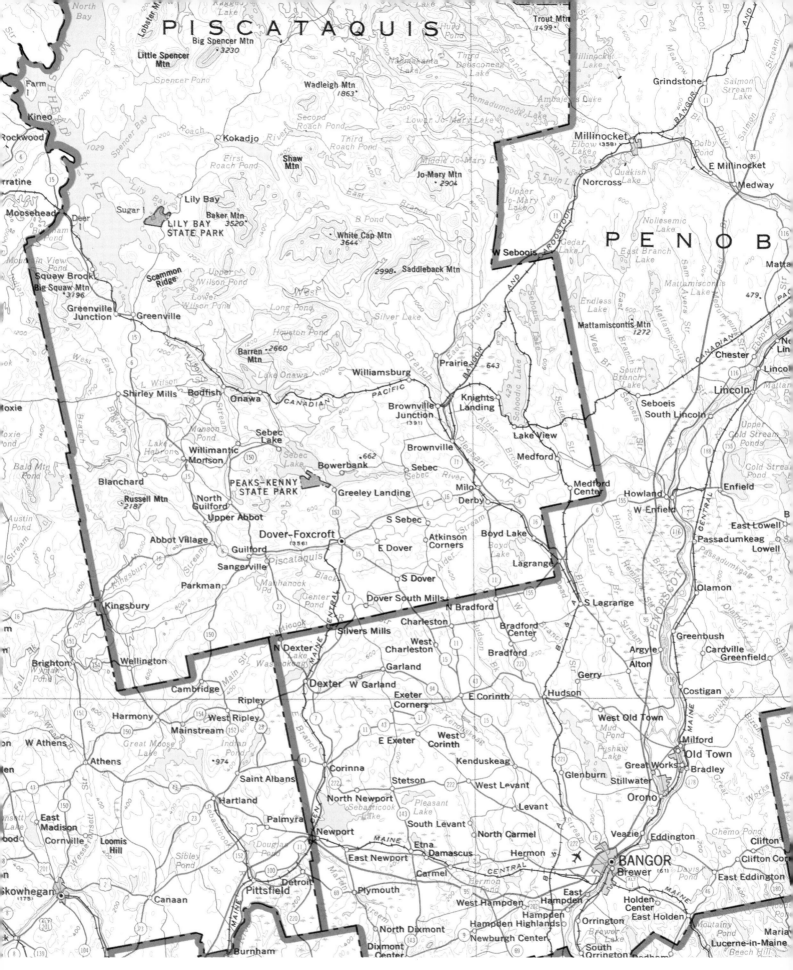

FIGURE 110. Portion of highway-and-contour edition of Maine State map at 1:500,000 scale.

Topographic Maps

125

FIGURE 111. Portion of shaded-relief edition of Maine State map at 1:500,000 scale. On older shaded-relief State maps, contours were omitted.

Geological Survey Cartographic Products

The essential specifications for the State map series are: Separate 1:500,000-scale map for each State, except for the following combinations of more than one State on a single 1:500,000-scale map—New Hampshire and Vermont; Connecticut, Massachusetts, and Rhode Island; and Delaware and Maryland.

The State map for Connecticut, as an exception, has also been published separately at a scale of 1:125,000, by special arrangement with the State.

State maps are published in one sheet if possible. The following State maps are published in more than one sheet because the States are too large to be shown on one reasonably sized sheet at 1:500,000 scale: California (2), Michigan (2), Montana (2), and Texas (4). Alaska is the only State for which there is no 1:500,000-scale map; Alaska topographic State maps are published at scales of 1:1,584,000 (2 sheets) and 1:2,500,000. The map features included on a State map are limited to the area lying within the State. No overedge area in adjoining States is shown except for shorelines in coastal States to complete the depiction of water areas, and shorelines of double-line streams (more than 833 feet—254 m—wide) that form State boundaries.

The features on State maps are indicated in table 4. Some special practices for these maps are:

Δ   Built-up (urban) areas are indicated only for places with a population exceeding a number determined separately for each State; this number depends upon the number and distribution of built-up areas within the State.

Δ   The State capital and all county seats are shown. Other populated places are shown if space permits. Rural localities are shown in areas of sparse population density. In addition, locations for which quadrangles are named are shown if space permits.

Δ   Commercial airports are shown if regularly scheduled service is provided by major airlines.

Δ   Only standard-gage operating railroads, symbolized as single track, are delineated. Private or industrial railroads are shown if the length exceeds 25 mi (40 km). Railroad spurs are included only if they serve a feature which is portrayed on the map, such as a town or mining area.

Δ   All roads of the interstate, Federal, and State primary systems are shown. Secondary systems are added as needed to portray the overall road network. Interstate roads under construction are symbolized as completed if alinement is known; otherwise they are omitted.

Δ   Generally, the minimum length of natural streams portrayed is 5 mi (8 km); the minimum length of canals and ditches is 10 mi (16 km). Rivers and canals having a width exceeding 833 feet (254 m) are shown with a double-line symbol.

Δ   To portray the character of the coastal plain areas, a first supplemental contour is sometimes used.

Δ   The contour interval is normally 200 feet for States east of the Rocky Mountains, and 500 feet for States west of the Rocky Mountains.

The statement of compliance with National Map Accuracy Standards is omitted from State maps.

United States 1:1,000,000-Scale Maps

The 1:1,000,000-scale topographic maps published by the Geological Survey are available in two editions. The IMW edition is the United States contribution to the International Map of the World (IMW). The other edition is based on a series of 1:1,000,000-scale maps compiled by the Army Map Service; although they do not conform to the IMW specifications in all respects, these maps satisfy the same general purposes.

The IMW specifications (United Nations, 1963) were developed at a conference held at Bonn, Federal Republic of Germany, in 1962, under the sponsorship of the United Nations. The objectives of the specifications are:

Δ   To provide, by means of a general-purpose map, a document that enables comprehensive study of the world for preinvestment survey and economic development planning.

Δ   To provide a base map for sets of thematic maps (population, soil, geology, vegetation, resources, administrative limits, statistical evaluation). These maps are basic tools for efficient study.

In both editions published by the Geological Survey, each map is numbered in accordance with the designation system adopted for the IMW series (fig. 112) and is named for one of the principal localities or natural features within its area. The maps are derived from the latest 1:250,000-scale maps and other source material.

The essential specifications for the 1:1,000,000-scale series are: Maps of the United States having quadrangle dimensions of 4 degrees latitude by 6 degrees longitude (12 degrees longitude for Alaska).

Quadrangle ground area:
   from 73,734 to 122,066 mi²
   (123,000 to 204,000 km²).

The 1:1,000,000-scale maps (fig. 113) show the principal cities and towns, railroads, and political boundaries in black; the roads in red; the water features in blue; and topographic features by brown contour lines and gradient tints. Contour intervals vary from 50 m where the terrain is relatively flat to 500 m in mountainous regions. The 100-, 200-, 500-, 1,000-, 1,500-, 2,000-, 2,500-, 3,000-, 4,000-, 5,000-, 6,000-m contours are called principal contours, indicating the limits of hypsometric tints. Bathymetric lines and their values and depths in meters are shown in blue in seas and principal inland waters. The elevations of selected points are shown by a dot and a height above sea level expressed in meters.

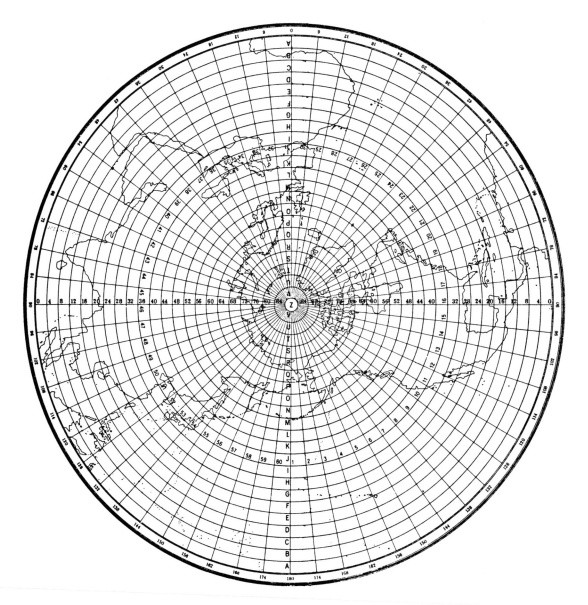

FIGURE 112. Sheet reference system for maps of the International Map of the World series lying in the Northern Hemisphere. The designation for any IMW map in the Northern Hemisphere begins with the Letter "N." For example, the map showing the southern part of Florida is designated NG 17.

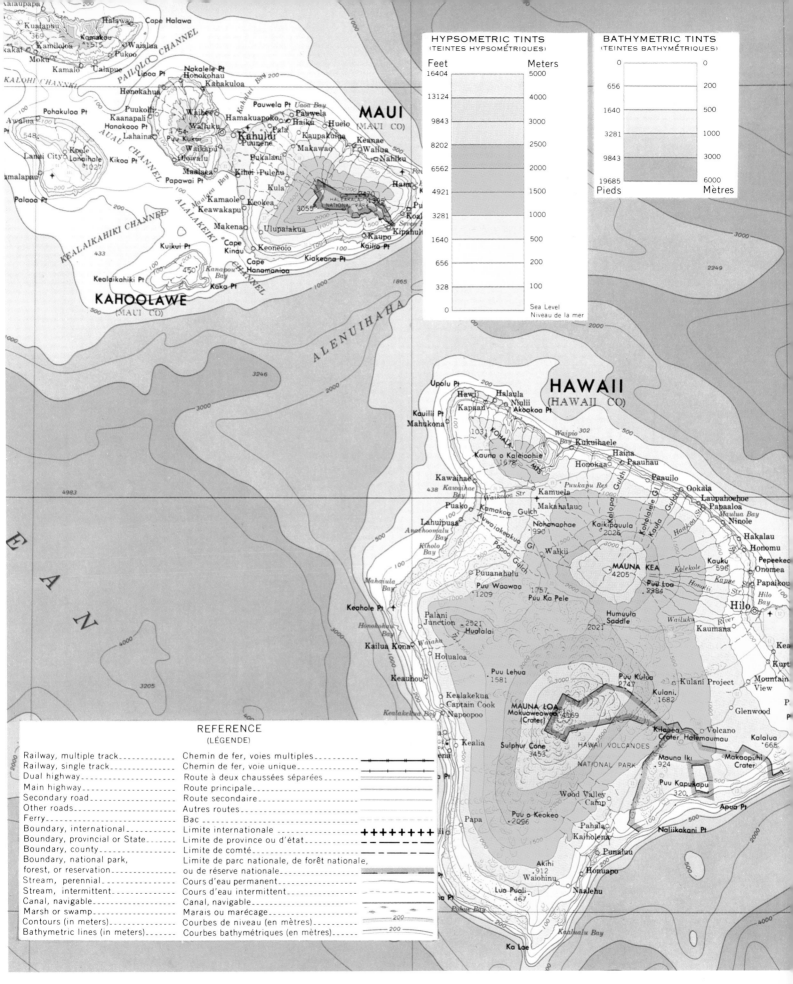

FIGURE 113. Portion of Hawaii sheet, International Map of the World, 1:1,000,000 scale. For this illustration, the reference and hypsometric tintblocks have been shifted from the margin to the body of the map.

Miscellaneous Map Series

The National Park Series of topographic maps, at various scales, covers national parks, monuments, and historic sites. Many of the maps are available in shaded-relief editions. The scales range from 1:960 for the map of the Franklin D. Roosevelt National Historic Site to 1:250,000 for the map of Mount McKinley National Park (fig. 114). In general, these maps conform to the specifications for standard quadrangle maps at the same scale, with special emphasis on map detail pertaining to recreational opportunities. Paper sizes vary from 17 × 21 inches to 46 × 61 inches.

Metropolitan area maps are composed of several 1:24,000-scale quadrangle maps of the national topographic map series covering selected cities and their adjacent areas. Although each map is generally printed as a single sheet, larger cities, such as New York, Chicago, Los Angeles, Philadelphia, and Detroit require two or more sheets. Because of the continual growth of metropolitan areas, the task of keeping these maps up-to-date is difficult and costly. The paper size ranges from 22 × 37 inches to 50 × 72 inches.

United States maps showing the entire country are published at various scales ranging from a letter-size page at 1:16,500,000 scale to large wall maps at a scale of 1:2,500,000. Representative United States maps published by the Geological Survey are:

Δ Wall map showing State and county boundaries and names, State capitals, and county seats in black; water features in blue. State boundaries are accentuated by yellow overprint; metropolitan areas are pink. A land tint background distinguishes the United States. Insets show Alaska, Hawaii, and other outlying areas of the United States. 1972. Two sheets (each 41 × 54 inches). 1:2,500,000 scale.

Δ Wall map showing State boundaries and names. State capitals and principal cities in black; water features in blue. State boundaries are accentuated by gray overprint. Major metropolitan areas shown in yellow. Also shown in black are boundaries of national forests, national parks and monuments, Indian reservations, and national wildlife refuges. Insets show Alaska, Guam, principal islands of Hawaii, American Samoa, Puerto Rico, Virgin Islands of the United States, and the Canal Zone. 1965. 42 × 65 inches. 1:3,168,000 scale.

Δ Wall map showing State and county boundaries and names in black; water features in blue. Insets show Alaska, Hawaii, Canal Zone, Puerto Rico, and the Virgin Islands of the United States. 1933. 27 × 41 inches. 1:5,000,000 scale.

Δ Wall map showing water features in blue, major metropolitan areas symbolized by a yellow tint within black circles, and railroads in black. State boundaries and boundaries of selected national recreation areas are also in black. This map portrays Alaska and Hawaii in their proper size and position relative to the other 48 States. 1975. 44 × 56 inches. 1:6,000,000 scale.

Δ Map showing State boundaries and principal cities in black, water features in blue, and contours in brown. Alaska, Hawaii, Canal Zone, Puerto Rico, and the Virgin Islands of the United States are not shown. 1916, with minor revisions 1974. 20 × 30 inches. 1:7,000,000 scale.

Δ Map showing State boundaries and boundaries of selected national parks, monuments, national recreation areas, cities, and railroads in black, water features in blue, highways in red, and major metropolitan areas symbolized by a yellow tint within black circles. This map portrays Alaska and Hawaii in their proper size and position relative to the other 48 States. 1975. 24 × 36 inches. 1:10,000,000 scale.

Δ Map showing State boundaries and principal cities in black; water features in blue. Alaska, Hawaii, Canal Zone, Puerto Rico, and the Virgin Islands of the United States are not shown. 1911. 9½ × 13 inches. 1:16,500,000 scale.

Separate sheets of selected thematic and general reference *National Atlas* maps are available from the Geological Survey. The original *National Atlas of the United States of America* was published in 1970; it contains 765 maps printed on 335 pages of 14 × 19-inch format. Many of these maps are spread across two pages. The content ranges from physiographic information to environmental and economic trends (fig. 115). One set of maps (also available singly) covers the United States in 21 sections at 1:2,000,000 scale; another details the 25 largest urban areas at 1:500,000 scale. Selected outlying areas are covered by maps at scales of 1:1,000,000 and 1:250,000.

Special-subject maps at scales of 1:7,500,000, 1:17,000,000, and 1:34,000,000 occupy 281 pages of the atlas. They depict national characteristics such as:

Δ Physical—relief, geology, climate, water resources.
Δ Historical—discovery, exploration, territorial growth.
Δ Economic—agriculture, minerals and mining, manufacturing, trade, transportation.
Δ Sociocultural—population, income, education.
Δ Administrative—counties, Standard Metropolitan Statistical Areas, judicial districts, congressional districts.

A series of maps describing the coverage by aerial photographs, maps, and charts is also included.

The gazetteer of 41,000 place names includes, where appropriate, geographic coordinates, populations, and other types of information.

A paper jacket inside the back cover contains six transparent overlays matching the special subject map scales. The overlays provide county boundaries and names of populated places.

Generally, the atlas text is limited to map captions and explanations. Whenever possible, references are provided to more detailed sources. A second edition of the atlas is planned for publication in the 1980's.

FIGURE 114. Portion of the 1:250,000-scale shaded-relief edition, Mount McKinley National Park, Alaska.

Topographic Maps

131

TOTAL PETROLEUM MOVEMENT: 1974

This is one of a series of nineteen maps prepared in 1976 by the U. S. Geological Survey and originally published as part of a report by the Committee on Energy and Natural Resources and the Committee on Commerce, Science and Transportation, U. S. Senate. The energy transportation data were provided by the Congressional Research Service, Library of Congress. Copies of the report "National Energy Transportation," stock #052–070–04018–1, are available from the Superintendent of Documents, U. S. Government Printing Office, Washington, D. C. 20402. Copies of the maps, individually or in sets, are available from the U. S. Geological Survey at the addresses shown below.

FIGURE 115. Portion of map showing petroleum movements in the United States in 1974, scale 1:7,500,000. This map is one of many thematic maps, published separately subsequent to 1970 and not included in the original volume, that are considered to be part of the *National Atlas of the United States of America*.

TYPICAL ATLAS SHEET. The *National Atlas of the United States of America* presents economic, social, and cultural data in cartographic form, as well as maps and charts showing physical features such as climate, landforms, geology, soil, and vegetation.

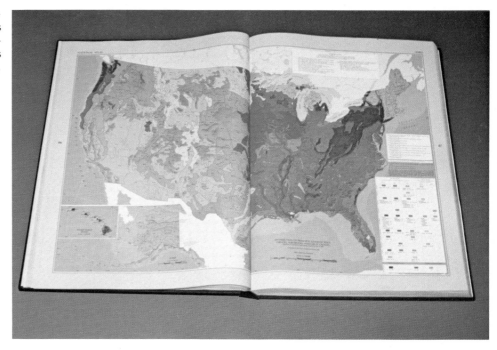

Antarctic Maps

The Geological Survey in cooperation with the National Science Foundation prepares and publishes topographic maps of selected areas of Antarctica needed to support the U.S. Antarctic Research Program (USARP). Aerial photographs and logistic support are supplied primarily by the U.S. Navy.

The international Scientific Committee on Antarctic Research (SCAR) promotes cooperation in Antarctic scientific activities. Maps and mapping data are automatically exchanged among the SCAR member nations, all of which are signatories to the 1959 Antarctic Treaty that set aside Antarctica for peaceful purposes only. The SCAR Working Group on Geodesy and Cartography has made recommendations concerning Antarctic mapping specifications and standards. Accordingly, Geological Survey topographic maps of Antarctica published since 1965 are on a subdivision of the International Map of the World (IMW) system and use SCAR-approved symbols.

The following series of Antarctic maps are available:

Δ **Topographic reconnaissance maps at 1:250,000 scale,** mapped, edited, and published by the Survey in cooperation with the National Science Foundation. This series is the primary USARP map source for planning, logistic support, and multidisciplinary investigations. It provides the base maps for the geologic reconnaissance map series. Topographic reconnaissance maps are generally compiled from U.S. Navy tricamera aerial photographs. The basic contour interval is 200 m. Maps covering coastal areas also include bathymetric data.

Δ **Geologic reconnaissance maps at 1:250,000 scale,** prepared by the Institute of Polar Studies, Ohio State University, under the auspices of the National Science Foundation and published by the Survey. The contour interval is 200 m.

Δ **Topographic reconnaissance shaded relief maps at 1:500,000 scale,** prepared by the Survey in part using trimetrogon (one vertical and two oblique cameras with metrogon lenses) aerial photographs taken by a U.S. Naval Task Force during Operation Hi Jump, 1946–47. These maps were compiled and published by the Survey in support of the International Geophysical Years (1955–58) and are available for coastal areas of Wilkes Land and Enderby Land.

Δ **Satellite image maps at 1:500,000 scale,** prepared and published by the Survey in cooperation with the National Aeronautics and Space Administration. The imagery is recorded by the multispectral scanner on board the Landsat satellites.

Δ **Sketch maps at 1:500,000 scale,** prepared and published by the Survey in cooperation with the National Science Foundation. This is an interim series compiled from the best source data and control available at the time of compilation. The features shown may be subject to redelineation when the area is mapped as part of the 1:250,000-scale topographic reconnaissance series. No contours are shown.

Δ **Topographic maps at 1:1,000,000 scale,** mapped, edited and published by the Survey in cooperation with the National Science Foundation. These maps are often compiled from Survey 1:250,000-scale maps or from new compilation and revisions from Landsat imagery. Production of maps of Antarctica on the IMW format using SCAR symbology was initiated in 1974, with contour intervals of 100, 300, and 500 m (fig.116).

FIGURE 116. Portion of 1:1,000,000-scale IMW map, McMurdo Sound, Antarctica.

△ **Satellite image maps at 1:1,000,000 scale,** prepared and published by the Survey in cooperation with the National Aeronautics and Space Administration. Landsat imagery is accurately related to ground positions that have been identified on the photographs obtained via satellite.

△ **Reconnaissance sketch and topographic map of the Ross Ice Shelf at 1:2,188,800 scale,** prepared and published by the Survey in cooperation with the National Science Foundation in support of the Ross Ice Shelf Geophysical and Glaciological Program.

Examples of all the above-described maps, an Antarctica map index, and a list of published Antarctica maps are given in the leaflet, *Maps Published of Antarctica by the U.S. Geological Survey,* available free from the National Cartographic Information Center, U.S. Geological Survey National Center, Reston, Va. 22092. In addition to the maps described in the leaflet, a new series of topographic maps at 1:50,000 scale was introduced in 1977. This series was undertaken in support of multidisciplinary investigations in the dry valley area of southern Victoria Land.

Photoimage Maps

In addition to the series of conventional line maps at scales of 1:20,000 to 1:1,000,000, the Geological Survey now has a series of photoimage maps. These maps are produced quickly, economically, and accurately by modern techniques and instrumentation known as "orthophoto" systems (Southard, 1975). There are a number of different kinds of orthophoto products, and there is some variation in nomenclature. The definitions that follow are in accord with the terms appearing on orthophoto products of the Survey.

△ **Orthophotograph.** A photograph having the properties of an orthographic projection. It is derived from a conventional perspective photograph by simple or differential rectification so that image displacements caused by camera tilt and terrain relief are removed.

△ **Orthophotographic map.** One or more orthophotographs brought to a specified scale and assembled in a map format.

△ **Orthophotomap.** An orthophotographic map with contours and extensive color-enhanced cartographic treatment, presented in standard quadrangle format and related to the standard horizontal and vertical reference systems.

△ **Orthophotoquad.** A monocolor orthophotographic map presented in standard quadrangle format and related to the standard horizontal reference system. It has no contours and has little or no cartographic treatment.

△ **Quad-centered photograph.** A quad-centered aerial photograph is the middle exposure of a photo-triplet (three consecutive aerial photographs) taken so that the middle photograph is exposed directly above the center of the quadrangle and the leading and following photographs are exposed directly above the boundaries of the quadrangle within specified tolerances. The flying height is set at an altitude such that the quad-centered photograph covers the entire area of the quadrangle.

ORTHOPHOTOMAPS. The combination of orthophotoimagery and cartographic line-map treatment called an "orthophotomap" is the most effective way to represent certain types of areas in map form when the usable information of the photobase exceeds what can be shown practically on conventional line maps. Flat swamp- and marshlands and flat sandy terrain, for example, are suitably portrayed by the image on orthophotomaps. Highly eroded, arid areas, where contours do not adequately portray the physiographic details are likewise best shown on orthophotomaps. When produced for an area, the orthophotomap replaces the conventional line map as the published map coverage.

The first 16 published orthophotomaps were the 1:24,000-scale quadrangles of the Okefenokee Swamp in the southeastern United States (fig. 117). Orthophotomaps are ideal for this terrain because there are few contours, there is a low density of cultural features, and standard maps show almost nothing but the marsh symbol pattern. The orthophotoimage presents a portrait of the terrain that would be impractical by cartographic symbolization. The Survey has published over 100 orthophotomaps covering the Everglades in southern Florida (fig. 118) and more than 200 quadrangles in the flat swamp and lake country of northern Minnesota. Orthophotomaps of areas with similar terrain characteristics have also been compiled for southern Louisiana (fig. 119), the coastal plains of Virginia and North Carolina, and other localities.

In 1970, 12 orthophotomaps were compiled of the Prudhoe Bay region of Alaska (fig. 120). The terrain in this area is mostly flat, consisting of marsh and lake country with few cultural features. The orthophotomaps were needed for oil exploration and planning studies, and they were compiled and published a few months after the aerial photographs were taken. In this case, two important requirements were satisfied better by orthophotomaps than by line maps: ground detail is much more complete, and the maps were available promptly.

Orthophotomaps at 1:24,000 scale are not suitable for all types of subjects. For example, in areas of high relief, where there is a high contour density over a large portion of the area, overprinted contours tend to obscure the photoimage, and the legibility of contours is impaired. Orthophotomaps of urban areas at 1:24,000 scale are generally not appropriate because high-rise

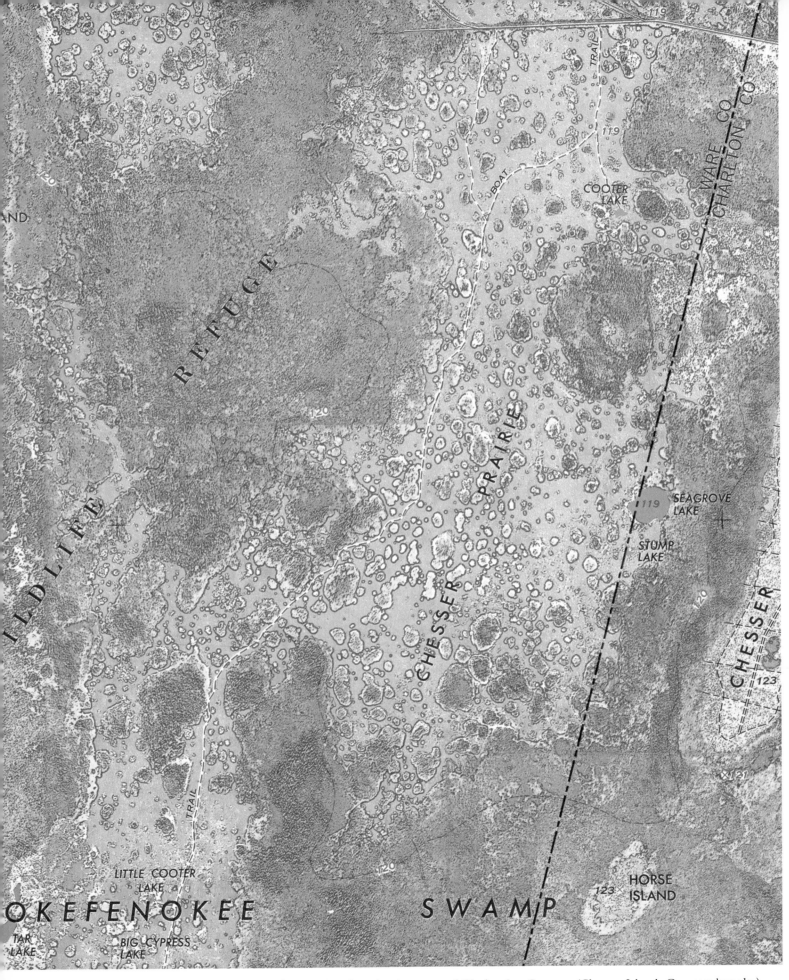

FIGURE 117. Portion of 1:24,000-scale orthophotomap of Okefenokee Swamp. (Chesser Island, Ga., quadrangle.)

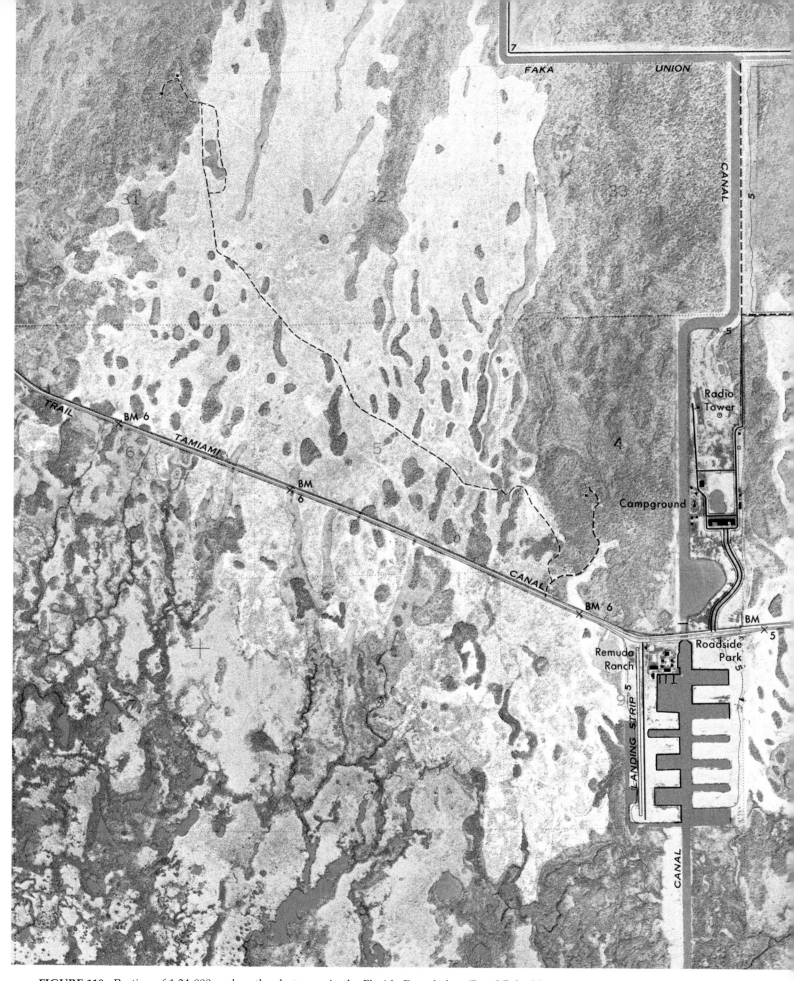

FIGURE 118. Portion of 1:24,000-scale orthophotomap in the Florida Everglades. (Royal Palm Hammock, Fla., quadrangle.)

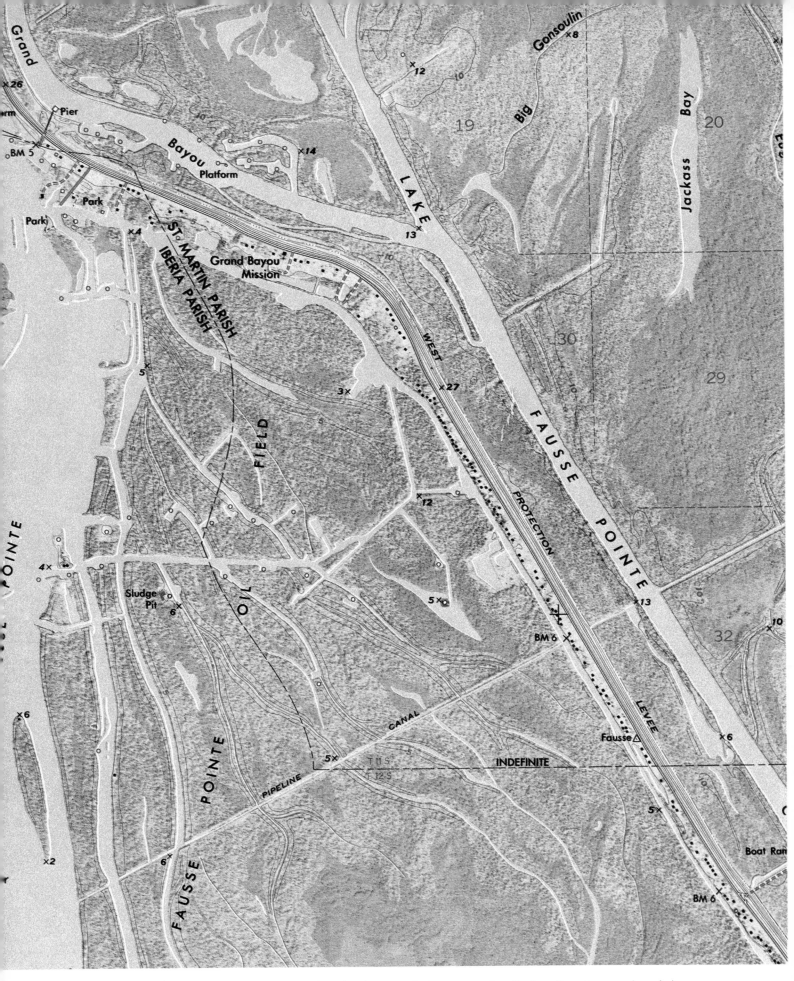

FIGURE 119. Portion of 1:24,000-scale orthophotomap in bayou country. (Jackass Bay, La., quadrangle.)

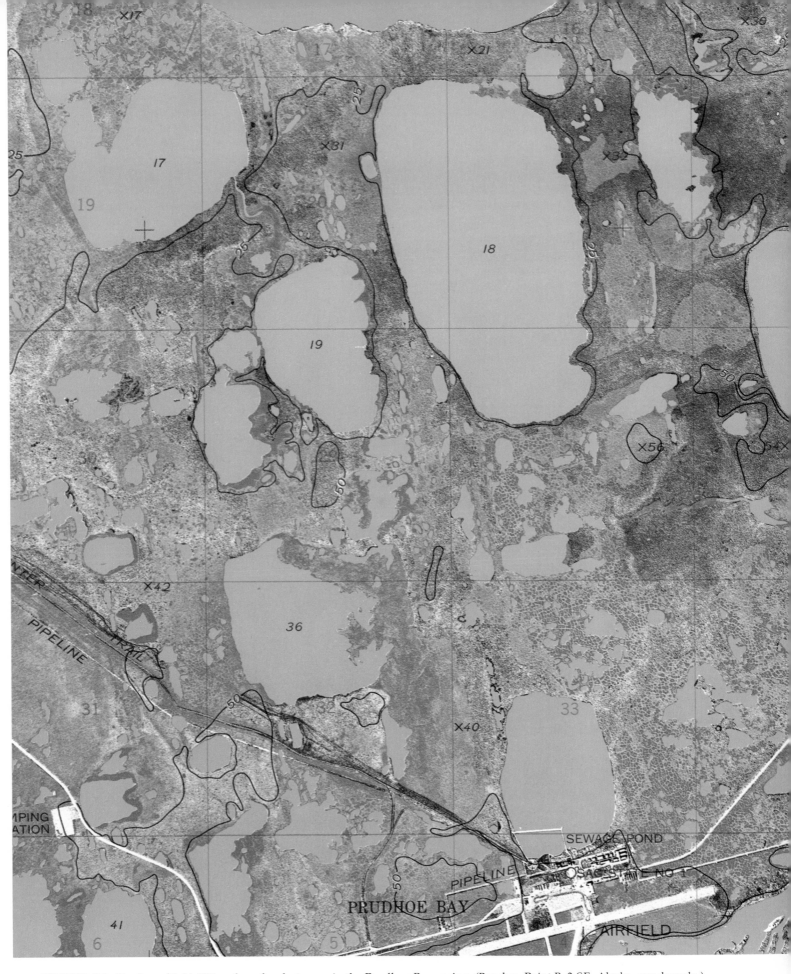

FIGURE 120. Portion of 1:24,000-scale orthophotomap in the Prudhoe Bay region. (Beechey Point B–3 SE, Alaska, quadrangle.)

manmade objects cause anomalies in the rectified photoimagery at that scale. Overprinting orthophotoimages with line-map symbols to enhance roads and buildings, usually the main features in urban areas, is often impractical because of the exaggerated dimensions of the symbols. The result is similar to the example of contour overprinting cited above. The degree and extent of the relief and the density of cultural development vary between areas; therefore, project areas are studied individually before the method of treatment is selected. In areas where the photoimage treatment is clearly best, it is used, and the resulting orthophotomaps become the standard product for the area.

The types of areas for which orthophotomaps are considered appropriate are ranked below in the order of preference:

1. Flat swampy areas where the line map is little more than symbolic; that is, full of swamp symbols and widely spaced contours. (Simple rectification required.)
2. Flat desert areas including salt flats and dry lakes, where much detail is symbolized or omitted on line maps. (Simple rectification required.)
3. Arid (desert) areas with moderate relief. (Some differential rectification required.)
4. Areas with sparse cultural development and complex vegetative cover where timber boundaries are indefinite but contours are not close enough to obscure the photoimagery. (Differential rectification required.)

Areas are considered inappropriate for orthophotomapping if they have: a concentration of cultural features; dense planimetric detail where the line-map symbols and photoimagery positions may not coincide because of line-map displacement of detail to accommodate symbols; considerable relief where densely spaced contours obscure photoimage information; or extensive dense vegetative cover that has a uniform appearance.

ORTHOPHOTOQUADS. These are published in a 7.5-minute 1:24,000-scale standard map series. They are usually made from quad-centered aerial photographs taken at altitudes ranging from 37,000 to 42,000 feet (11,000-13,000 m), providing full coverage of a 7.5-minute quadrangle in a single exposure (fig. 121).

Methods used to prepare orthophotoquads are designed to meet National Map Accuracy Standards, the same criteria used for the national topographic map series. Orthophotoquads can be prepared in a relatively short time and for a fraction of the cost of a standard line map. Therefore, for unmapped areas orthophotoquads are useful interim maps, and they are also valuable complements to existing line maps—especially when those maps are in need of revision.

Orthophotoquads are in great demand for use as base maps by State and regional planners for land use information; hydrologic and geologic studies; site selection for industries, utilities, and public transportation; urban renewal and urban-suburban growth studies; tax assessment; development and conservation of natural resources; and flood hazard, pollution, and coastal wetland studies. Data such as timber, soil, and crop inventories can be expeditiously plotted directly on the orthophotoquad, and a reliable determination of acreages can be made. The orthophotoquad can be used to revise other maps or to serve as a base for making special-purpose maps. It is conceivable that, with the merits of a short production time and up-to-date information, orthophotoquad coverage of an area will serve as the source material for developing and maintaining digital data banks.

In response to the growing demand for orthophotoquads, the Survey has produced some 18,000 orthophotoquads. Each covers a standard 1:24,000-scale 7.5-minute quadrangle. In ground area, 18,000 quadrangles cover approximately 1,000,000 mi^2 (2,600,000 km^2), which is about 27 percent of our 50-State area. Information on published orthophotoquads and orthophotomaps is available for each State from the National Cartographic Information Center (see p. 216-218).

LARGE-SCALE ORTHOPHOTOGRAPHIC MAPS. In the mid-1970's the Geological Survey conducted a study to determine what type of map would be most helpful to State and city agencies concerned with the growth and development of metropolitan areas. The primary objective of the study was to develop standards for a uniform urban map series that can serve as the foundation for the more specialized maps needed for the many specific city functions.

Four cities were selected for experimental projects, each with some unique characteristics and problems. In selecting the pilot cities, discussions were held with many local officials to insure complete cooperation in evaluating the experimental urban map products. The areas included:

1. Fort Wayne, Ind., with low, rolling topography; population 180,000.
2. Charleston, S.C., a coastal city with relatively flat terrain; population 75,000.
3. San Francisco, Calif., also a coastal city, with topography ranging from flat terrain to very steep hills and tall buildings; population 700,000.
4. Frederick, Md., a city with rolling topography in the city and high hills in the area outside the city limits; population 25,000.

Responses from the cities indicated that a suitable scale would be 1:2,400 (1 inch equals 200 feet). Moreover, it was recognized that 1:2,400-scale photoimage maps could be reduced or enlarged without seriously affecting readability. Because of the sharp relief and high buildings, an exception was made in selecting the scales for the San Francisco maps. All of San Francisco county was mapped at 1:6,000 scale, but small segments within the area were mapped at 1:2,400 and 1:1,200 scales.

FIGURE 121. Reduced orthophotoquad; original scale 1:24,000. (Palm Springs, Calif., quadrangle.)

Fort Wayne was the first city selected for the urban mapping study. The Fort Wayne 1:2,400-scale orthophotographic maps were completed, and reports on their acceptance and suitability are encouraging. The 440 sheets in this project cover 220 mi². Several departments in the city engineer's office are using the maps in a variety of applications. The principal scales used are 1:2,400 (1 inch equals 200 feet) and 1:600 (1 inch equals 50 feet). The enlargements were made on stable base material from the 1:2,400-scale originals (fig. 122). From these, comparatively inexpensive diazo copies can be made to be used as worksheets. Some of the applications reported by city officials are:

▲ Street engineering
   Δ Designing highways (fig. 123).
   Δ Estimating quantities of curbing and resurfacing for streets.
▲ Traffic engineering
   Δ Reviewing effect of recommended street closings on traffic flow.
   Δ Reviewing intersection layouts to plan improvements, such as widening turning lanes.
   Δ Preparing construction drawings for placing new cables for traffic signal interconnections.
▲ Water and sewer engineering
   Δ Preparing preliminary waterline designs.
   Δ Preparing storm and sanitary sewer designs.
▲ Park department
   Δ Master planning.
   Δ Selecting bicycle trails.
▲ City planning
   Δ Updating existing land use plans.
   Δ Locating zoning violations.
   Δ Preparing site maps for planning developments and locating access points.

Mosaics composed of several orthophotographic maps at 1:2,400 scale present a broad picture for area studies. For example, they can be used effectively for studying highway relocation and street widening, locating sewer interceptor lines, and selecting bicycle trails. The school authority in Fort Wayne has mosaics that cover the area of each of the four school districts, including pickup stations; these mosaics are used to plan schoolbus routes.

In less than a year, the list of applications for the Fort Wayne orthophotographic maps became quite lengthy and has continued to grow because new applications are continually being found. Feedback from Fort Wayne and other cities on the utility of the maps will influence the design of future urban mapping projects.

Shaded-Relief Maps

The Geological Survey publishes shaded-relief editions of certain topographic quadrangle maps showing physiographic features of special interest, selected maps of the 1:250,000-scale series, State maps, Antarctic maps, and some national park and monument maps. On these editions the shading accentuates the physical features by simulating in color the appearance of sunlight and shadows on the terrain, thereby creating the illusion of a three-dimensional land surface (fig. 124; see also figs. 111, 114, 116).

The maps (numbering more than 300) for which a shaded-relief edition is available are listed in a folder which may be obtained from the Survey.

Slope Maps

Although standard topographic maps clearly indicate by the spacing of contours which areas are flat, steep, or moderate in slope, there are many instances in which there is a need to portray the extent of specified slope zones. Such portrayals are particularly useful in studies related to land use because of the many ways in which the configuration of the terrain influences soil, drainage, vegetation, and construction. For land use analysis, data from slope maps can be combined with information from maps showing other elements of terrain, such as topography, hydrology, surficial geology, soils, vegetation, and flood plains. Because there normally is a direct relationship of terrain slope to rock exposures, to the geologic structure of an area, and to drainage and runoff of a basin, clinometric or slope mapping has become a matter of increasing interest.

The Geological Survey does not produce slope maps as a standard series. Rather, they are produced for selected areas based on the special need for such maps.

Recently, the Survey has developed methods of slope map preparation that appear to be feasible, practical, economical, and acceptable to both producers and users. These methods entail the use of photomechanical techniques and equipment (Gilman, Richter, and Brownworth, 1972) for semiautomatically deriving slope zones on the basis of distances between adjacent contour lines on existing topographic maps.

By various techniques the contour lines are widened by predetermined amounts so that when they touch each other, specific slope zones are indicated. Then, in a series of line-weight reduction and masking steps, the zones are recorded permanently on film for reproduction. The resulting slope maps may contain some recognizable anomalies but nevertheless are preferred over costly, manually compiled slope maps.

Slope or gradient of a land surface is conventionally expressed in degrees of inclination, as a percentage, as a ratio, or as a simple descriptive term. On Survey maps and related publications, slope is indicated as a percentage. As an additional aid, the legend on each slope indicates the angle of inclination and the gradient ratio.

Slope maps can be designed with a wide range in the number of slope zones. A simple map may include

FIGURE 122. Portion of orthophotographic map of the Fort Wayne, Ind., area at 1:2,400 scale.

Topographic Maps

143

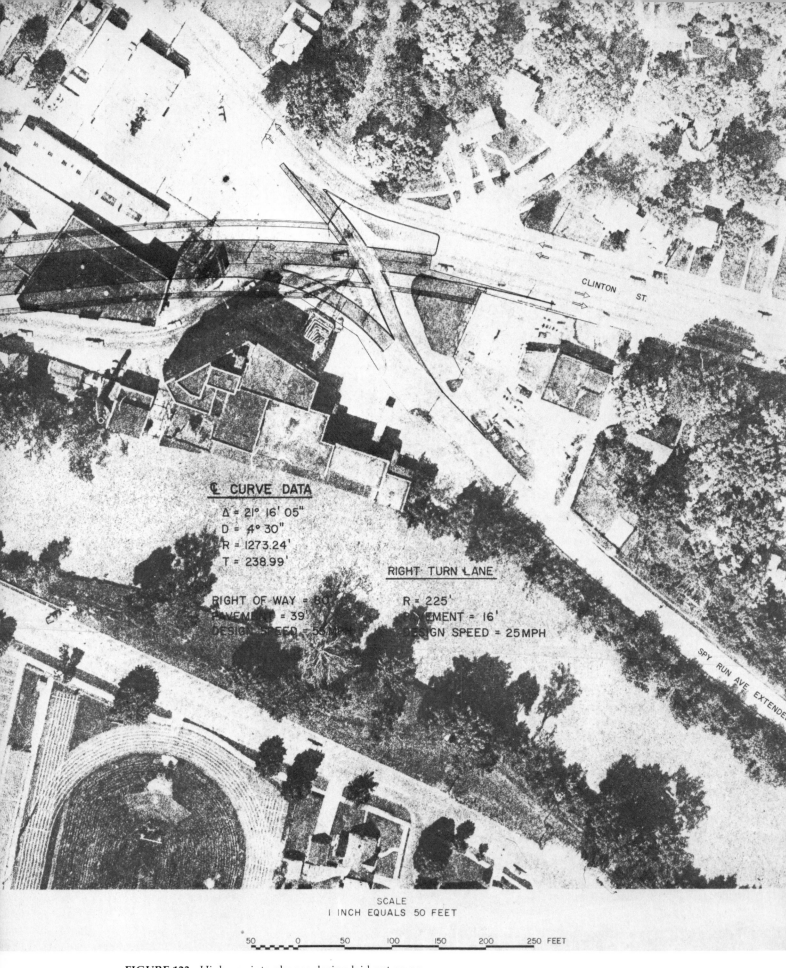

FIGURE 123. Highway interchange design laid out on an orthophotographic map. Original scale 1:600; shown here at approximately 1:1,200. (Fort Wayne, Ind.)

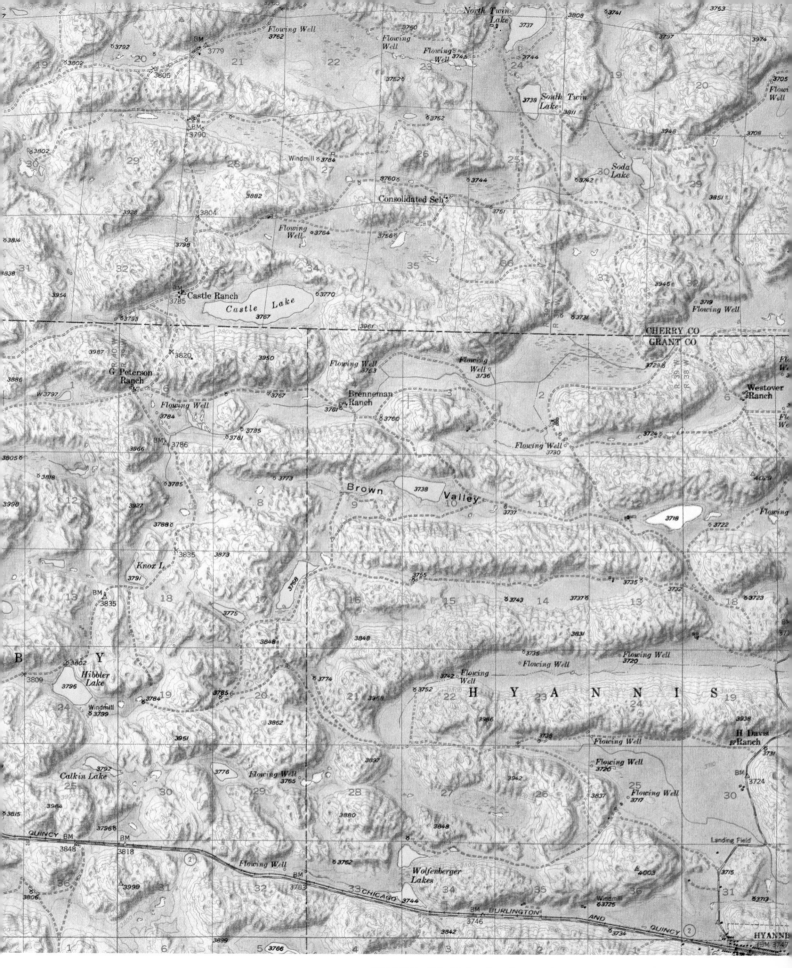

FIGURE 124. Nebraska dune ridges dramatically portrayed by shaded-relief treatment. (Ashby, Nebr., 1:62,500-scale 15-minute quadrangle.)

three zones (as 0–30, 30–60, and 60 percent and greater) whereas a detailed, large-scale map might contain 10–15 zones, normally with smaller increments in the lower gradients (usually land of greater economic value) and larger increments in the steeper gradients (for example, 0–2, 2–5, 5–10, 10–20, 40–70, and 70 percent and greater).

Multizone maps provide slope information for a quadrangle, county, watershed, national park or forest, or geographic region. On these maps the location, size, shape, and aspect of each unit of a particular slope zone are readily identifiable (fig. 125).

One use for such a map is in a hydrologic evaluation of a watershed. The influence of slope on snow accumulation, runoff rates, and soil erosion can be better understood and evaluated with the help of complete graphic slope data. Potential problem areas can be located, and plans developed to better manage water resources and minimize erosion and flood damage.

Other uses include (1) identifying forested areas where logging should be restricted because of soil and erosion factors, (2) predicting forest-fire behavior and planning appropriate control measures, (3) locating transportation corridors to minimize construction costs, and (4) defining zoning district boundaries for restricting certain forms of construction, strip mining, or other development.

On multizone slope maps, there are several ways to portray the slope information. Distinctive colors can be used, one for each zone; several densities of a single color can be used to reduce preparation and printing costs; or the slope map itself can be produced in the form of a film transparency, with each slope zone in a different percentage screen to overlay the published base map. The clarity of slope information is preserved by including only enough map detail for orientation— the geographic graticule, selected contour lines, streams, and open-water areas. Selected geographic names may be added, and in some instances, civil boundaries.

Special two-zone slope maps can be made to define certain social engineering problems in terms of desirable and undersirable gradients. For example, if a county ordinance requires that septic fields be sited on slopes less than 15 percent to protect water supplies, then all the areas within the county that meet this criterion could be defined on a two-zone slope map.

Thus a dual-zone map produced from one set of line-widening and reduction exposures, which shows slopes only above and below that particular gradient, might suffice for users interested only in a particular critical slope. Such a product can be prepared relatively quickly and inexpensively for users who are satisfied with a raw, unedited product generated directly from a contour negative. These special-request items are reproduced as film overlays, registered to the published base maps, and are devoid of all map features except the required slope information and an identifying label.

Coastal Maps

Following passage by Congress of the Coastal Zone Management Act of 1972, it became apparent that improved maps of these coastal areas were needed. As the coastal zone includes both land and water, the task of producing a set of maps for the entire coastal zone of the United States devolves on both the Geological Survey and the National Ocean Survey (see Ellis, 1978).

The Coastal Zone Management Act of 1972 defines the coastal zone as

. . . the coastal waters (including the lands therein and thereunder) and the adjacent shorelands (including the waters therein and thereunder), strongly influenced by each other and in proximity to the shorelines of the several coastal states, and includes transitional and intertidal areas, salt marshes, wetlands, and beaches. The zone extends, in Great Lakes waters, to the international boundary between the United States and Canada and, in other areas, seaward to the outer limit of the United States territorial sea. The zone extends inland from the shoreline only to the extent necessary to control shorelands, the uses of which have a direct and significant impact on the coastal waters. Excluded from the coastal zone are lands the use of which is by law subject solely to the discretion of or which is held in trust by the Federal Government, its officers, or agents.

LAND AREAS. The Geological Survey is devoting a significant effort to the completion of 7.5-minute quadrangle mapping of the land areas in the coastal zone and to the revision of published maps on a 5-year cycle. Approximately 3,600 7.5-minute quadrangles are included in the coastal zone of the conterminous United States, Alaska, Hawaii, and Puerto Rico. This number includes shoreline quadrangles plus adjacent inland quadrangles (fig. 126). Quick-response products, such as orthophotoquads and interim revisions, are provided for areas where timely completion of conventional maps is not feasible.

Although the topographic map offers the greatest wealth of information for land areas, the problems of coastal-zone management may require that supplemental data be provided from thematic maps covering such fields as geology, land use, land ownership, utilities, and population distribution. Thematic data may be obtained from aerial photographs and photographic products, or from spacecraft imagery. Orthophotographic maps are especially useful for ascertaining the extent of wetlands and for studying vegetation.

WATER AREAS. The greatest single source of data for water areas is the series of nautical charts and related products produced by the National Ocean Survey. These

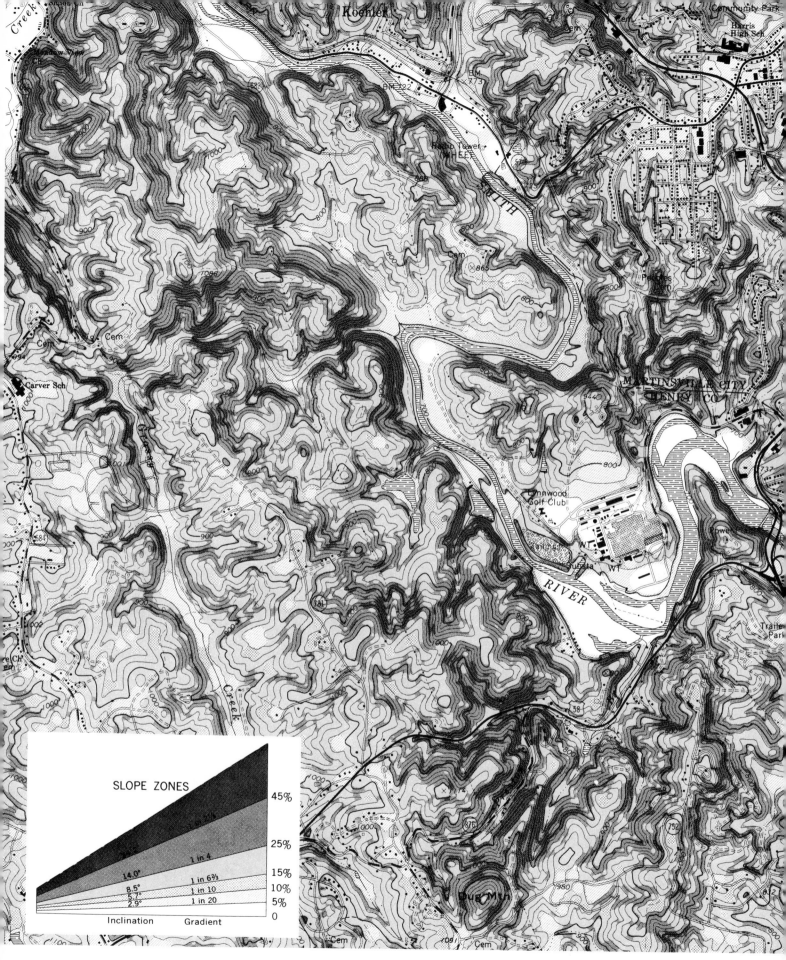

FIGURE 125. Portion of 1:24,000-scale monocolor slope map with six slope zones. (Martinsville West, Va., quadrangle.)

Topographic Maps

147

FIGURE 126. Coastal areas as designated for coastal-zone management.

charts may be subdivided according to type, all of which contain similar information but differ mostly in scale and intended use. There are also a number of special-purpose maps, charts, and diagrams dealing with water areas.

Another very useful water-related map product is the bathymetric map, produced by the National Ocean Survey at various scales and with varying content. Some bathymetric maps show magnetic and gravity data in addition to the water depths. They generally cover extensive offshore areas and are helpful in planning offshore resource development.

TOPOGRAPHIC-BATHYMETRIC MAPS. For the production of coastal maps with significant areas of both land and water, the National Ocean Survey provides bathymetric data to be added to Geological Survey coastal maps. These joint "topo-bathy" maps incorporate into one format and one edition the data previously shown separately on the topographic map and the bathymetric map of the area. The integrated product

serves the cartographic needs of oceanographers, marine geologists, land use planners, physical scientists, conservationists, and others having an interest in management of the coastal zone, the wetlands, and the offshore environment.

A portion of the 1:250,000-scale topographic-bathymetric map for Los Angeles is shown in figure 127. Other maps have been prepared at that scale and at 1:100,000 scale.

UPDATING. Coastal areas are dynamic biologically, geologically, demographically, legally, and in other ways. So, also, are coastal boundaries and the administration of the land and water areas they encompass. Maps depicting coastal information, therefore, cannot be considered permanent, and have to be updated frequently. This updating is facilitated by using overlays on a good base map.

Geological Survey Cartographic Products

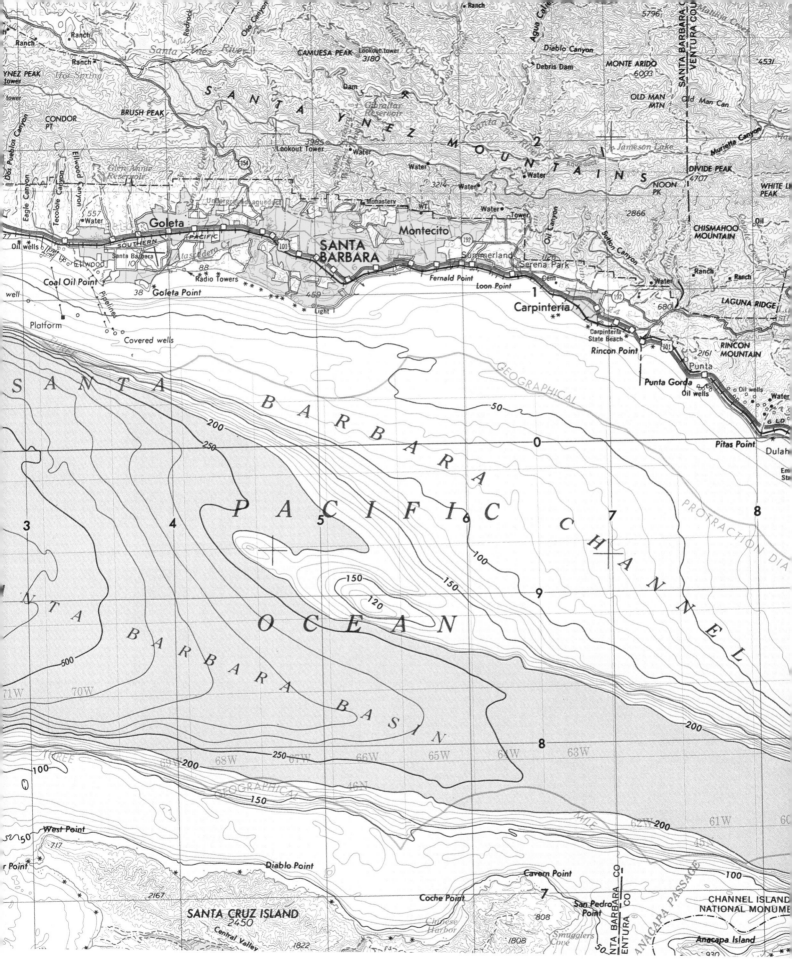

FIGURE 127. Portion of Los Angeles 1:250,000-scale topographic-bathymetric map produced jointly by Geological Survey and National Ocean Survey.

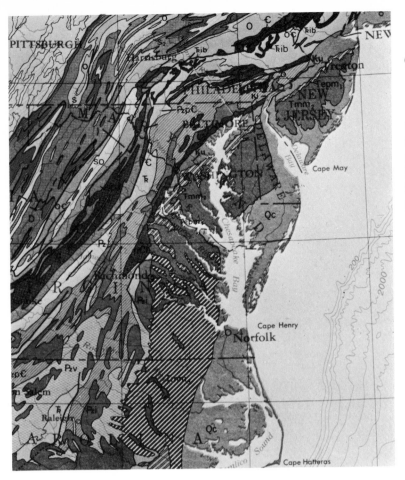

FIGURE 128. Geologic portrait of part of the eastern coast region, from a small-scale geologic map of North America.

FIGURE 129. Individual layers of rock along the walls of the Grand Canyon are clearly shown in this drawing (made in the 1870's by W. H. Holmes).

Geologic Mapping

Geologic maps (White, 1970) show the distribution of rocks and surficial material by age, and their physical and structural relations with one another. Inferences can be drawn from these maps about an area's geologic history, geologic processes, orientation of rock layers, faults, fractures, and shape of rock bodies beneath the surface (fig. 128).

Panoramic Views

The first natural scientists to make meaningful predictions about what lies beneath the Earth's surface seem to have acquired their insight not from making geologic maps, but from the large panoramic views one sees from cliffs and steep mountainsides. In the walls of the Grand Canyon of the Colorado River, for example, the eye can easily follow the course of individual layers of rock for miles, and one realizes that the layers occur in the same order at other places throughout the canyon (fig. 129). Such individual layers of rock are grouped by geologists into units called "formations." The thickness and physical features of a formation are sufficiently distinct to allow them to be traced continuously for long distances, and they are the basic units plotted on a geologic map. Geologists commonly name a formation for some locality near which the unit was first identified.

Where river valleys cut across mountain ridges like the Appalachians, one can see arches in the strata a few hundred yards across in a single view and learn from this that rocks do not always lie horizontally, as at the Grand Canyon, but that the layers may, instead, be tipped and folded.

In walking along such a river valley, one might notice that the layers sloping one way in one ridge resemble layers sloping in the opposite direction in the next ridge. Figure 130 shows two ridges and a valley between as seen from a river flowing from left to right. The ridges and the valley extend away from us, so we are looking at the ends of the ridges and can see something of their internal structure. The figure clearly shows that the sandstone beds, with gray shale beds above and red shale and limestone beds below, bend down under the valley to make a trough. This cross section of the two ridges suggests how the rocks might look if we were able to dig a trench deep into the Earth along the course of the river and look at the rocks in the walls of the trench. It is easy to see how the rock layers must connect beneath the valley. By drawing cross-sectional views like this, one can estimate how deep a hole would have to be drilled in the middle of the valley to reach the limestone bed beneath the red shale.

From cross-sectional views like this, where the vertical dimensions of things can be seen directly, the earliest geologists learned how the formations of the Earth occur in recognizable sequences, and that what can be seen at the surface may, with a little imagination, be used to make intelligent estimates about what lies at depth.

Plotting on Base Maps

Unfortunately, the number of places where the Earth shows its internal structure (figs. 129 and 130) is very small compared to the area where the underlying structure is hidden. Consequently, geologists organize their direct observations by plotting them on base maps.

Making a geologic map is one way by which a geologist can predict the presence and position of certain rock layers beneath the Earth's surface. First, he makes a systematic search for places where rock appears in natural outcrops or artificial exposures. Second, he records the location of such outcrops on a map. Third, he places symbols on the map to record the observations that appear to be most significant about each outcrop. Generally these observations are placed on a base map (fig. 131A) which shows roads, streams, and houses. The base map eventually becomes covered with symbols representing the geologist's observations of the scattered outcrops that he has examined (fig. 131B). Each of the symbols on this field map (circles, dots, dashed lines, wavy lines) represents an outcrop that he has examined. Each symbol, plotted in its correct relationship to the stream, house, roads, and other outcrops, represents a different kind of rock. Dots, for example, are often used to represent sandstone; circles, conglomerate; straight lines, shale; wavy lines, schist or gneiss. The flat T-shaped symbols with numbers like 3°, 10°, 25°, and 40° are strike-and-dip symbols, which give the amount and direction of slope of the layers in the various outcrops. If this symbol were to be used to describe a sloping roof, the long (strike) line would parallel the ridgepole, and the short (dip) line would point directly down the slope of the roof in the direction water would drain (see fig. 132). The number gives the inclination (dip) of the roof in degrees measured below a horizontal plane. For a flat roof, the dip would be 0°, and for a vertical wall, 90°. The other numbers (82 to 96) near some of the outcrops refer to entries in the geologist's field notebook in which he records the numerous additional observations on the rocks that he cannot conveniently represent by map symbols.

The geologist's final step is to add boundary lines between different kinds of rock and to differentiate (usually by color) the sections to show how he thinks the area would look if the soil were completely stripped away. Figure 131C, finally redrawn to show the important features more distinctly, is an example of the completed geologic map.

The reliability of this map depends on the number of exposures of the rocks and their distribution. In drawing the final geologic map, the geologist assumes that each rock type represents a layer that was once continuous over the whole area. He also assumes that these layers occurred in the same order, from top to bottom, over the whole area. If the final geologic map is consistent with everything he knows about this and surrounding areas, and does not, for example, imply that one

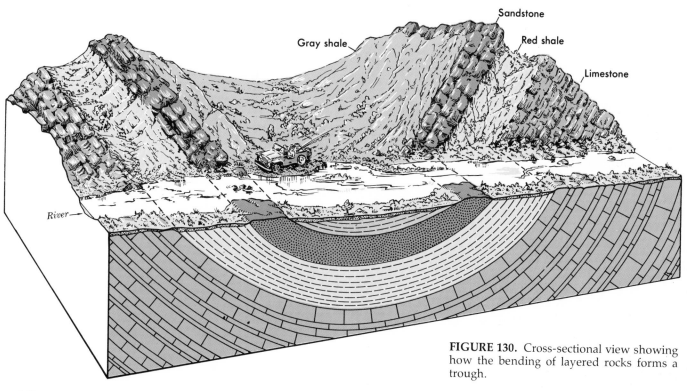

FIGURE 130. Cross-sectional view showing how the bending of layered rocks forms a trough.

151

FIGURE 131. Steps in geologic mapping.

FIGURE 132. Strike and dip of a rock outcrop.

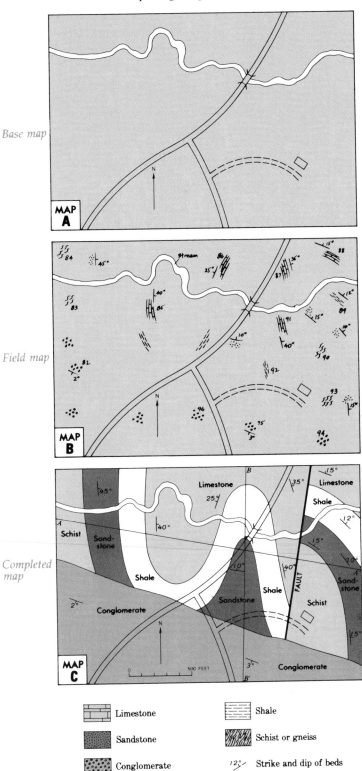

Base map

Field map

Completed map

Limestone

Sandstone

Conglomerate

Shale

Schist or gneiss

Strike and dip of beds

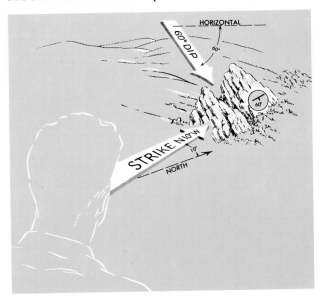

situations in which the outcrops might be connected in several different ways, with no one way being obviously more or less credible than the others. Such situations can readily occur where there are few exposures, less clear-cut contrasts in rock types, and more complicated geology. To find the best solution, the geologist relies on additional evidence that may not be readily shown on the map. Such evidence might consist of particular types of fossils or of pebbles of one rock layer in another; both kinds of evidence show which layers are older and which are younger. The geologist might notice that the rocks along a line running north from the house shown in figure 131B appear to be more fractured than normal, suggesting that these outcrops lie near an important break or fault in the rocks (see fig. 133). Finally, he may rely heavily on what he has learned in areas of good exposure about the sequence of rock layers and about the characteristic fold or fault patterns of these particular rocks in this region.

FIGURE 133. Movement along a fault has brought older rocks into contact with younger rocks.

layer is older than another when fossils show the opposite, the map is inferred to be a correct representation of the surface distribution of rock formations. These tentative assumptions severely limit the number of ways in which the distribution of outcrops can reasonably be explained. Most geologists would draw about the same final map (fig. 131C) from the particular set of data given in figure 131B. It is not difficult, however, to imagine

Geological Survey Cartographic Products

152

In the completed geologic map, the geologist has a map that shows what he could see from an airplane if all the rocks were bare and the different rock units were easily distinguishable by color or other characteristics. The strike-and-dip symbols tell whether the layers at each place are going down into the Earth at a steep or gentle angle and in what direction. The geologist can predict the subsurface geology by the strike-and-dip symbols and the distribution pattern of the rock formations, even though no cliffs or other steep cuts show the vertical dimensions and depths directly.

By drawing cross sections in different directions across the area covered by figure 131C, the geologist can depict the subsurface geology (fig. 134). He can predict what might be seen in the walls of trenches 400–500 feet deep were they dug along the lines A–A' and B–B'. The top line of each cross section represents the surface of the ground. Proceeding from A toward A' along this top line, the map shows schist, symbolized by wavy lines. About 250 feet from A the schist gives way to sandstone, symbolized by a stipple pattern. The strike-and-dip symbol just north of the stream (fig. 131C) indicates that this sandstone layer is inclined toward the east at an angle of 45°. Since it is known by scaling from the map (see bar scale, fig. 131C) how far it is from A to the top and bottom of the sandstone layer, and since it is known that the sandstone extends downward into the Earth towards the east at an angle of 45°, the inclination can be tentatively drawn in for at least a few hundred feet below the surface in the cross section.

FIGURE 134. Cross sections A—A' and B—B'; locations given in figure 131C on the opposite page.

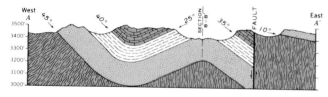

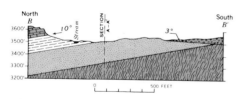

Proceeding eastward, the geologist can complete the near-surface part of the section from A to A'. The heavy faultline on the cross section and map represents a break in the Earth's crust. The strike-and-dip symbols don't give the fault's attitude, so it is assumed to be vertical. If the boundary lines of the various rock units are extended downward, parallel to their dips, and the patterns are filled in, the rock formations in the western two-thirds of the section probably would join below the surface in a trough-shaped structure. Familiarity with

similar folded structures elsewhere leads the geologist to round off the bottom as is shown in the cross-section. Though different geologists might round the trough off in slightly different ways, the differences would normally be too small to have much effect on the predicted depth to the sandstone in the center of the trough.

The east side of the trough (syncline) is the west side of an upwarp (anticline), and everything down to the top of the sandstone can be drawn without any serious stretch of imagination. From the cross section alone, the thickness of the sandstone at the anticline is unknown. However, if the geologist knows the sandstone thickness in other places, he may be able to predict its thickness in the anticline fairly closely and complete this part of the cross section with some confidence. Otherwise he might use the thickness of the sandstone layer he found in the western part of the section, and dash the base of the section to show his uncertainty. The upper surface of the schist is the floor on which the sandstone was deposited. The attitude of the schist layers suggested by wavy lines need not conform to the dip of the layers in the sandstone and overlying rocks.

The fault is a break or dislocation in the rock layers, and each rock layer ends against it on the west side and starts anew on the east. If the layers almost aline across the fault, the displacement is small, but if the fit is poor, as it is here, we know that the displacement is large. Good estimates of the actual vertical displacement can be made by measuring how far the rocks on one side of the fault must be shifted to bring the bases of the sandstone to the same level. Cross sections can be drawn in other directions and places to determine, with greater or less certainty, what lies below the surface of the whole area. In section B–B', drawn nearly north-south, the dip of 10° measured in sandstone gives the same thickness for the shale that was obtained from the construction of section A–A'. Such a check for internal consistency between geologic maps and sections makes both the maps and the sections more credible.

The conglomerate formation (open circle pattern) in the southern part of the area is shown as a thin sheet inclined gently south as the 3° dip of the bedding suggests. Figure 131C shows a discontinuity between the conglomerate and the rocks to the north—the northward limit of the conglomerate is a straight line that cuts across other formation boundaries. This suggests a fault, but the map does not indicate that a fault is necessarily present. If the conglomerate were known from included fossils to be younger than the other rocks, or if it contained pebbles or rock units to the north, it would be possible to interpret the conglomerate as a broad gravel bank that lies on the top of the other rocks; under these circumstances, no fault need be present. This latter interpretation is shown in cross section B–B'. The existence of these two possible interpretations illustrates how a geologic map may correctly represent the distribution of rocks at the surface and still be ambiguous below the surface.

Time Sequences

The sample geologic mapping (figs. 130, 134) is concerned wholly with understanding the spatial relations of the different rock formations—their geologic structure. The analysis of the geology of the area is not complete, however, without consideration of time. Geologic history attempts to put all the geologic events of an area into the proper sequence.

A basic premise of geology is that most rock layers were originally laid down as horizontal or near-horizontal sheets, either in the bottom of a sea or lake, or on land in a valley or plain. Cross section A–A' shows that the layers have been folded and broken since they were orginally laid down, and that the present surface of the land cuts across the various layers just as though a giant planer had been run across the area after the rocks were deformed. The processes that accomplish this planing effect are collectively called erosion. Most people are familiar with this term as it is applied to the spectacular gullies formed when soil is eroded on hillslopes, but the geologist sees the results of erosion in a broader sense whenever he looks at a geologic map or cross section, or at a landscape. Were it not for the combined effects of deformation and erosion, the most ancient rocks of the Earth would be the most deeply buried, and we would never see them at the surface. But, because the crust of the Earth has been periodically buckled and broken and then planed off by erosion, its layering and structure are exposed to view just as a knife cut reveals the inner structure of an onion.

With these principles in mind, one can gain an insight into the geologic history of an area by studying the cross section. In the example (fig. 134), the sandstone was orginally laid down as a sheet on a relatively flat surface that cuts across the layering in the schist. This indicates that, still earlier, the schist must have been deformed, and that erosion had then carved a level surface on this rock before the sandstone was deposited. Layers of shale were then deposited on the sandstone and this shale was overlain in turn by limestone. Detailed study of these formations would probably reveal whether they were laid down on the sea floor, in lakes, or on land, because each kind of rock has physical or chemical characteristics that reflect its environment of deposition. Fossils in the rock provide information about both the environment and the time of deposition.

After the limestone was deposited, the area was crumpled and broken as shown by the folds and faults. Again the area was subjected to erosion and a relatively flat surface was cut across all the rocks. The conglomerate was deposited on this surface. The area was then tilted slightly toward the south to give the conglomerate its present low dip in that direction. The latest event that produced the present land surface was the erosion that is still going on. Thus, the cross section serves as a geologic diary, recording the sequence of events long past.

Uses of Geologic Maps

In this account of geologic mapping, it has been convenient to describe a series of steps taken in a regular sequence, with each completed before the next is begun. Actually, because a geologic map is an interpretation, it is used to test hypotheses. It may be drawn and redrawn many times before a version satisfies all pertinent facts. If more than one version survives these tests, additional field or laboratory observations may be needed to decide among them.

A geologic map, therefore, really plays three distinct roles. First, it is a convenient means of recording observations about rocks in a way that preserves their spatial relationship to each other. Second, along with the cross sections that can be drawn from it, it is a device for study and analysis of many kinds of geologic features such as sequence and thickness of formations, their geologic structure, and their history. Trial versions of the map suggest conditions that a satisfactory hypothesis of the local geology must meet, and these lead the geologist to critical localities where alternative hypotheses can be tested. Finally, when the geologist has deciphered the significant geologic relationships of an area, his map is the most compact way to illustrate many of these relationships so they can be readily grasped and used by others. It would take volumes of text to describe the features of a structurally complex area that can be portrayed on a geologic map and cross section.

Scientists and engineers in many fields use geologic maps as basic tools. Because we know, for example, that certain kinds of rock or geologic structures are associated with certain kinds of mineral deposits, geologic maps can help the exploration geologist find new places where favorable conditions exist. The highway or construction engineer can use geologic maps to locate sources of construction materials and to predict foundation and excavation conditions. Hydrologists use geologic maps to locate sources or movement paths of underground water. And because soil is commonly a product of the disintegration of the bedrock beneath, geologic maps are helpful to soil scientists in classifying soils for agricultural purposes.

Geologic maps can be used for these and other purposes whether or not the geologist who made them had such purposes in mind. Even though the map is interpretive, it is primarily a method of recording and presenting data in compact and systematic form. A map originally made as part of a program of petroleum exploration may turn out, ultimately, to have far greater value in a search for uranium or potash. One prepared solely to solve a geologic problem may later help an engineering geologist choose between potential construction sites, or determine that the presence of a major fault precludes heavy construction in that area.

TABLE 5. Scales of geologic maps commonly used by the Geological Survey

Map scale	Percentage of U.S. covered by 1976 at this or larger scale	Type of information	Purpose
1:2,500,000	100	Very general distribution of limited number of very large and heterogeneous rock units.	General planning and resource evaluation over very large regions (Federal regions, very large States).
1:500,000	73	General distribution of a larger number of somewhat less heterogeneous rock units. Little information on depth.	General planning, and resource evaluation over large regions (large States, river basins). Common scale for older State maps.
1:250,000	44	Semidetailed distribution of large numbers of fairly homogeneous rock units. Some information on depth. Often has topographic base.	More detailed planning and resource evaluation in medium-sized areas (small States, large counties, national forests, mineralized belts).
1:100,000 1:63,360 (Alaska) 1:62,500	25	Detailed distribution of large number of homogeneous rock and surficial units and considerable information on thickness and depth. Generally has topographic base.	Detailed planning, land-management, and resource studies (mining districts, urban areas, many counties).
1:24,000 1:20,000 (Puerto Rico)	15	Very detailed distribution of large number of quite homogeneous rock units. Surficial deposits may be shown on separate map. Much information on thickness and vertical extent of rock units. Has topographic base.	Detailed planning, zoning, site selection, resource evaluation, and exploration (cities and towns, subdivisions, mining, districts, mine sites, large construction projects).

The Geological Survey makes many kinds of geologic maps as part of a continuing program to fulfill one of its missions: ". . . to examine the geological structure . . . of the national domain." These maps may be published singly in one of several series that include geologic quadrangle maps (fig. 135), mineral investigations maps, mineral resource maps, oil and gas maps, and hydrologic investigations atlases; or they may be published as folded sheets in envelopes bound with book-type reports such as bulletins, water-supply papers, and professional papers. The texts of such reports contain descriptive and interpretive material that geologic maps cannot alone provide.

Geologic maps published by the Survey range in scale from 1:20,000 to 1:2,500,000 depending on the type of information to be portrayed and the purpose of the mapping (table 5). Geologic maps at 1:250,000 or larger scales are available for nearly 50 percent of the United States.

In addition to the commonly used geologic maps, the Survey prepares a wide range of special geologic maps for specific purposes. For example, maps are prepared, generally at a scale of 1:7,500,000, that are useful for understanding environmental problems and for making decisions on land use and mineral and energy resource development on a national scale. The following maps of the National Environmental Overview Program have been completed in preliminary form:

Δ Map showing areas of karst topography and related terrains.
Δ Map showing areas subject to volcanic hazards.
Δ Map showing areas of possible landslides.
Δ Map showing present and proposed nuclear reactor sites.
Δ Map showing streams with flow rates of 300 feet³/s or more.
Δ Map showing surficial clay, sand, silt, and gravel deposits.

Another program in special geologic mapping is the compilation of engineering geologic maps of such areas as the Arctic Coastal Plain between Prudhoe Bay and the Canadian border, which covers the route of the proposed Alaska Arctic Gas Pipeline. Such mapping is useful in understanding the effects of geologic processes and materials on man's use of the land and on the design and construction of manmade structures.

Hydrologic Maps

The Geological Survey is charged with gathering and publishing information about water resources for use by the public and by agencies that have the responsibility for managing or developing these resources. As a result of water-resources investigations, hundreds of different water reports and maps by Survey personnel are made available every year in Federal, State, and local publications, in technical journals, or in depositories for public inspection.

FIGURE 135. Portion of a geologic quadrangle map, scale 1:24,000. (Adam Weiss Peak, Wyo., quadrangle.)

For each State, the Survey issues a folder containing a brief description of its water-resources investigations in that State. The folder includes a principal map that shows the location of hydrologic data stations and the extent of the hydrologic investigations; smaller maps in the folder depict variations in hydrologic characteristics. Also available are State Hydrologic Unit Maps (fig. 136).

Hydrologic Investigations Atlases

Hydrologic atlases fulfill a major objective of the water-resources investigations of the Survey. The atlases, developed from basic-data collection and special studies, present a wide range of hydrologic and hydrogeologic facts concerning the Nation's water resources. Some hydrologic information is difficult and cumbersome to express meaningfully in text but can be depicted clearly and simply in map form for ready interpretation, especially when supplemented by other graphics and notes.

More than 600 hydrologic atlases have been published by the Survey. Most of these atlases have been prepared in cooperation with State, county, and municipal agencies and cover areas of existing and potential water problems or areas where general hydrologic mapping and inventory were desired. Currently, atlases cover natural hydrologic units, such as drainage basins. These atlases provide a meaningful presentation relating to the future development of the Nation's water resources. Each atlas consists of one or more sheets whose basic format is a map presentation that may cover any combination of subjects. Subjects most frequently treated in this manner are water availability and delineation of flood areas. Frequently used combinations of subjects may include information on surface drainage, precipitation and climate, geology, availability of ground and surface water, water quality and use, and streamflow characteristics.

The scale of maps used for hydrologic atlases depends on the type of presentation and on the availability of base maps. The principal maps are most frequently presented at a scale of 1:24,000. Atlases dealing with large regions, however, may require a scale of 1:250,000 or smaller. Hydrologic information is shown on the map superimposed on either a topographic or a planimetric base map of the study area. The principal maps are supplemented by smaller maps, graphs, tables, and text that illustrate facts and present relevant data and analyses. Photographs are occasionally used to illustrate changes caused by significant hydrologic events, landforms with hydrologic significance, important hydrologic structures, or other information. References to sources of additional information relating to the areas are also given.

Water Availability Maps

Figure 137 is a sample map from a hydrologic investigations atlas sheet that depicts the general availability of ground water. It contains, superimposed on a 1:24,000 scale topographic map, symbols that represent the ground-water potential throughout the areas shown. The map legend also shows, for areas where data are available and where the yield per well is sufficient, the depth to ground-water level. Limits of yield and depth to water level in unstudied areas are estimated on the basis of the best geologic and hydrologic data available and are subject to revision. Such maps are intended for use as a convenient guide in planning water-supply projects for domestic, municipal, industrial, and irrigation uses.

In recent years, work on determining water availability has advanced on over 1,000 separate projects per year, but less than half of the country is covered. Present work is aimed toward the acquisition of generalized or detailed coverage for 75 percent of the Nation, with some information for the remainder. Mapping is selective and places greater stress on those areas where population and water use are growing the fastest.

Flood-Prone-Area Maps

The 89th Congress (1966) in House Document 465 recommended preparation of flood-prone-area maps (Edelen, 1976) to assist in minimizing flood losses by quickly identifying areas of potential flood hazards. The intent of Congress obviously was to obtain a nationwide "reconnaissance level" of information quickly. A basic premise of the recommendation is that a hydrologist quickly can identify potential flood areas from his assessment of readily available data and from skills obtained through experience. Although the greatest confidence cannot be placed in the exact position of the flood boundaries, the flood-prone-area map serves as a general warning of potential flood hazards and as a basis for setting priorities of future detailed studies.

House Document 465 suggested that the Survey prepare the flood-prone-area maps, in recognition of the competent staff of hydrologists who are familiar with local flood conditions throughout the United States. In 1968 maps showing "approximate areas occasionally flooded" were prepared. In the 1969 fiscal year the project was changed to delimit the approximate boundaries of the 100-year flood. This change was undertaken to assist the Federal Insurance Administration (FIA) which was charged with identification of the Nation's flood plains in the August 1968 flood insurance legislation. The FIA has defined the flood plain as the area subject to inundation by a 100-year flood.

Flood-prone-area maps produced under this program have been put to good use by individuals, private organizations, and local, State, and Federal governmental agencies. The maps have been particularly useful in

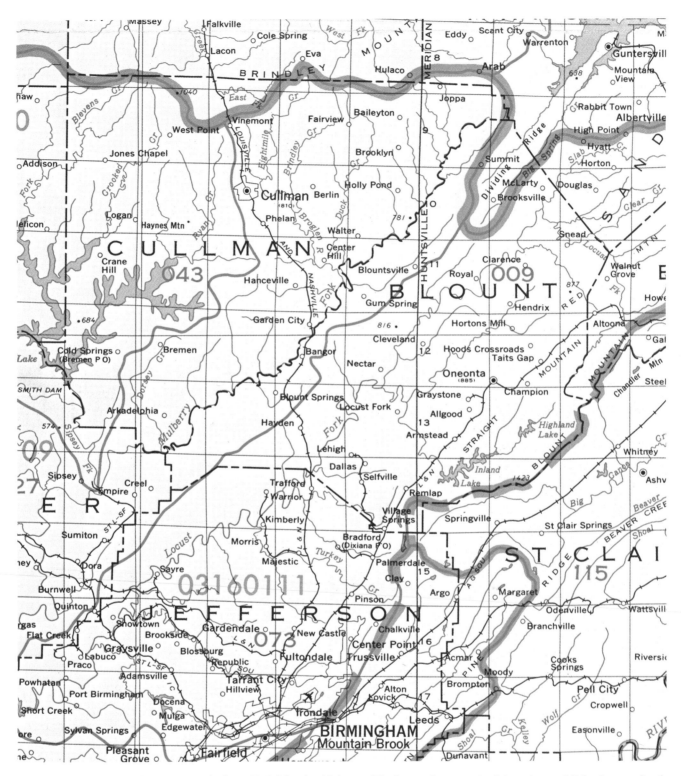

FIGURE 136. Portion of the State Hydrologic Unit Map for Alabama. The four-color maps in this series, published at a scale of 1:500,000, delineate river basins in the United States that have drainage areas greater than 700 square miles. A distinctive numeric code is assigned to each river basin (hydrologic unit). The maps show culture in black, hydrography in blue, hydrologic unit boundaries and eight-digit hydrologic unit codes in red, and political subdivision codes in green.

FIGURE 137. Portion of 1:24,000-scale map showing availability of ground-water resources. (From Hydrologic Investigations Atlas HA–540 (Winner, 1975), Ground-water Resources of the Cape Hatteras National Seashore, N.C.) ▶

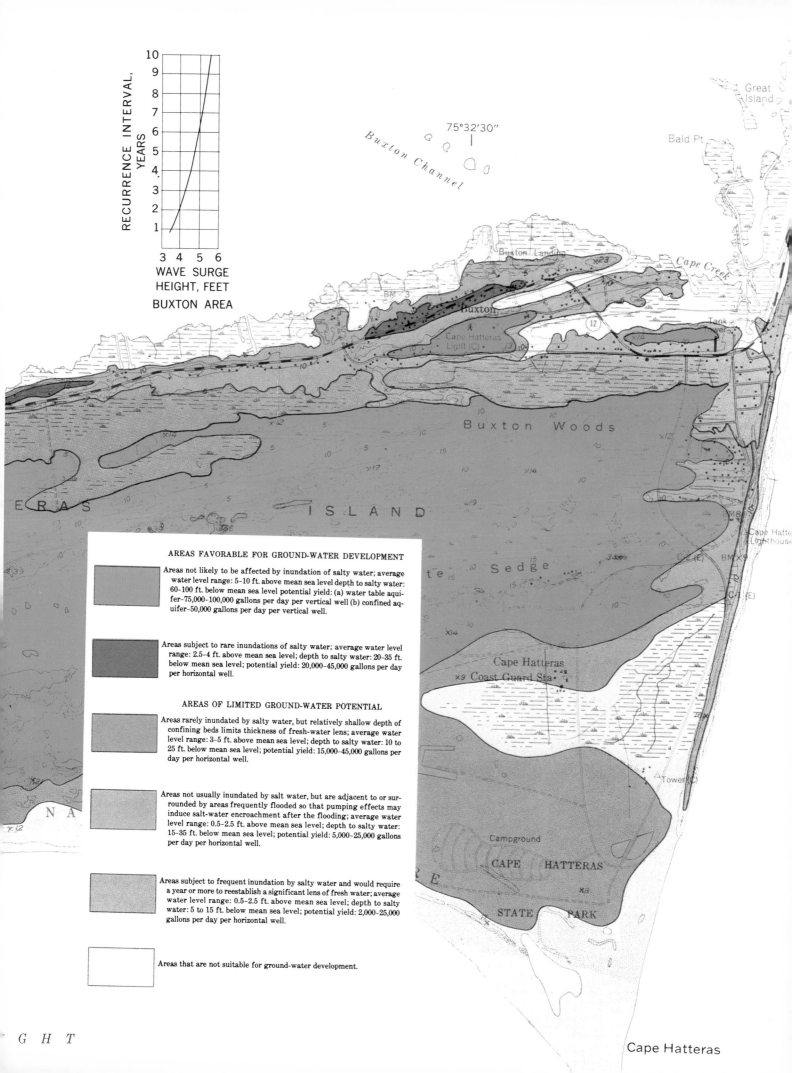

RECURRENCE INTERVAL, YEARS

10
9
8
7
6
5
4
3
2
1

3 4 5 6

WAVE SURGE HEIGHT, FEET

BUXTON AREA

AREAS FAVORABLE FOR GROUND-WATER DEVELOPMENT

Areas not likely to be affected by inundation of salty water; average water level range: 5–10 ft. above mean sea level depth to salty water: 60–100 ft. below mean sea level potential yield: (a) water table aquifer–75,000–100,000 gallons per day per vertical well (b) confined aquifer–50,000 gallons per day per vertical well.

Areas subject to rare inundations of salty water; average water level range: 2.5–4 ft. above mean sea level; depth to salty water: 20–35 ft. below mean sea level; potential yield: 20,000–45,000 gallons per day per horizontal well.

AREAS OF LIMITED GROUND-WATER POTENTIAL

Areas rarely inundated by salty water, but relatively shallow depth of confining beds limits thickness of fresh-water lens; average water level range: 3–5 ft. above mean sea level; depth to salty water: 10 to 25 ft. below mean sea level; potential yield: 15,000–45,000 gallons per day per horizontal well.

Areas not usually inundated by salt water, but are adjacent to or surrounded by areas frequently flooded so that pumping effects may induce salt-water encroachment after the flooding; average water level range: 0.5–2.5 ft. above mean sea level; depth to salty water: 15–35 ft. below mean sea level; potential yield: 5,000–25,000 gallons per day per horizontal well.

Areas subject to frequent inundation by salty water and would require a year or more to reestablish a significant lens of fresh water; average water level range: 0.5–2.5 ft. above mean sea level; depth to salty water: 5 to 15 ft. below mean sea level; potential yield: 2,000–25,000 gallons per day per horizontal well.

Areas that are not suitable for ground-water development.

Cape Hatteras

planning the evacuation of areas likely to be flooded. By the end of 1976 fiscal year flood-prone areas had been delineated on more than 12,000 quadrangles.

House Document 465 recommended a three-stage program to delimit major flood hazards: (1) listing of towns and streams with flood problems, (2) outlining the flood plain on maps or aerial photographs, and (3) accelerating the present program of flood hazard information reports. The Survey was assigned primary responsibility for stage 2. The U.S. Army Corps of Engineers has completed stage 1 and has accelerated its program relative to stage 3.

The objective of the mapping program is to identify quickly those areas subject to flooding, without regard to detailed accuracy that will be provided at a later date under stage 3. Areas inundated by a 100-year flood on all streams are to be outlined on topographic maps or on photomosaics.

The project includes all areas of the United States where flooding from streams, lakes, and tides is a problem. Priority is given to areas in and near the 4,000 urban places with flood problems as listed by the Corps of Engineers and to those communities interested in participating in the Federal Flood Insurance Program. In addition, flood-prone areas are identified in rural areas where bottom lands subject to flood damage are extensively farmed. Following this, maps are produced for areas in the public domain where management or planning decisions are required and for undeveloped areas with recreational potential.

Maps showing flood-prone areas are distributed to Federal and State flood-control agencies, planning commissions, civil defense groups, lending-agency officials, public officials, and the local citizenry. The maps are open-file releases; press releases are issued with the completion of groups of maps. Copies of flood-prone area maps are available upon request to the Geological Survey.

The flood-prone-area mapping program does not include areas for which flood-plain information reports are already available or are being prepared by the Corps of Engineers or other agencies. Quadrangles in which very large areas are protected from flooding by major levee systems (areas along the lower Mississippi River, for example) are omitted from the program.

Where the quadrangle map extends beyond the borders of the United States into a foreign country, flood-prone areas in the foreign country are not delineated.

MAP CONTENT. Lines marking the boundaries of flood plains of streams are drawn on 7.5- or 15-minute topographic maps or photomosaics. Areas subject to inundation are marked "FLOOD-PRONE AREA."

A brief text is shown on each map. The text describes the need for flood-plain management and the nature, accuracy, and intended use of the information on the map.

Reliability of the depicted flood-plain boundaries is a function of the flood information available, and of the scale and contour interval of the maps. About 75 percent of the 4,000 urban places with flood problems are covered by 7.5-minute topographic maps and an additional 18 percent by topographic maps in the 15-minute series.

Any quadrangle selected for flood-plain mapping is completely mapped, including both the rural and urban areas. Flood plains are delineated at least for all streams having drainage basins of the following extent:

Δ Urban and suburban areas where the upstream drainage area exceeds 25 mi² (65 km²), and preferably for much smaller streams.
Δ Rural areas in humid regions where the upstream drainage area exceeds 100 mi² (259 km²).
Δ Rural areas in semiarid regions where the upstream drainage area exceeds 250 mi² (647 km²).

The flood-prone-area map (fig. 138) for the Montezuma, N.Y., quadrangle illustrates the treatment of maps in this category. Figure 139 shows the eastern half of an index indicating quadrangles for which flood-prone-area maps are available.

Flood Maps Included in Hydrologic Atlas Series

The Geological Survey has published an extensive series of flood maps identified as "hydrologic investigations atlases." Each atlas consists of a topographic map (or maps) or of a photomosaic base map on which is shown the area covered by one or more outstanding floods of the past or by hypothetical floods of specified frequencies. Generally, the scale of each map is 1:24,000. Each flood map is accompanied by explanatory data that describe the stages and profiles of the flood.

These maps have been prepared in cooperation with State, county, and other governmental agencies. The flood maps are important planning documents for those zoning, planning, construction, and insurance groups concerned with the orderly development and economic use of flood-plain areas. An example of this series, a portion of Hydrologic Investigations Atlas HA–498 showing the floods in the Capron quadrangle, Illinois, is given in figure 140. This atlas also includes a representative index map showing the location of atlases in this series for northeastern Illinois.

Land Use Maps

Knowledge about land use and land cover has become increasingly important as the Nation plans to overcome the problems of haphazard, uncontrolled development, deteriorating environmental quality, loss of

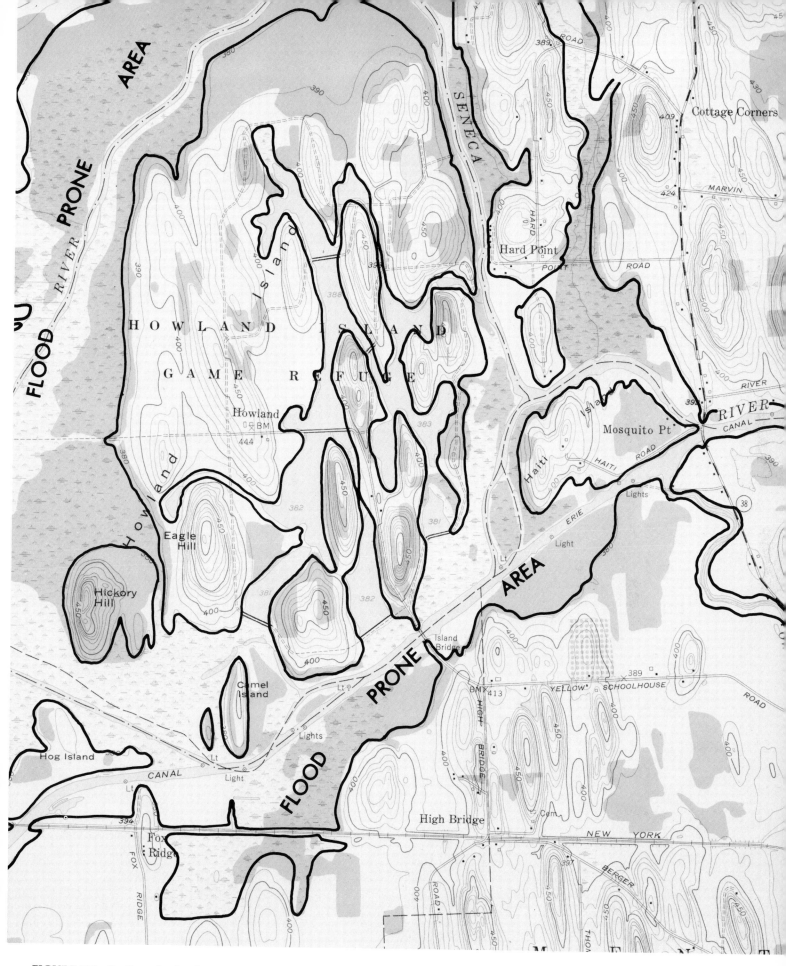

FIGURE 138. Portion of a flood-prone-area quadrangle map, scale 1:24,000. (Montezuma, N. Y., quadrangle.)

FIGURE 139. Eastern half of the index map showing the location of flood-prone areas mapped as of 1975.

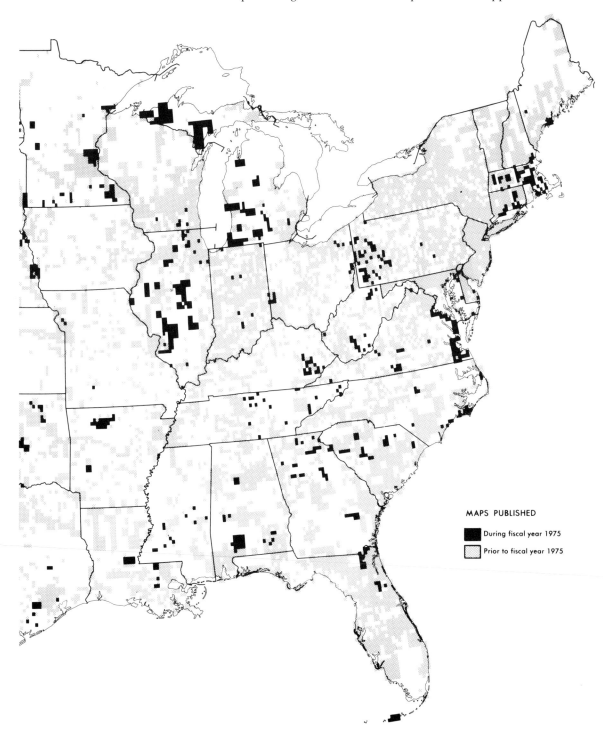

MAPS PUBLISHED

■ During fiscal year 1975

☐ Prior to fiscal year 1975

prime agricultural lands, destruction of important wetlands, and loss of fish and wildlife habitat. Land use data are needed in the analysis of environmental processes and problems that must be understood if living conditions and standards are to be improved or maintained at current levels.

One of the prime prerequisites for better use of land is information on existing land use patterns and changes in land use through time. Knowledge of the present distribution of agricultural, recreational, and urban lands,

as well as information on their changing proportions, is needed by legislators, planners, and State and local governmental officials to determine better land use policy, to project transportation and utility demand, to identify future development pressure points, and to implement effective programs for regional development.

Geological Survey Cartographic Products

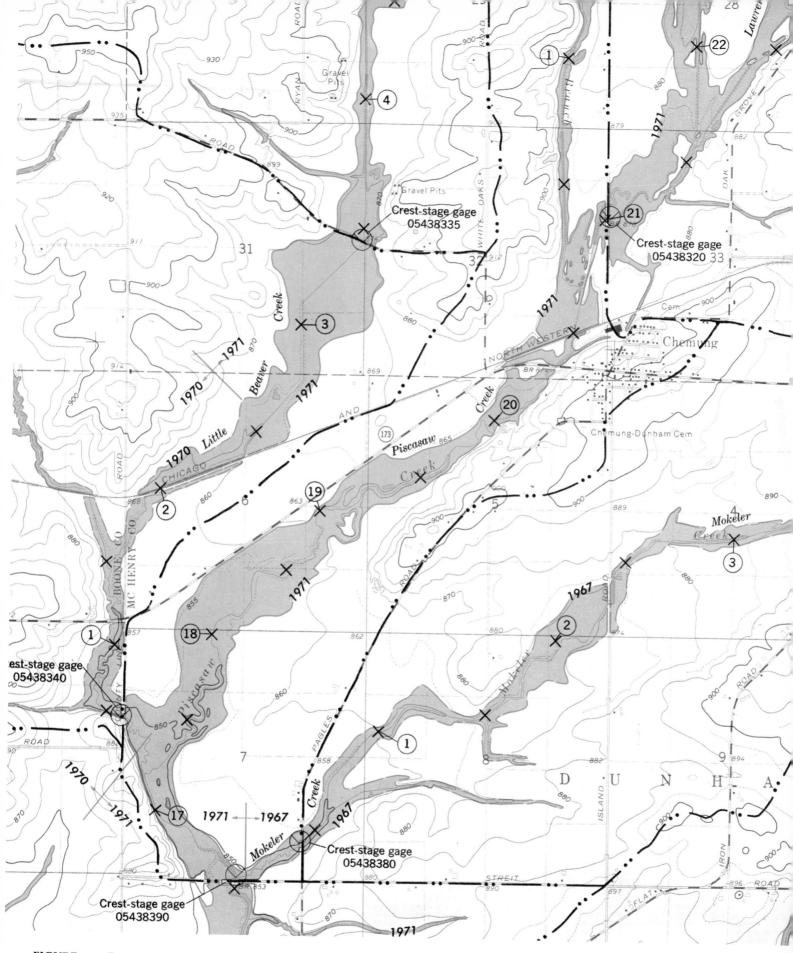

FIGURE 140. Portion of Hydrologic Investigations Atlas HA–498 (Grant and Durek, 1973), Floods in Capron quadrangle, northeastern Illinois, 1:24,000 scale.

Land Use Maps

Classification Principles

There are no ideal methods of land use and land cover inventory or classification of natural resources. One detailed inventory will not be adequate for more than a relatively short period of time. Land use patterns change as our demands for resources change. Few users of land use information are satisfied with an inventory that cannot reflect change and does not satisfy most of their specific or major needs.

Depending on user needs, a land use classification system can be people- or resource-oriented. From the standpoint of wide acceptance and use, the combination of both is preferable.

As remote-sensing technology improves, more and more inventories are made with reliance on source material obtained from both aircraft and satellite sensors. This source material, whether it consists of an aerial photograph or a Landsat image in digital tape format, requires interpretation in order to be used in the inventory. Even though supplemental material may be necessary, the inventory that is made primarily from remote-sensor data will be limited as to what can be identified to an acceptable degree of accuracy. Remote sensors provide many desirable features for inventory use which may outweigh the limitations. The source material is relatively inexpensive, generally unbiased, and provides information at a known time and under conditions that can usually be identified.

The Geological Survey uses the following criteria as a land use/land cover classification system that can effectively employ orbital and high-altitude remote-sensor data (Anderson and others, 1976):

Δ   The minimum level of accuracy in identifying land use and land cover categories from remote-sensor data should be at least 85 percent.

Δ   The accuracy of interpretation for the several categories should be about equal.

Δ   Repeatable or repetitive results should be obtainable from one interpreter to another and from one time of sensing to another.

Δ   The classification system should be applicable over extensive areas.

Δ   The categorization should permit vegetation and other types of land cover to be used as surrogates for activity.

Δ   The classification system should be suitable for use with remote-sensor data obtained at different times of the year.

Δ   Effective use of subcategories that can be obtained from ground surveys or from the use of larger-scale or enhanced remote-sensor data should be possible.

Δ   Aggregation of categories should be possible.

Δ   Comparison with future land use data should be possible.

Δ   Multiple use of land should be recognized when possible.

The Survey land use and land cover classification system (table 6) has been developed to meet the needs of Federal and State agencies for an up-to-date overview of land use and land cover, using a system of categories that are uniform at the generalized first and second levels. The classification is intentionally open ended to provide flexibility in developing more detailed land use classifications at the third and fourth levels that meet particular user needs while retaining compatibility with the national system.

Figure 141 depicts a typical map produced at a scale of 1:250,000 using the Survey land use and land cover classification system. Most of the maps in this series have been compiled by conventional interpretation techniques from high-altitude color-infrared photographs.

TABLE 6. U.S. Geological Survey land use and land cover classification system for use with remote-sensor data

[Single-digit classes are in Level I category; two-digit classes are in Level II category.]

1. Urban or built-up land
    11. Residential
    12. Commercial and services
    13. Industrial
    14. Transportation, communications, and utilities
    15. Industrial and commercial complexes
    16. Mixed urban or built-up land
    17. Other urban or built-up land

2. Agricultural land
    21. Cropland and pasture
    22. Orchards, groves, vineyards, nurseries, and ornamental horticultural areas
    23. Confined feeding operations
    24. Other agricultural land

3. Rangeland
    31. Herbaceous rangeland
    32. Shrub and brush rangeland
    33. Mixed rangeland

4. Forest land
    41. Deciduous forest land
    42. Evergreen forest land
    43. Mixed forest land

5. Water
    51. Streams and canals
    52. Lakes
    53. Reservoirs
    54. Bays and estuaries

6. Wetland
    61. Forested wetland
    62. Nonforested wetland

7. Barren land
    71. Dry salt flats
    72. Beaches
    73. Sandy areas other than beaches
    74. Bare exposed rock
    75. Strip mines, quarries, and gravel pits
    76. Transitional areas
    77. Mixed barren land

8. Tundra
    81. Shrub and brush tundra
    82. Herbaceous tundra
    83. Bare ground tundra
    84. Wet tundra
    85. Mixed tundra

9. Perennial snow or ice
    91. Perennial snowfields
    92. Glaciers

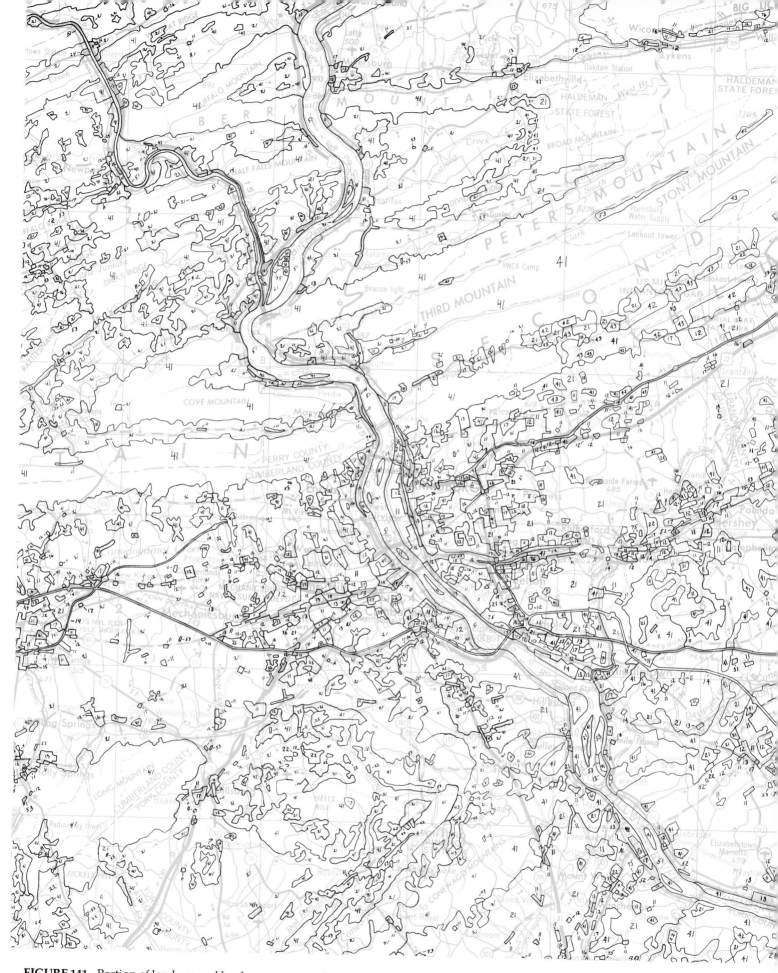

FIGURE 141. Portion of land use and land cover map, scale 1:250,000 (Harrisburg, Pa., quadrangle). For a computer-assisted display derived from the same digital data base, see page 235. A timely computer-drawn application in polygon format, using the same data base, is shown on page 236.

FIGURE 142. Map showing status of land use and land cover mapping. Mapping units are 1°×2° quadrangles (1°×3° in Alaska) shown on indexes to topographic maps at 1:250,000 scale or 30'×60' quadrangles shown on indexes to topographic maps at 1:100,000 scale.

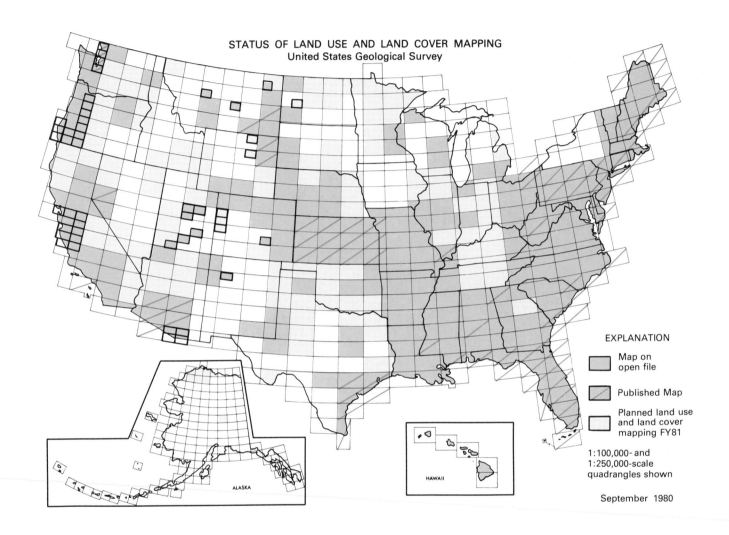

Land Use Mapping Program

In 1975, the Geological Survey embarked upon a new program (Anderson, 1976) to provide land use and land cover maps and ancillary data for the entire United States within 8 years. A systematic update of these maps and related data is a part of the program. This mapping program relates closely to the Survey's long-standing activities in the collection, analysis, and publication of accurate information about the Nation's mineral, land, and water resources. The following products are being provided:

▲ Land use and land cover maps for use with the 1:250,000-scale base maps and with the new 1:100,000-scale base maps as these become available (see fig. 142 for mapping status).

▲ Associated maps showing political units (counties and States), hydrologic units (drainage areas), census county subdivisions including census tracts, and areas of Federal land ownership.

▲ Magnetic tapes containing digital data obtained by digitizing in polygon format the land use and land cover maps. Documented software, necessary for the effective use of the digital data, is also provided.

▲ Land use and land cover statistics by political units, hydrologic units, census county subdivisions, and areas of Federal land ownership. Such statistics are to be made available mainly by States. However, statistics may also be made available for such areal units as coastal areas, Standard Metropolitan Statistical Areas, and major river basins.

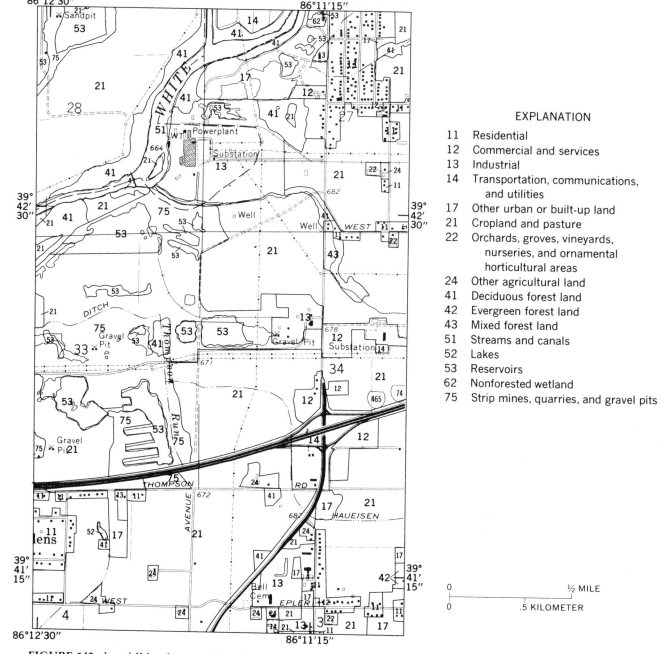

FIGURE 143. Level II land use and land cover in a part of the Maywood, Ind., 1:24,000-scale quadrangle.

EXPLANATION

11 Residential
12 Commercial and services
13 Industrial
14 Transportation, communications, and utilities
17 Other urban or built-up land
21 Cropland and pasture
22 Orchards, groves, vineyards, nurseries, and ornamental horticultural areas
24 Other agricultural land
41 Deciduous forest land
42 Evergreen forest land
43 Mixed forest land
51 Streams and canals
52 Lakes
53 Reservoirs
62 Nonforested wetland
75 Strip mines, quarries, and gravel pits

In close association with the products indicated above, research and development is being carried out on the following topics:

▲ Experimentation with and demonstration of land use and land cover mapping at scales of 1:24,000 (fig. 143) and 1:50,000 to determine
1. the level of categorization appropriate for such scales,
2. the kind of land use and land cover data obtainable from different remote sensors which can be used at such scales,
3. the minimum areal extent of a given category suitable for delineation at such scales, and
4. the relationship between data compiled at such scales with data derived from mapping at scales of 1:100,000 and 1:250,000.

▲ Research to determine the possible use of Landsat data in association with higher resolution source materials for Level II land use and land cover mapping requirements to provide
1. suitable remote sensor data for mapping areas such as Alaska, for which other suitable remote sensor data do not exist over extensive areas, and
2. a part of the remote sensor data that will be necessary for a future systematic updating of the land use and land cover maps of the Survey.

▲ Continuing refinement of a geographic information system for handling and disseminating land use and land cover data that will provide
1. graphic display of land use and land cover data either as a total thematic presentation or by separate or varying combinations of categories,
2. opportunity for the users of the digital tapes containing land use and land cover data to generate statistics for other areal units,

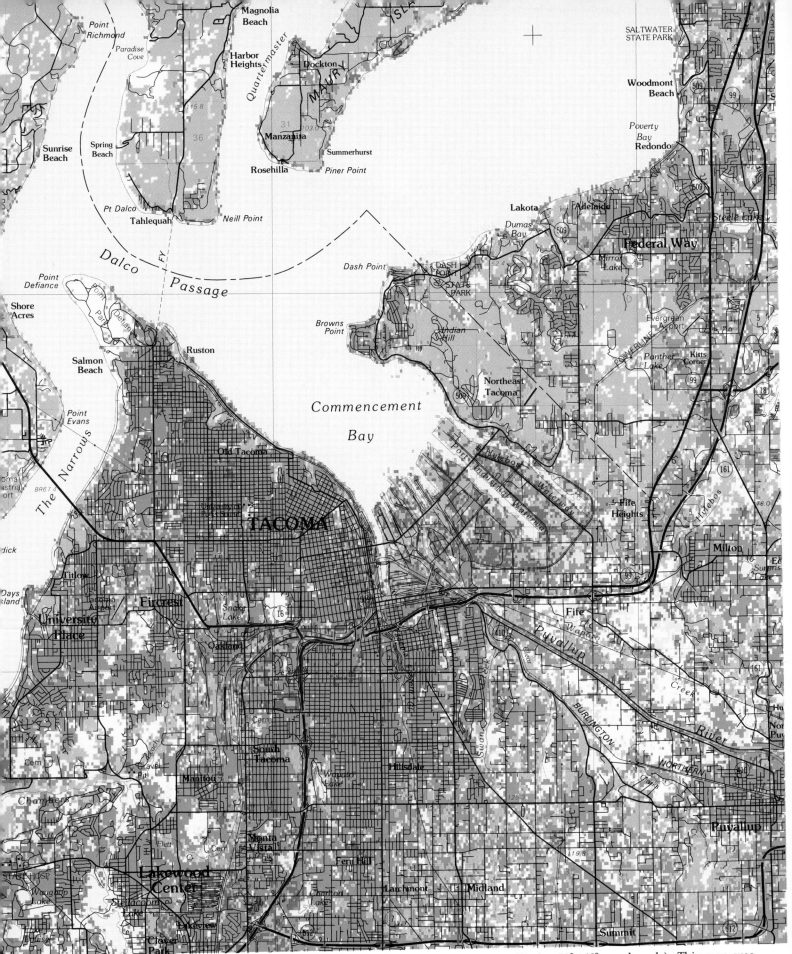

FIGURE 144. Portion of digital land cover map, scale 1:100,000 (Tacoma, Wash., 30°×60° quadrangle). This map was prepared on a large-format laser plotter from satellite data in a digital format, with land use coded in color.

3. land use and land cover statistics for the standard map units being used by the Survey (political units, hydrologic units, census county subdivisions, and areas of Federal land ownership),
4. capability to relate effectively land use and land cover data by use of computers, with other data sets such as soils, topographic, hydrologic, geologic, socioeconomic, and demographic,
5. satisfactory color separation plates for publishing land use and land cover maps in solid color (fig. 144 and p. 235) or with a combination of line patterns and color for selected maps, and
6. preparation of reproducibles (such as negative or positive transparencies) for thematic maps.

▲ Demonstration, analytical, and interpretive studies in which land use and land cover data are being applied to the solution of "real world" problems. Some examples of studies already completed or being carried out are
1. climatology of land use patterns,
2. modeling the effects of land use on the urban temperature field,
3. streamflow characteristics: improved prediction using land use data,
4. shore zone land and land cover,
5. impact of the oil and gas industry on the Louisiana coast,
6. land use and land cover analysis for Chattahoochee River quality assessment,
7. land use impacts of strip mining phosphate in southeastern Idaho, and
8. analysis of selected land use patterns in relation to environmental problems in the Little Rock, Ark., four-county area.

Further information on the status of land use and land cover mapping and the availability of indexes, maps, and data may be obtained from the Chief Geographer, U.S. Geological Survey, Mail Stop 710, Reston, Va. 22092.

Space-Age Maps

Modern science has created new tools that are not only revolutionizing techniques for making maps, but are also giving rise to new types of map products. These new tools include automation techniques, remote sensing technology, and applications of space science.

Automation is the operation of a system or device automatically or by remote control. The key element in recent advances in automated mapping systems is the continuing development of powerful computer techniques and equipment for complex computations, graphic-to-digital or digital-to-graphic transformations, and the ability to process vast amounts of data.

Remote sensing is defined by the American Society of Photogrammetry as the measurement or acquisition of information of some property of an object or phenomenon, by a recording device that is not in physical or intimate contact with the object or phenomenon under study; e.g., the utilization at a distance (as from aircraft, spacecraft, or ship) of any device and its attendant display for gathering information pertinent to the environment, such as measurements of force fields, electromagnetic radiation, or acoustic energy. The technique employs such devices as the camera, lasers, radio-frequency receivers, radar systems, sonar, seismographs, gravimeters, magnetometers, and scintillation counters.

The mushrooming space technology of the 1960's, including projects that brought mankind new information concerning the Earth, Moon, and Mars, demonstrated that monitoring and cataloging Earth's resources from space would be feasible. In 1966, the Secretary of the Interior established the Earth Resources Observation Systems (EROS) Program. The program, administered by the Geological Survey, provides for developing techniques to obtain and analyze remotely sensed data and for promoting the use of these techniques in fulfilling the resource and environmental inventory and management responsibilities of the Department of the Interior. A vital aspect of this program is the production of cartographic products from remotely sensed data obtained via spacecraft (figs. 144, 149–152). Thus, the technologies of automation, remote sensing, and space science have been blended to produce maps and map-related products.

Maps From Satellite Data

EARLY EARTH-ORBITING MISSIONS. Most of the photographs on the early Earth-orbiting missions in the Mercury, Gemini, and Apollo programs (Lowman, 1969) were taken with hand-held cameras using 70-mm roll film and interchangeable lenses of 60-, 80-, and 250-mm focal length. These historic pictures were examined by scientists worldwide, who demonstrated the utility of a synoptic view for geologic, hydrologic, and geographic interpretation; early cartographic applications were meager. A few Gemini frames over Cape Canaveral were shown to contain detail that would be useful in revising existing 1:250,000-scale line maps, and some frames from Apollo 6 over the Dallas-Fort Worth area were measured to determine their cartographic integrity, but not actual maps were made (Doyle, 1975).

In March 1969 the first scientific space photographic experiment was performed on Apollo 9. Four 70-mm cameras with 80-mm lenses were mounted on a metal frame that fit the command module hatch window. Three of the cameras carried black-and-white film appropriately filtered to record the green, red, and near-infrared spectral bands. The fourth camera carried color infrared film. Two frames of the red band covered approximately the area of the standard 1:250,000-scale Phoenix, Ariz., map sheet. These frames were rectified to eliminate the effect of camera tilt and enlarged nearly

10 times by fitting to detail points identified on the map and the photographs. The frames were mosaicked and then printed as an image base for the standard line map. A number of different color schemes were tried, and these versions were produced both with and without contours.

On a standard line map, wherever white paper appears there is no information for that area; but on an image base the terrain morphology, the field patterns, and other land-surface characteristics are shown over the entire area. At the same time, all the information from the conventional line map is also available. The 1969 Phoenix photoimage base disclosed needed corrections to both position and content on the published 1:250,000-scale line maps.

A similar base for a 1:500,000-scale aeronautical chart was prepared from the same photographs. These two projects demonstrated the utility of a space-image base for a conventional line map.

LANDSAT MISSIONS. Landsat 1 (originally named the Earth Resources Technology Satellite, ERTS-1), launched in July 1972, was the first NASA spacecraft designed specifically to record images of the Earth (fig. 145). It carried a three-camera television system known as return beam vidicon (RBV), and a four-channel multispectral scanner (MSS). Because of power switching problems the RBV cameras were turned off after the first few weeks of operation, and virtually all subsequent data were collected by the MSS.

FIGURE 145. Landsat 1.

The MSS has exceeded the most optimistic predictions and has produced thousands of nearly flawless images (McEwen and Schoonmaker, 1975). The image quality is excellent, and the geometric distortions are surprisingly small.

The MSS is a continuous scanning device which creates an adjoining series of scan lines transverse to the orbital direction (fig. 146). The length of a single scan line is 185 km on the ground, and the width is 79 m.

FIGURE 146. Landsat ground coverage pattern. There are 14 revolutions per day; global coverage is obtained in 18 days.

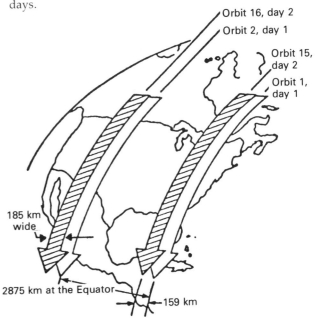

Assembly of sequential scans creates a continuous strip of image data covering 185 km and centered on the ground track. There is no inherent frame sequence for the MSS. An artificial frame is created in converting the MSS data to images on 70-mm film using an electron beam recorder. Each frame is centered on the exposure station previously defined for the RBV and covers 175 km. As the RBV exposure stations are 159 km apart, the MSS frames have an artificial overlap of 16 km. This overlap is not from two separate observations of the same ground area from two exposure stations, as is common with aerial frame-format photographs; it is rather the result of writing some of the MSS scan lines twice, once on each of two adjacent artificial frames. Consequently, the MSS does not have alongtrack stereocapability but does have sidelap stereo where coverage from one orbit sidelaps the adjoining one.

The Geological Survey has defined a series of normal Landsat scenes based on the repetitive coverage of the Landsat ground tracks and framing sequence. The geodetic coordinates of all nominal image centers were obtained from NASA, and a nominal scene was formed by lines drawn midway between the centers as shown in figure 147.

Geological Survey Cartographic Products

FIGURE 147. Landsat nominal scenes.

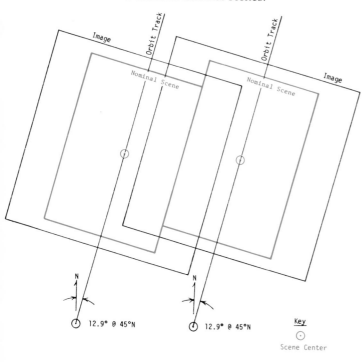

The nominal scenes are areas on the Earth that, if plotted on a map, create a unique set of quadrangular units, or "pigeonholes," for all the Earth covered by Landsat 1. An example for Georgia is shown in figure 148. There is no overlap between nominal scenes and therefore no ambiguity about which scene covers which area. Actual images obtained on the 18-day repeating cycle will generally center on the nominal scene and will overlap adjacent scenes. The amount of image overlap alongtrack is constant as described for the RBV and MSS, but the sidelap between orbits varies with latitude. It is about 13 km at the Equator and 32 km at 40° latitude. The actual drift of the orbit also affects the sidelap between images from different 18-day cycles.

The unique identification code for each nominal scene is based on the geodetic coordinates of the scene center. The 11 characters specify north or south latitude and east or west longitude in degrees and minutes. The system is intelligible to both humans and computers.

LANDSAT IMAGE FORMAT MAPS. The first Landsat image-format map printed in a color lithographic edition was the Lake Tahoe area, Calif.-Nev. (fig. 149). It was prepared by the Survey in September 1972 from a scene acquired on July 25, 1972, two days after launch of Landsat 1.

FIGURE 148. Landsat nominal scenes covering the State of Georgia.

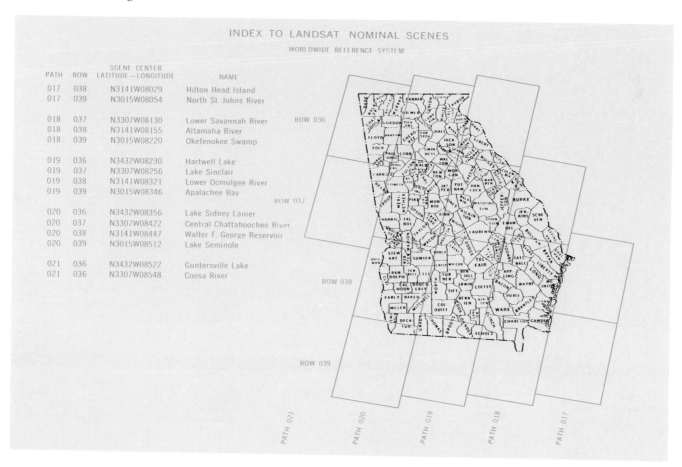

PATH	ROW	SCENE CENTER LATITUDE—LONGITUDE	NAME
017	038	N3141W08029	Hilton Head Island
017	039	N3015W08054	North St. Johns River
018	037	N3307W08130	Lower Savannah River
018	038	N3141W08155	Altamaha River
018	039	N3015W08220	Okefenokee Swamp
019	036	N3432W08230	Hartwell Lake
019	037	N3307W08256	Lake Sinclair
019	038	N3141W08321	Lower Ocmulgee River
019	039	N3015W08346	Apalachee Bay
020	036	N3432W08356	Lake Sidney Lanier
020	037	N3307W08422	Central Chattahoochee River
020	038	N3141W08447	Walter F. George Reservoir
020	039	N3015W08512	Lake Seminole
021	036	N3432W08522	Guntersville Lake
021	036	N3307W08548	Coosa River

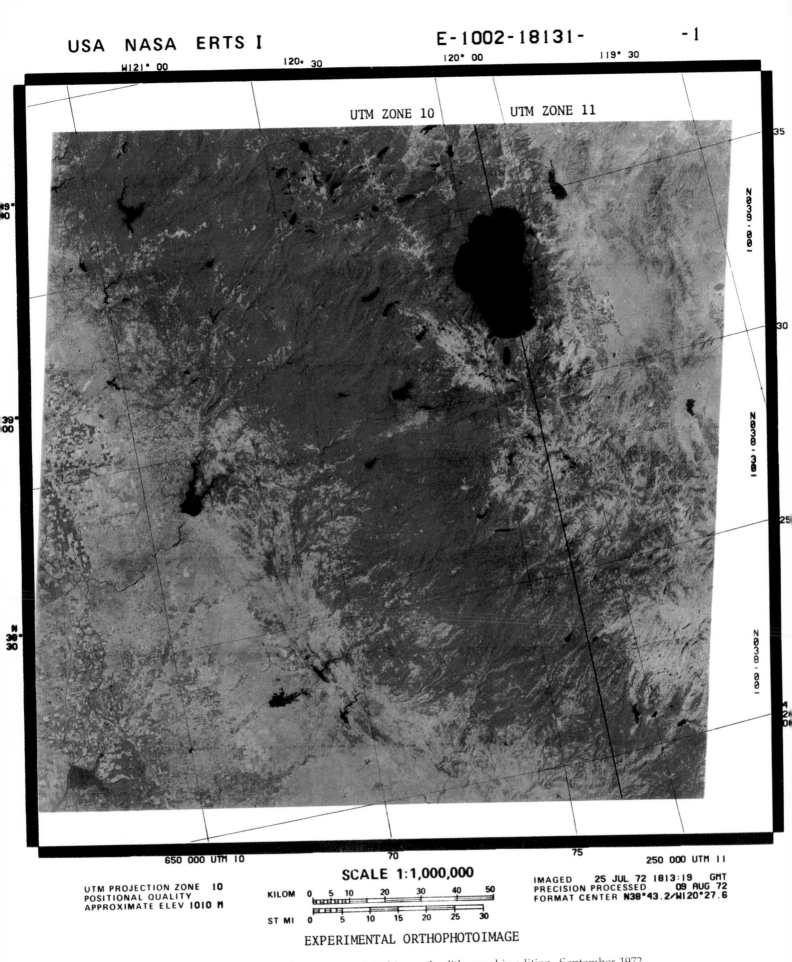

UTM ZONE 10   UTM ZONE 11

SCALE 1:1,000,000

UTM PROJECTION ZONE 10
POSITIONAL QUALITY
APPROXIMATE ELEV 1010 M

KILOM   0   5 10   20   30   40   50

ST MI 0   5   10   15   20   25   30

IMAGED   25 JUL 72 1813:19   GMT
PRECISION PROCESSED   09 AUG 72
FORMAT CENTER N38°43.2/WI20°27.6

EXPERIMENTAL ORTHOPHOTO IMAGE

FIGURE 149. First Landsat image-format map printed in a color lithographic edition, September 1972.

The two immediate advantages of using single Landsat images to define a map series are the inherent register between MSS spectral bands and the elimination of mosaicking between separate images. The system of nominal scenes, previously described, allows a series of Landsat image-format maps to be prepared. Each Landsat image covers 32,375 km² (about the same area as two 1:250,000-scale maps).

A second image-format map, Upper Chesapeake Bay (fig. 150) was printed by the Survey from an image acquired October 11, 1972. It was the first Landsat map with a completely designed and specified cartographic collar (information in map margin). The collar includes a location map in color prepared from portions of the 1:2,000,000-scale plates of the National Atlas. There is also an index to nominal scenes and to the 1:250,000-scale line maps of the area. If possible, an image map should be used in conjunction with a line map.

Other image-format maps are in preparation. Each map is identified by its latitude and longitude code and is given a distinctive name, for example, Upper Chesapeake Bay. The names selected are approved by the Domestic Names Committee of the Board on Geographic Names. Usually major water bodies are favored for a name because they show the greatest contrast and are quickly recognized.

Almost all color composites of Landsat multispectral images have adopted the false-color convention of color-infrared film. Although human vision can differentiate many thousands of color variations, the individual detectors of the eye respond only to three primary colors; all other colors are mixtures of the primary colors for light (not pigment): blue, green, and red. Thus any printed color image must assign the primary colors in some rational way.

Color-infrared film is commonly filtered to exclude the waveband from 0.4 to 0.5 μm that we call blue, and adds an emulsion layer sensitive to the near-infrared waveband (about 0.7–0.8 μm) for which the eye has no sensitivity and experience has assigned no color response. The film has two other layers sensitive to the wavebands 0.5–0.6 μm and 0.6–0.7 μm which we normally call green and red. However, the dye color introduced into the layers provides a color shift from green to blue, red to green, and infrared (invisible, no color) to red.

This conventional assignment of false colors was not haphazard but rather for the special purpose of camouflage detection during World War II. Increasing civilian use of the film has preserved the color convention for several major reasons:

Δ Healthy vegetation appears in shades of red and contrasts with unhealthy vegetation appearing blue-green.

Δ Water appears dark blue or black unless sediment laden, in which case it takes on a light blue tone.

Δ Most cultural features appear as a steely blue-gray.

The experience of many image interpreters has shown that the convention described provides the best separation of the major themes of vegetation, water, and culture. Other false-color combinations are possible and may have practical or esthetic advantages in special situations. However, the evidence for the conventional false-color rendition is well established for general ease of image interpretation. For example, vegetation, or the lack of it, which is the predominant theme on any Earth scene, is assigned a color variation between red and blue-green.

The MSS on Landsat senses four spectral bands:

| Band 4 | 0.5–0.6 μm | Band 6 | 0.7–0.8 μm |
| Band 5 | 0.6–0.7 μm | Band 7 | 0.8–1.1 μm |

(Bands 1, 2, and 3 designate the visible light bands of the three RBV cameras which were inoperative on Landsat 1.) MSS bands 4, 5, and 6 correspond to the three emulsion layers on color-infrared film. Band 7 extends further into the infrared wavelengths and provides a high-contrast image between water and vegetation. Most Landsat false-color composites have used bands 4, 5, and 7, with band 4 depicted in blue, band 5 depicted in green, and band 7 depicted in red.

The Upper Chesapeake Bay image-format map was printed according to the false-color combination just described.

LANDSAT MAP MOSAICS. The first printed color Landsat map incorporating more than one image was the image mosaic covering the state of New Jersey (fig. 151). It was assembled from three images of a single orbit, acquired on October 10, 1972 (the day before the orbit that produced the images used for Upper Chesapeake Bay). The New Jersey image mosaic illustrates the condition where a large area enjoying several days of clear weather can be completely imaged if the orbital cycle coincides. The joining of the images was aided by the continuous scan pattern of the MSS along the orbit. (Because of the effect of earth rotation during the scanning, the production of an extensive continuous-strip image on one piece of film is not feasible. The practical solution to this problem is the creation of artificial frames by the electron beam recorder which converts MSS data to images; these frames can readily be mosaicked.)

After the first successful use of film mosaicking for color-image maps, the Survey published a Landsat mosaic of Florida (fig. 152). This presented new cartographic problems, not the least of which is the fact that the Florida State boundaries extend across seven Landsat orbits. Further inspection showed that at least 16 nominal scenes contained part of Florida; one is over the Dry Tortugas, 75 miles west of Key West. Although southern Florida has a nonseasonal vegetation pattern,

FIGURE 150. Portion of Upper Chesapeake Bay 1:500,000-scale image-format map. Improved techniques in printing from the original Landsat imagery acquired October 11, 1972, have resulted in successively better versions of this map.

174

UNITED STATES
DEPARTMENT OF THE INTERIOR
GEOLOGICAL SURVEY

NEW JERSEY

NASA ERTS-1
SATELLITE IMAGE MOSAIC

SCALE 1:500,000
1 centimeter equals 5 kilometers

FOR SALE BY U. S. GEOLOGICAL SURVEY, RESTON, VIRGINIA 22092. PRICE $1.25

NEW JERSEY
SATELLITE IMAGE MOSAIC
1972

FIGURE 151. Satellite image mosaic of New Jersey, assembled from three images of a single Landsat orbit. This mosaic, originally prepared at a scale of 1:500,000, is shown here at a scale of approximately 1:1,700,000.

FIGURE 152. Satellite image mosaic of Florida, with the panhandle shown as an inset. This mosaic, originally prepared at a scale of 1:500,000, is shown here at a scale of approximately 1:3,000,000.

Geological Survey Cartographic Products

the northern panhandle has seasonal agriculture and deciduous forests to compound the difficulty of tone matching winter and summer images.

Although two or three Landsat images may be successfully enlarged and mosaicked into a map simply by applying a scale factor, the assembly of groups of images demands a geodetic control network. The Florida mosaic was controlled photogrammetrically with a planimetric block adjustment to UTM coordinate values. Due to width limitations of the printing press, the panhandle must be printed as an inset, and it was decided to control images in each zone separately.

The legend for the Florida mosaic, carefully designed to serve as a guide for other State mosaics, includes nominal scenes, the images used, and the index of existing 1:250,000-scale line maps. The text of the legend explains some of the characteristics of Landsat and the image features (fig. 152). A fitted UTM grid is on the Florida mosaic and on the separate image-format maps.

All the individual image-format maps (fig. 153) of Florida can be prepared as a byproduct of the mosaic. After each image is enlarged to the proper size by fitting it to control, an extra copy is prepared and screened. These copies are individually mounted in image-format collars with text, National Atlas inserts, and appropriate coordinates. Because the image-format area is a standard size, the cartographic collars can be prepared independently of the images, and can be inserted and gridded when available.

Mapping with Landsat and other satellite data is still in its infancy (Colvocoresses, 1975). Landsat 2 was launched January 22, 1975, and Landsat 3 was launched March 5, 1978. The return-beam vidicon (RBV) camera system on Landsat 3, which is significantly different from the RBV systems on the previous Landsats, works very well; figure 154 reproduces a photograph of the Cape Canaveral area received from the Landsat 3 RBV camera.

SKYLAB EXPERIMENTS. The three manned Skylab missions (Doyle, 1975) provided an opportunity to recover original photographic film from orbit. The Earth Resources Experiment Package (EREP) on Skylab contained three imaging systems. The first was a six-camera system, identified as S-190A, designed for experimentation in the multispectral approach to identification of terrain features, at higher resolution than is provided by Landsat. A black-and-white mosaic of four frames from band 5 (0.6 to 0.6 μm) was assembled at 1:250,000 scale as an image base for the Hartford, Conn., quadrangle. The S-190A photographs show most map-worthy features, but in general the resolution is inadequate for land use classification.

The second photographic experiment on Skylab utilized a long-focal-length camera known as S-190B. Sev-eral different films were used at different times, but most of the pictures were taken with color or color infrared film. The coverage for S-190B was similar to that for S-190A, except that the ground track was narrower and only one kind of film could be used at a time.

The third system in EREP consisted of a conical MSS (S-192) with 13 channels. This system has advantages in simplicity, but it had an image-recording disadvantage that resulted in degraded resolution and geometry.

In addition to the three imaging systems described above (S-190A, S-190B, and S-192), EREP carried three non-imaging sensing systems. These consisted of S-191 (infrared spectrometer), S-193 (microwave radiometer, scatterometer, and altimeter), and S-194 (L-band radiometer).

Experiments in the use of Skylab imagery for thematic mapping, specifically to develop a photographic procedure for extracting themes of cartographic interest were carried out in 1975 with some useful results. Photomechanical isolation techniques were used with black-and-white film to extract themes from S-190A, S-190B, and S-192 images. The Skylab theme extractions for open water, infrared-reflective vegetation, and woodland (fig. 155) are useful in themselves and also proved suitable for use as color separates for printing the Hartford, Conn., N.Y., N.J., Mass., 1:250,000-scale photomap (fig. 156).

Skylab completed its mission after 171 days of manned operation in 1973–74. The vehicle reentered Earth's atmosphere in 1979.

Maps of the Moon and Planets

In 1960, the Geological Survey established an astrogeology program on behalf of NASA to support lunar and planetary exploration. One of the primary activities of the program is the systematic mapping of the stratigraphy and structure of the Moon, Mars, and Mercury.

LUNAR MAPS. In July 1969, the Lunar Excursion Module Eagle settled to a landing on the Sea of Tranquility, and mankind first set foot on another celestial body. The site had been selected and mapped photogrammetrically by the Geological Survey with two satellite programs (McEwen and Tyler, 1972). The first was the Lunar Orbiter (fig. 157A) program, from which a series of photographs were obtained. In the second program, appropriately called Surveyor, sequences of pictures were taken from several satellites that softlanded on the Moon. In both programs, the images were transmitted and reconstructed in film format on Earth.

The Lunar Orbiter and Surveyor programs produced thousands of photographs for photomosaics and landing zone charts. They supported the successful lunar landings of the Apollo program, including the historic *Eagle* landing in 1969 (fig. 157B, p. 183).

FIGURE 153. Portion of satellite image map, Florida Keys, Fla.; scale 1:500,000.

14MAR78 C N28-00/W080-41 D016-041 N N27-20/W080-17 RA   DXCI SUN EL44 A125 S2S- P-N L2 NASA LANDSAT E-30009-15095-A

FIGURE 154. RBV (return beam vidicon) image of Cape Canaveral, Fla., received from Landsat 3, launched March 5, 1978, orbital altitude 919 km.

FIGURE 155. Woodland theme extraction from Skylab imagery covering Hartford 1:250,000-scale quadrangle; shown here at scale of approximately 1:650,000.

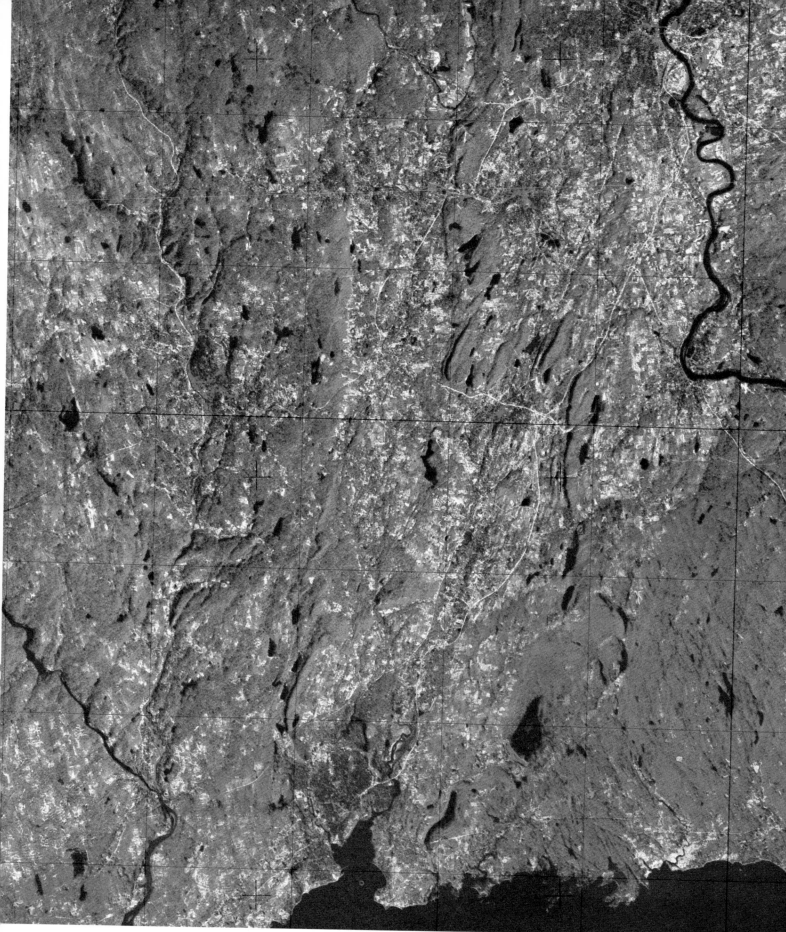

FIGURE 156. Portion of Skylab satellite photomap, 1:250,000-scale series. (Hartford, Conn., N.Y., N.J., Mass., quadrangle.)

FIGURE 157*A.* The lunar orbiters were designed to obtain data from various orbital paths. Flown at different altitudes, they provided picture coverage of almost the entire surface of the Moon. These photographs were the primary means of selecting landing sites for manned missions. (*See also* lunar topophotomap, fig. 170.)

Geological Survey Cartographic Products

FIGURE 157B. Footprints on the Sea of Tranquility. Apollo 11 astronaut "Buzz" Aldrin walks on the Moon near a footpad of *Eagle*.

The cameras carried on the Lunar Orbiter and Surveyor missions were not specifically intended for cartographic purposes, and many photographs could be used only for their pictorial value. Starting with the Apollo 15 mission, the spacecraft have carried an increased payload with better cameras and lunar staytime capability (see fig. 170 in chapter 8), thereby providing improved photography for subsequent lunar mapping, an essential requirement for basic research on the nature and geologic history of the Moon.

MARTIAN MAPS. The Mariner 9 spacecraft was launched in 1971 and placed in orbit around Mars in September of that year. A primary objective of the mission was to map the topography and geology of Mars as a part of the sequence of events leading to the unmanned Viking spacecraft landing on Mars in 1976 (fig. 158). At least 70 percent of the Martian surface was scheduled for mapping at a scale of 1:5,000,000, and it may be possible to prepare partial maps of Phobos and Deimos, the two moons of Mars.

FIGURE 158. Portion of panoramic view of the surface of Mars taken with electro-optical camera minutes after Viking I landed on July 20, 1976. The camera scanned the surface vertically and sent electronic signals 220,000,000 miles to Earth.

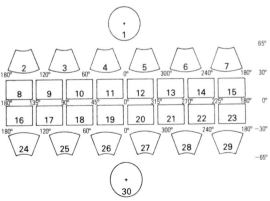

FIGURE 159. Map layout for 1:5,000,000-scale mapping of Mars.

An arrangement of 30 maps at the 1:5,000,000 scale was selected (fig. 159). Each map is rendered in shaded relief by airbrush. Topographic information is developed from spot heights measured by radar and tracking data together with photogrammetric plotting from a few convergent stereoimages, which allows the display of some contour lines. Figure 160 shows a portion of a Mars map.

SATURN AND BEYOND. In 1980, Voyager 1 passed Saturn after a journey of more than 940 million miles and sent back a bountiful harvest of remarkable images of that planet (fig. 161).

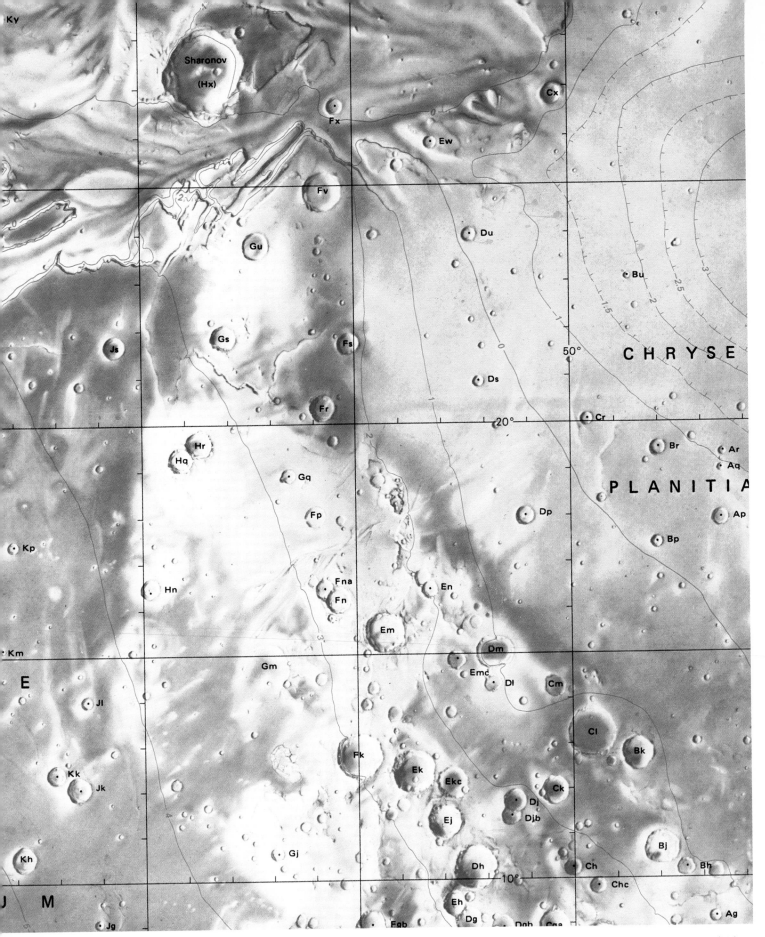

FIGURE 160. Portion of topographic map of the Lunae Paulis quadrangle of Mars. Scale 1:5,000,000; contour interval 1 km.

FIGURE 161. Cartography in future exploration of the Universe. Spectacular new achievements in the exploration of space provide a fertile field for application of cartographic science to the gathering of important information concerning extra-terrestrial bodies. This photograph of Saturn was acquired by the Voyager I spacecraft on October 5, 1980, from a distance of 1.5 billion kilometers (940 million miles) from Earth and less than 6 weeks away from its November 12, 1980, closest approach to Saturn. Closer photographs showing smaller areas in more detail can be used for mapping the planet.

Automated Theme Extraction

To conduct a complete remote-sensing program, it is necessary to process the remotely sensed data by some means which isolates and extracts the particular resource data (theme) desired. EROS draws heavily upon Earth imagery obtained from the Landsat and Skylab space flights, which use multispectral imagery, wherein each scene is subdivided into three or more separate frequency bands by means of filters, gratings, or other devices. Each spectral band portrays a selected theme as a slightly different hue or density relative to other components of the scene. A particular hue or density band can be isolated or enhanced by color-filtering and density-slicing techniques.

To isolate and extract a specific theme, it must possess a unique spectral signature or autograph (Smith, 1973) by which it can be readily identified. Four gross themes under active study are open water, vegetation, ice-snow cover, and concentrated works of man.

The isolated theme data are customarily stored in the form of easily reproducible two-level or binary graphic extractions, usually as a photographic transparency or color-foil overlay. Figure 162 shows a Landsat MSS image of a section of southern Maryland and northern Virginia. Figure 163A is the open-water theme graphic, and figure 163B is the infrared-reflective vegetation graphic derived from this scene. Other graphics derived from this scene show forested areas, fields and grassland, urban areas and swamps, high-density urban and suburban areas, and concrete surfaces and bare ground.

FIGURE 162. Landsat MSS (multispectral scanner) scene, portion of southern Maryland and northern Virginia.

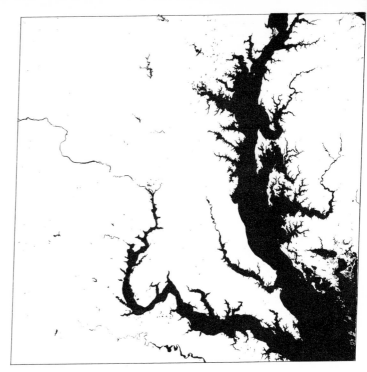

FIGURE 163A. Open-water theme graphic.

FIGURE 163B. Infrared-reflective vegetation theme graphic.

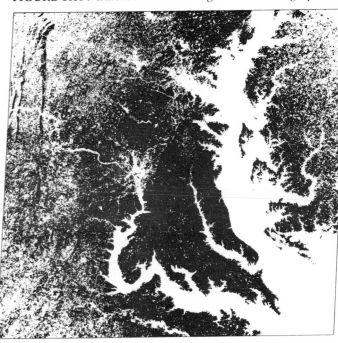

Theme graphics of appropriate scale and fitted with an appropriate reference grid are cartographic products usable in many applications. They can be used to assess snow packs in otherwise arid regions, to track and document some types of pollution, and to monitor the creep of urban sprawl. Many other distinct themes that can be isolated are of direct economic benefit in analyzing land use.

Digital Cartographic Data

It would not be unreasonable to estimate that the average Geological Survey topographic quadrangle map contains over 100 million separate bits of information. While maps are extremely efficient devices for the storage of spatially associated data, even more information about an area, together with positional coordinates, can be stored in computer systems.

A major advantage of cartographic data in digital form is the convenient interface with other geographically related information and management systems. Such interfaces provide a means for machine-readable data to be used in complex modeling and problem analysis. Examples of the types of data in various systems are positions and elevations of manmade or natural features, transportation routes, lakes, streams, shorelines, terrain slopes, land use, cadastral and political boundaries, population distribution, soils, geology, and hydrology. When these data are digitized, the end product can be in a variety of forms and at any scale.

Digital data can be manipulated rapidly to produce maps at different scales or projections and with selected contents. In the past, cartographers have mapped specific areas of interest at a scale commensurate with the units in use that best satisfied the average map user requirement. The level of content was limited by the scale selected. Past technology has also assumed that the end product is to be a hard copy at a single scale with limited and generalized content.

Map users often find it necessary to produce their own maps because of their need for specific content or particular scale. Of course the scale of the general map can be changed by using a copy camera, but the content must be treated separately and manually. These analog processes are sometimes expensive and are limited by optical or mechanical constraints. Today, digital techniques in cartography can be applied to develop new and different forms of presentation.

Maintaining existing maps is often just as important as compiling new maps. Several methods for revising maps are in use today, each requiring review of recent source material and manual cartographic procedures. Automated processes using the digital computer are seen as the means of map revision in the future. In digital form, cartographic information can be updated continuously from reliable sources, permitting current graphical display on a truly timely basis.

1:250,000-Scale Map Data

The Survey has acquired the bulk of the digital terrain tapes of the contiguous United States which were developed by the Defense Mapping Agency. These tapes are composed of a latticework of elevation points digitized from 1:250,000-scale topographic quadrangle maps. The tapes have broad applications for the study of difficult terrain and land management problems by direct computer processing. The 1:250,000-scale maps from which the tapes were compiled usually cover 1 degree of latitude by 2 degrees of longitude; two 1-degree grids were prepared during the original digitizing of each quadrangle. These tapes are now available for most of the United States, including Alaska, in the new *DMA standard format:* 1-degree by 1-degree blocks with data points at 3-second latitude-longitude spacing.

An index and complete ordering information for the 1:250,000 digital data are available from the User Services Section, National Cartographic Information Center (NCIC). (See "Cartographic Information Sources," p. 216–218.) As this data bank consists only of elevation data derived from small-scale (1:250,000) maps having a large contour interval (100 or 200 feet), its usefulness is limited to applications wherein the requirement is for only approximate elevation information.

Types of Data

The National Mapping Program of the Survey has as one of its primary missions the development of a digital cartographic data base (McEwen, 1980) that initially will contain 11 types of base map data:

1. Reference systems—geographic and other coordinate systems except the public land survey network.

2. Hypsography—contours, elevations, and slopes.

3. Hydrography—streams and rivers, lakes and ponds, wetlands, reservoirs, and shorelines.

4. Surface cover—woodland, orchards, vineyards.

5. Nonvegetative features—lava rock, playas, dunes, slide rock, barren waste areas.

6. Boundaries—portrayal of political jurisdictions, national parks and forests, military reservations. This category does not fully set forth land ownership or use.

7. Transportation systems—roads, railroads, trails, canals, pipelines, transmission lines, bridges, tunnels.

8. Other significant manmade structures such as buildings, airports, and dams.

9. Identification and portrayal of geodetic control, survey monuments, other survey markers, and landmark structures and objects.

10. Geographic names.

11. Orthophotographic imagery.

In 1975, a preliminary proposal for a digital cartographic data base was prepared and sent to numerous interested Federal and State agencies along with a questionnaire. The proposal defined the base data categories listed above and described a pilot data base consisting of five categories: county and State boundaries, public land survey system (not included in the list of base data categories), surface hydrography, terrain surface elevation, and transportation systems. Analysis of the returned questionnaires revealed that most users requested data compatible with 1:24,000-scale map content and accuracy. The most frequently requested categories of data were the same as those in the proposal.

In 1977, the Survey formed a Digital Applications Team to conduct digitizing research projects, to refine the data base description, and to define system alternatives for the National Mapping Program. Research conducted by this team resulted in the identification of strengths and weaknesses of available hardware and software for actual digitizing operations . It also resulted in the development of data structures and storage formats for planimetric and elevation data as well as procedures for encoding planimetric networks.

Digital Cartographic Data Files

Digital cartographic data files may be grouped into two basic forms. The first form is a Digital Elevation Model (DEM) and consists of a sampled array of elevations for a number of ground positions that are usually, but not always, at regularly spaced intervals. The second form, a Digital Line Graph (DLG), is line map information in digital form and includes information on planimetric base categories such as transportation, hydrography, and boundaries.

The DEM files may be built from a number of data sources, such as contour plates, profiles or terrain models scanned in stereo photogrammetric equipment, or digitizing orthophoto equipment. A DEM may be classified at one of three levels depending on editing, enhancement, and spatial structuring:

DEM-1. A network of raw elevation data that have only been edited for gross blunders and have not been keyed to planimetry.

DEM-2. Elevation data that have been smoothed for consistency, enhanced to remove noise, and filtered to reduce data volume. The data have not been keyed to planimetry.

DEM-3. Elevation data that have been edited and modified to be consistent with planimetric features, such as streams, roads, and shorelines.

The DLG files may be formed from a number of data sources, such as stable-based map separates or stereomodels in digitized photogrammetric equipment; manual or automated digitizing may be used. A DLG may also be classified at one of three levels depending on editing, enhancement, and spatial structuring:

DLG-1. Line map information that has been collected and coded to prescribed standards and edited to remove data acquisition blunders.

DLG-2. Line map information that has been edited to add additional attribute codes and to remove visible errors and inconsistencies.

DLG-3. DLG-2 information that has been spatially structured to define all topological relations.

National Digital Cartographic Data Base

In 1980, a National Digital Cartographic Data Base (NDCDB) was established with the object of providing a wide range of cartographic data in computer-compatible form. Major priorities were assigned by the Survey to five base categories of data for which it has production capability. These are (1) digital elevation models (fig. 164), (2) public land net, (3) boundaries, (4) hydrography, and (5) transportation.

By the end of 1980, NDCDB contained digital elevation data for some 4,000 7.5-minute quadrangles and boundary and land net data for about 2,000 quadrangles. In addition, plans were underway to include both the land use/land cover data prepared on a 1:250,000-scale base and the National Atlas base maps being digitized at 1:2,000,000 scale for the entire country. The elevation data prepared by DMA was in process of being reformatted and edited by DMA for entry in the NDCDB. The Survey has concluded an agreement with the National Bureau of Standards to standardize the computer representation of data elements in the earth sciences.

Most of the present and near-term digital data production will be from aerial photographs or from relatively simple planimetric map layers. Any extensive program to convert the more complex planimetric layers or the contours from the 40,000 published maps to digital form must await the development of an automated map digitizing system, now expected about 1982.

FIGURE 164. Mount St. Helens, Washington, before (upper drawing) and after (lower drawing) the eruption of May 18, 1980. These 3-D perspective views, as seen from the northeast, were produced from digital elevation models by USGS.

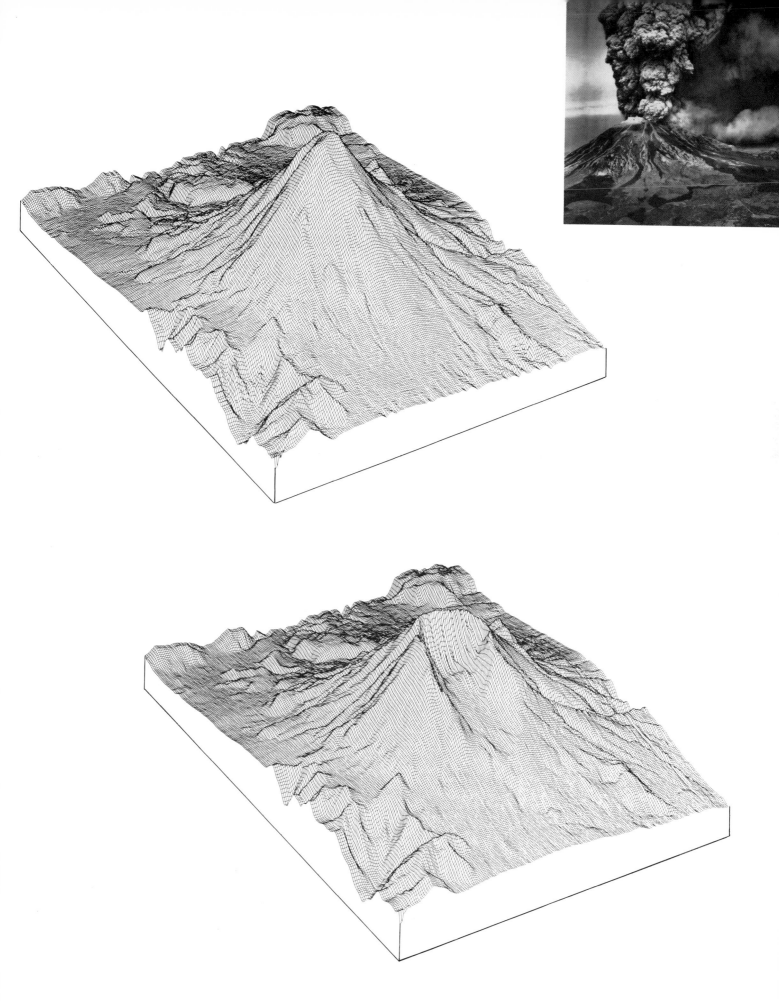

8:

Maps from Other Agencies

Major producers of maps include the National Ocean Survey, the Defense Mapping Agency, the U.S. Army Corps of Engineers, the Tennessee Valley Authority, the U.S. Department of Agriculture, the National Park Service, the Bureau of Land Management, the Department of Transportation, the Bureau of the Census, State and local agencies, and commercial and geographical organizations.

In discussing general mapping principles, we have described the cartographic products of the Geological Survey. These products form but a part of the entire production of maps for America, however, and a comprehension of the role of Geological Survey maps in the spectrum of American cartography can be obtained only if other mapping programs are recognized. These other programs complement, supplement, and intertwine with the Geological Survey program; they are, in general, equally important, and their products are of high quality.

Some of the other programs merit a detailed treatment, but that treatment is left to those intimately concerned with the respective programs. Here, we will be limited to general descriptions, sufficient to provide a background for understanding Geological Survey maps.

National Ocean Survey

The National Ocean Survey (NOS; formerly Coast and Geodetic Survey), an agency of the National Oceanic and Atmospheric Administration, Department of Commerce, is responsible for producing cartographic information in three principal categories: nautical charts, aeronautical charts, and geodetic data (Powell, 1976).

Nautical Charts

The NOS nautical charting program consists of nine categories of charts and publications, with a production of over 2 million copies annually.

1. Sailing charts with scales smaller than 1:600,000 are used for planning and navigation in open coastal waters and between ports.

2. General charts with scales from 1:150,000 to 1:600,000 are designed for visual and radar navigation offshore using landmarks.

3. Coastal charts (fig. 165) with scales from 1:50,000 to 1:150,000 are for navigation nearshore, in harbors, in bays, and in inland waters. These are the most widely used nautical charts.

4. Harbor charts (fig. 166) with scales larger than 1:50,000 are for navigation in harbors and smaller waterways, and for anchorage.

5. Small-craft charts with scales from 1:10,000 to 1:80,000 include specific information pertinent to small-craft operators. They show a great variety of information, such as tide and current data, marina and anchorage facilities, and courses. These charts are published in several different formats for convenience in handling on small boats.

6. Coast pilots and Great Lakes pilots are published in nine volumes to provide detailed navigation information which cannot be conveniently shown on charts, such as radio service, weather service, port data, sailing directions, and natural features.

7. Nautical chart catalogs (see "Cartographic Information Sources," p. 219) are issued as required to show all of the nearly 1,000 charts of various types available for coastal waters of the United States, Puerto Rico, the Virgin Islands, Hawaii, Guam, Samoa, and the Great Lakes; *Dates of Latest Editions of Nautical Charts* is a separate publication.

8. Special maps and data, byproducts of the nautical charting program that are generally for nonnavigational uses, include topographic surveys and planimetric shoreline maps, aerial photographs, hydrographic smooth sheets, graphic depth records, descriptive reports of surveys, and sedimentology sample data.

9. Notice to Mariners is a pamphlet issued weekly by the Defense Mapping Agency in cooperation with NOS, the Coast Guard, and the Corps of Engineers to keep mariners advised of new publications and information on marine safety.

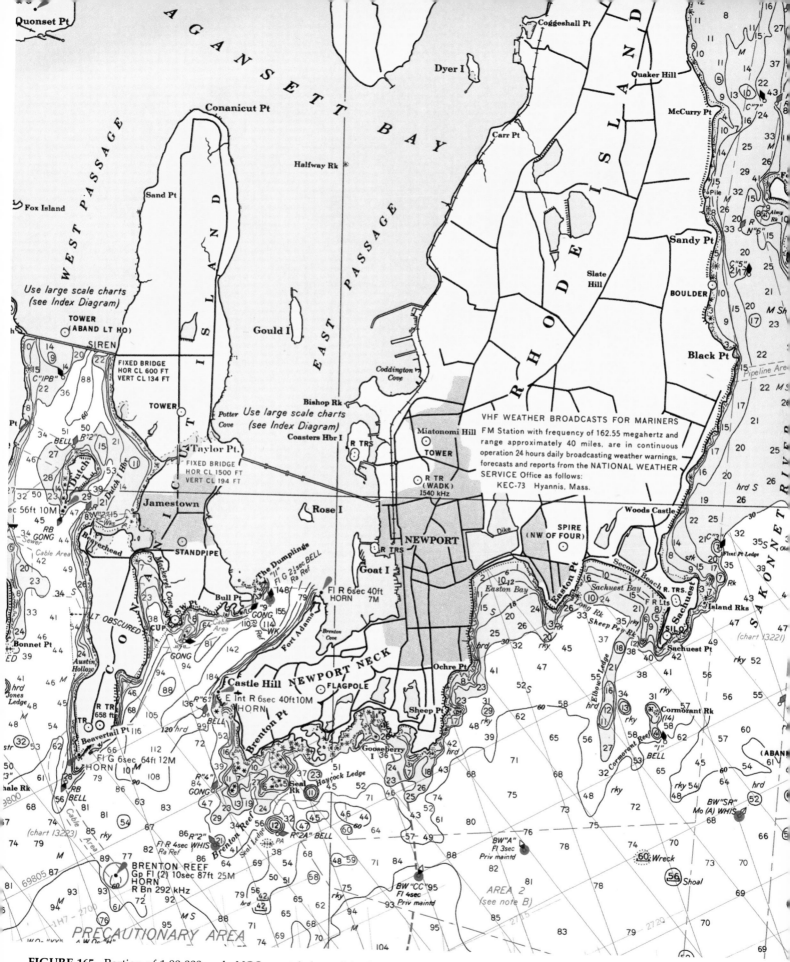

FIGURE 165. Portion of 1:80,000-scale NOS coastal chart. (Martha's Vineyard to Block Island, No. 13218, July 17, 1976.)

National Ocean Survey

191

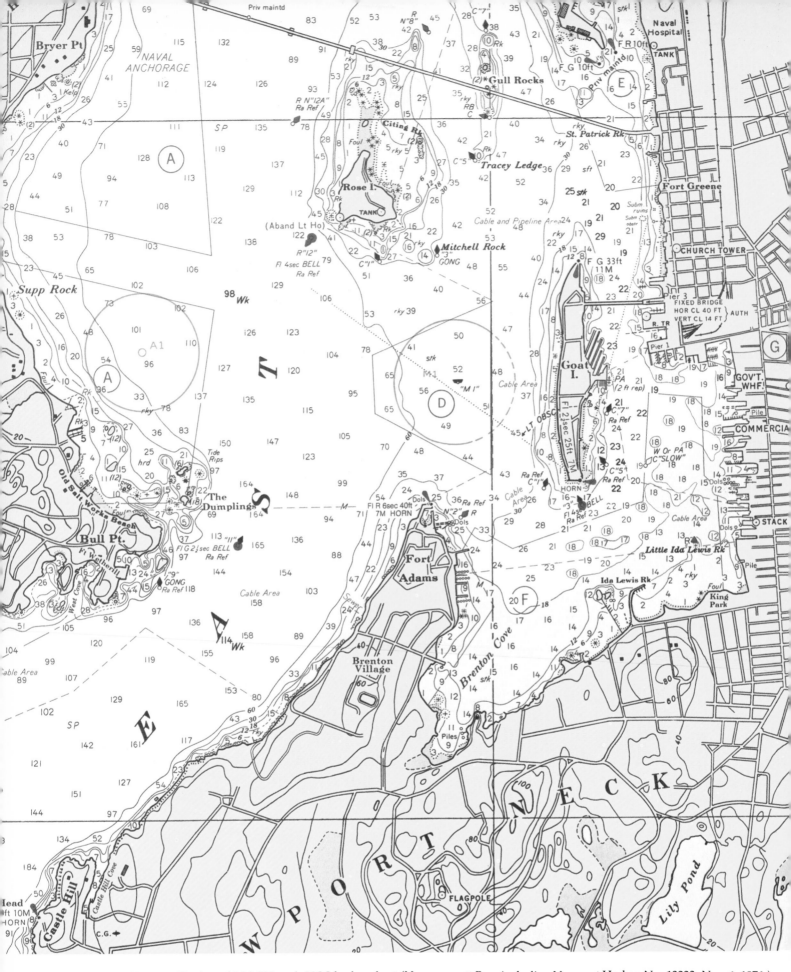

FIGURE 166. Portion of 1:20,000-scale NOS harbor chart.(Narragansett Bay, including Newport Harbor, No. 13223, Nov. 6, 1976.)

Maps from Other Agencies

In July 1974 NOS started using a new numbering system for its nautical charts. Developed in cooperation with the Defense Mapping Agency Hydrographic Center, the new system provides a uniform worldwide system for identifying nautical charts. The area of coverage and chart numbers for each of the nine regions of the world included in the system are given on **page 225.**

For greater efficiency in producing the *Notice to Mariners* documents, data are formatted for computer input and output and are listed according to chart number and geographical location. NOS archives data from more than 9,500 hydrographic surveys covering the 2.5-million mi² area for which it is responsible.

In terms of new charts and chart revisions, the average annual production is from 6 to 20 new charts, and about 500 revised and reprinted charts.

Aeronautical Charts

Passage of the Air Commerce Act in 1926 gave the Department of Commerce, among other duties, the authority and responsibility to produce and publish charts of the Nation's airways. The first aeronautical chart, published in 1927, was in strip form and covered the air route from Kansas City to Moline, Ill. This early chart portrayed prominent topographic features for contact (visual) flying, and the newly installed airport lighted beacons for night flights. The strip chart concept was extended to other lighted air routes between the major air terminals until about 1930, when it became evident that area charts were needed to provide complete coverage. A series of sectional charts was then developed to cover the entire United States; these are the basic charts for contact flying.

With the advent of radio navigation aids, all-weather flying, air traffic control, and more aircraft operating at faster speeds and higher altitudes, new types of charts were required. The result was two categories of charts—for visual flying and for instrument navigation. (See catalog lists in the chapter, "Cartographic Information Sources.") Visual aeronautical charts now published include 2 planning charts, issued every 4 months; 54 sectional charts, with the majority issued every 6 months and others annually; 21 terminal control area charts, issued every 6 months; 26 world aeronautical charts, issued annually; 1 helicopter chart for the Los Angeles area, issued annually; and 1 local chart for Puerto Rico and the Virgin Islands, issued annually (fig. 167).

Instrument aeronautical charts now published include 20 radio facility en route charts, issued every 56 days; 2 high-altitude en route charts and 5 high-altitude navigation charts, issued every 56 days; 1 standard terminal arrival route volume, issued every 56 days; 1 Alaska terminal volume, issued every 56 days; over 4,000 instrument approach procedures plus supplementary data and 200 taxi charts, issued as required; 7 aircraft position charts, issued every 6 months; 1 Alaska supplement, issued every 56 days; 1 Pacific supplement, issued every 56 days; and 2 standard instrument departure volumes issued every 56 days.

Geodetic Data

NOS is authorized to conduct all phases of geodetic surveying and related data. It also has the lead role in integrating all geodetic control surveys into a unified national system. An interagency agreement between the Geological Survey and the National Oceanic and Atmospheric Administration (NOAA) regarding geodetic data management was signed on June 13, 1974. The agreement covers policies and procedures for the exchange, maintenance, and dissemination of geodetic control data and the maintenance of geodetic indexes. Within NOAA the functions are handled by the National Geodetic Information Center (NGIC); within the Geological Survey, by the National Cartographic Information Center (NCIC). The intent of the agreement is to provide for the transfer of all Geological Survey control data to NGIC, and to clarify responsibilities and establish a communication link between NGIC and NCIC so that anyone seeking maps and aerial photographs at NCIC offices can also select and order geodetic control data.

Geodetic control data relate to marked recoverable points whose latitude, longitude, and (or) elevation above sea level are known to a high accuracy. These data are presently available in published lists (figs. 168 and 169) consisting of the geodetic position, elevations, and descriptions of marked, recoverable control points that are part of or are connected to the national horizontal or vertical control networks (see appendix, p. 244). NGIC has undertaken a program to digitize its lists.

The major responsibilities under the agreement are as follows:

Δ   NCIC provides a geodetic data-ordering service to assist users who query NCIC, in accordance with the provision of this agreement.

Δ   All available geodetic control data of the Geological Survey are transferred to NGIC in digital form.

Δ   NOS adjusts into the national networks all new Geological Survey second- or third-order monumented surveys and adds the results to the National Geodetic Control File.

Δ   NOS is responsible for the maintenance of the Geological Survey geodetic control data, once they are placed in the National Geodetic Control File, and applies datum shifts when needed and makes corrections as given on recovery notes.

Other Cartographic Products

In cooperation with the National Weather Service, NOS produces a series of storm evacuation maps covering the Atlantic and Gulf coasts. In 1975, second editions of six previously issued maps of the Galveston-Houston, Tex., area were published to show land subsidence up to 1973.

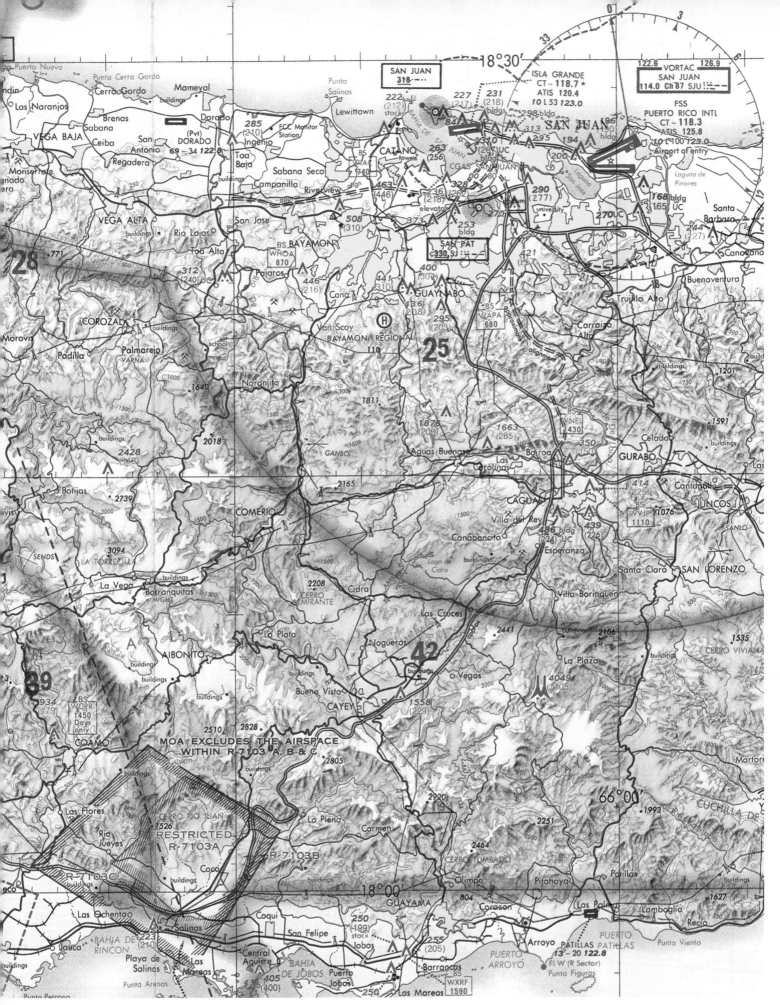

FIGURE 167. Portion of NOS 1:250,000-scale local aeronautical
chart. (Puerto Rico-Virgin Islands, Nov. 30, 1978.)

FIGURE 168. Horizontal control data for station Johanna, Monroe County, Ill.

DECEMBER 1960
U.S. DEPARTMENT OF COMMERCE
ENVIRONMENTAL SCIENCE SERVICES ADMINISTRATION
COAST AND GEODETIC SURVEY

HORIZONTAL CONTROL DATA
by the
Coast and Geodetic Survey
NORTH AMERICAN 1927 DATUM

QUAD 380902 STATION 1013
ILL-MO
LATITUDE 38°00' TO 38°30'
LONGITUDE 90°00' TO 90°30'
DIAGRAM NJ 15-6 SAINT LOUIS

Johanna (Monroe County, Ill., H. W. Hemple, 1931).—In yard of the Johanna Church, about 4½ miles, airline, west of Waterloo, in W½ sec. 29, T. 2 S., R. 10 W., 14 meters (46 feet) south of southwest corner of church, 16 meters (52 feet) southwest of southeast corner, and 17 meters (56 feet) north of south fork in road which forms south angle of triangle. To reach from Waterloo, go west 2.5 miles on Route 156 to dirt road on right marked "Camp Vandeventer 2 mi.", follow this road one-fourth mile to fork, take left fork 0.3 mile to another fork, keep left, and continue 1.8 miles to Johanna Church. Surface and underground marks are standard station disks in concrete, notes 1 (a) and 7 (a). Reference marks are standard reference disks in concrete, note 11 (a). No. 1 is 1 foot south of fence, 5 meters (16 feet) north of road, 11 meters (36 feet) west of southeast corner of cemetery near church, and approximately 400 meters (1,312 feet) from station in azimuth 237°13'10". No. 2 is about 1 foot south of southwest corner of church, and 14.06 meters (46.1 feet) from station in azimuth 145°46'. United States Geological Survey bench mark, brass capped pipe stamped "ILL" and "658 ft", is 1 foot east of southeast corner of church, and 16.83 meters (55.2 feet) from station in azimuth 195°36'.

ADJUSTED HORIZONTAL CONTROL DATA

NAME OF STATION: JOHANNA — YEAR 1931
STATE: Illinois — LOCALITY: Mississippi River, Cairo to St. Louis
First-order Triangulation — SOURCE: G-1323 — FIELD SKETCH: ILL 7-I

GRID DATA	COORDINATES (Feet)	PLANE AZIMUTH & ION & ANGLE	MARK
STATE I11 ZONE W CODE 1202	x 480,199.41 y 606,498.93	237°15'44"	R M 1 (AZIMUTH MARK)
STATE MO ZONE E CODE 2401	x 575,815.04 y 909,945.16	237 03 20	R M 1 (AZIMUTH MARK)

GEODETIC DATA — POSITION — SECONDS IN METERS — ELEVATION
LATITUDE: 38°19'56".614 — LONGITUDE: 90 14 08.501 — NORTH/WEST — METERS/FEET

TO STATION	GEODETIC AZIMUTH (From south)	LOGARITHM (Meters)	METERS
		DISTANCE	
REHLING	60°20'08".83	FIRST-ORDER 3.674 0167	4,720.81
ENGLE	88 48 01.63	4.232 2667	17,071.30
PATTERSON 1873	119 31 17.69	4.475 2256	29,869.34
KLEINSCHMIDT 1871	157 57 07.26	4.316 6781	20,733.76
KLEINSCHMIDT 2	157 57 40.92	4.316 7168	20,735.61
SCHILLING	344 31 50.98	4.058 6162	11,445.01
TWIN HOLLOW	159 11 44.7	SECOND-ORDER 4.150 341	14,136.5
WHITEHOUSE WATER TOWER	146 24 05.8	THIRD-ORDER 4.082 388	12,088.9
AZIMUTH MARK (R M 1)	237 13 10		
WATERLOO CATHOLIC CHURCH SPIRE	265 43 22.3	3.879 019	7,568.7
WATERLOO LUTHERAN CHURCH SPIRE	267 04 56.7	3.865 048	7,329.1
WATERLOO MUNICIPAL WATER TOWER	269 02 51.8	3.873 161	7,467.3
WARTBURG CHURCH SPIRE	324 52 10.5	3.771 462	5,908.3

FIGURE 169. Vertical control data listing of bench mark elevations in meters and feet. Additional pages of the vertical control data describe in detail the location and nature of each bench mark.

AUGUST 1970
U.S. DEPARTMENT OF COMMERCE
ENVIRONMENTAL SCIENCE SERVICES ADMINISTRATION
COAST AND GEODETIC SURVEY
REPLACES ELEV. OF NOV. 1959

VERTICAL CONTROL DATA
by the
Coast and Geodetic Survey
SEA-LEVEL DATUM OF 1929

QUAD 380902 PAGE NO. 1
ILL.-MO.
LATITUDE 38°00' TO 38°30'
LONGITUDE 90°00' TO 90°30'
DIAGRAM SAINT LOUIS NJ 15-6

LINE 101 (Second-order)

The field work (L-1572) was done in the spring of 1934 by a party supervised by A.C. Thorson. Releveling (L-4995) was done from E 59 through B 59 in January 1935 by a party supervised by J.D. Thurmond.

These elevations are all based on a supplementary adjustment of 1955.

BENCH MARK	ADJUSTED ELEVATION (Meters)	(Feet)
Y 58	127.604	418.647
Z 58	128.018	420.006
M 59	127.269	417.548
L 59	125.725	412.483
K 59	126.923	416.413
H 59	125.204	410.773
G 59 RESET 1940		412.584
F 59	126.504	415.039
E 59	134.097	439.950
L 129	133.939	439.432
RV 29 (MPRR)	133.749	438.808
D 59	137.384	450.734
RV 31 (MPRR)	134.127	440.048
K 129	128.253	420.777
RV 34 (MPRR)	127.646	418.785
C 59	127.756	419.146
*420 (USGS)	128.078	420.203
B 59	128.714	422.289
A 59	146.385	480.265
Z 57	142.542	467.657
Y 57	131.598	431.751
PBM M (MRC)	126.577	415.277
X 57	124.741	409.254
W 57	122.520	401.968
PBM N (MRC)	125.988	413.344
V 57	124.728	409.212
U 57	121.062	397.184
T 57	121.940	400.065
S 57	119.407	391.754
R 57	DESTROYED	
Q 57	DESTROYED	
RM 4 BRICKEYS MILL (USE)	117.378	385.098
P 57	119.023	390.495
N 57	120.566	395.557
M 57	119.368	391.627
L 57	120.396	394.999
K 57	121.844	399.750
RM 4 LITTLE ROCK (USE)	114.092	374.317
HM 1844 (USE)	118.916	390.144

LINE 102 (Second-order)

The field work (L-5909) was done in the spring of 1935 by a party supervised by J.D. Thurmond.

These elevations are based on a supplementary adjustment of 1955.

BENCH MARK	ADJUSTED ELEVATION (Meters)	(Feet)
RV 18 (MPRR)	125.926	413.142
G 115	125.358	411.279
RV 19 (MPRR)	125.739	412.529
H 115	125.327	411.177
RV 21 (MPRR)	125.459	411.610
J 115	DESTROYED	
K 115	125.729	412.496
RV 24 (MPRR)	126.362	414.573
RV 25 (MPRR)	127.307	417.673
L 115	125.676	412.322
RV 26 (MPRR)	123.898	406.489
RV 28 (MPRR)	123.518	405.242
M 115	124.218	407.539
N 115	123.909	406.525
RV 29 (MPRR)	124.261	407.680
P 115	124.072	407.060
RV 30 (MPRR)	123.554	405.360
RV 31 (MPRR)	124.823	409.523
406 (USGS)	123.533	405.291
Q 115	124.888	409.737
RV 32 (MPRR)	123.094	403.851
R 115	123.850	406.331
RV 33 (MPRR)	121.895	399.917
S 115	122.788	402.847
RV 34 (MPRR)	123.158	404.061
T 115	122.969	403.441
U 115	122.133	400.698
RV 35 (MPRR)	121.026	397.066
RV 36 (MPRR)	121.047	397.135
V 115	122.088	400.550
RV 37 (MPRR)	122.286	401.200
W 115	120.936	396.771
RV 38 (MPRR)	121.536	398.739
X 115	121.281	397.903
V 97	120.773	396.236
RV 39 (MPRR)	120.050	393.864
RV 40 (MPRR)	124.082	407.092
U 97	123.610	405.544
T 97	119.938	393.497
S 97	119.766	392.932

LINE 102 (Continued)

BENCH MARK	ADJUSTED ELEVATION (Meters)	(Feet)
R 97	119.996	393.687
RV 43 (MPRR)	119.895	393.356
Q 97	119.053	390.593
RV 44 (MPRR)	118.441	388.585
P 97	117.438	385.295
RV 45 (MPRR)	119.064	390.629
RV 46 (MPRR)	119.801	393.047
N 97	119.431	391.833
M 97 RESET	NO ELEV. AVAILABLE	
RV 49 (MPRR)	119.966	393.588
L 97	118.795	389.747
RV 50 (MPRR)	118.695	389.419
K 97	117.777	386.407
J 97	116.738	382.998
RV 51 (MPRR)	116.142	381.043

LINE 103 (Second-order)

The field work (L-4995) was done in the winter of 1935 by a party supervised by J.D. Thurmond.

These elevations are based on a supplementary adjustment of 1955.

BENCH MARK	ADJUSTED ELEVATION (Meters)	(Feet)
RV 37 (MPRR)	127.346	417.801
H 129	129.936	426.298
RV 38 (MPRR)	127.618	418.693
RV 39 (MPRR)	127.539	418.434
RV 40 (MPRR)	129.153	423.729
RV 41 (MPRR)	130.390	427.788
RV 42 (MPRR)	131.324	430.852
RV 43 (MPRR)	130.556	428.332
434 (USGS)	132.275	433.972
F 129 RESET 1967		438.776
RV 44 (MPRR)	134.375	440.862
RV 45 (MPRR)	133.997	439.622

*Changed elevation.

NOS is also engaged in a program to produce a series of maps for coastal areas and the continental shelf showing bottom topography, gravity anomaly data, and magnetic data. This series has proved to be of great value in crustal and sediment studies, offshore oil and gas development, facilities siting, ocean dumping, environmental studies, and coastal-zone planning. Overlays, data lists, printouts, tapes, and technical reports are prepared to accompany the basic maps. Maps of the continental margins are prepared at a scale of 1:250,000, and for the deep ocean areas, at 1:1,000,000 scale.

Recently, NOS published the first of five new international nautical charts it will produce as part of a multination program to provide a new series of small-scale charts covering the entire world. Sponsored by the International Hydrographic Bureau, Monaco, the program calls for standard presentation of navigational information such as depth curves, sounding spacing, aids to navigation, and nautical symbols. Depths and elevations are shown in metric units; scales are 1:3,500,000 and 1:10,000,000. Fifteen nations are producing such charts and each is authorized to reprint charts in its own language. The United States five-map series will cover the northern Pacific Ocean and the Bering Sea. The first map, at a scale of 1:3,500,000, covers an area off the West Coast of the United States and Canada. This is the first metric-unit nautical chart published by NOS.

Defense Mapping Agency

The Defense Mapping Agency (DMA) operates three principal centers for the production of charts and maps:

△ **DMA Hydrographic Center** (DMAHC) produces nautical charts, including extensive coverage of foreign waters.
△ **DMA Aerospace Center** (DMAAC) produces aeronautical charts covering foreign areas.
△ **DMA Topographic Center** (DMATC) produces topographic maps, including foreign and worldwide coverage.

Much of the mapping performed by DMA is intended for specific defense purposes; however, a substantial portion of the cartographic output is available to the public (see "Cartographic Information Sources"). Sheets of the following topographic map series can be purchased:

△ **World, series 1106, scale 1:5,000,000.** Topographic; multicolor with gradient tints.
△ **World, series 1142, scale 1:11,000,000.** General-purpose wall map composed of nine sheets; multicolor with gradient tints.
△ **World, series 1144, scale 1:22,000,000.** General-purpose wall map composed of three sheets; multicolor with gradient tints.
△ **World, series 1301, scale 1:1,000,000.** Topographic; multicolor, many sheets are plastic relief.
△ **World, series 1301P, scale 1:1,000,000.** Plastic relief; topographic; multicolor. Vertical exaggeration 4:1.

△ **World road maps, series 1304 W, scale 1:1,000,000.** Road map; multicolor. Series composed of six sheets covering Egypt, Middle East, and Iran.
△ **Middle East briefing map, series 1308, scale 1:1,500,000.** Physical; multicolor.
△ **Korea road map, series 1351, scale 1:700,000.** Topographic; multicolor. Series composed of two sheets.
△ **World, series 1404, scale 1:500,000.** Europe and Middle East. Topographic; multicolor.
△ **Africa, series 2201, scale 1:2,000,000.** Topographic; multicolor.
△ **Puerto Rico, series E502P, scale 1:250,000.** Plastic relief; topographic; multicolor. Vertical exaggeration 2:1.

The topographic map series listed above are described in more detail in DMA's *Price List of Maps and Charts for Public Sale.* In addition to these regular series maps, DMA also produces various kinds of special maps; for example, figure 170 shows a lunar topophotomap of the Apollo 17 landing area produced by DMA for NASA.

U.S. Army Corps of Engineers

The Corps of Engineers produces nautical charts of the Mississippi River and its tributaries. These charts show water depths and navigation data. Also available for these waterways are maps showing small-craft installations such as harbors, ramps, and landings. Another series of maps shows commercial river terminals. Information concerning these cartographic products is available from the district offices of the U.S. Army Corps of Engineers (see "Cartographic Information Sources").

Tennessee Valley Authority

Since its inception in 1933, the Tennessee Valley Authority (TVA) has operated a Mapping Services Branch (formerly Maps and Surveys Branch). This branch has produced a great variety of maps—too many for total identification here. The more important types are described below.

Valley Topographic Maps

The preparation of these topographic quadrangles started in 1937 under a cooperative agreement between TVA and the Geological Survey. The 763 7.5-minute quadrangle maps covering the TVA area were prepared entirely in accordance with Survey standards for 1:24,000-scale topographic maps. Mapping of the entire valley was completed in 1962, and since then a map-maintenance program has continued.

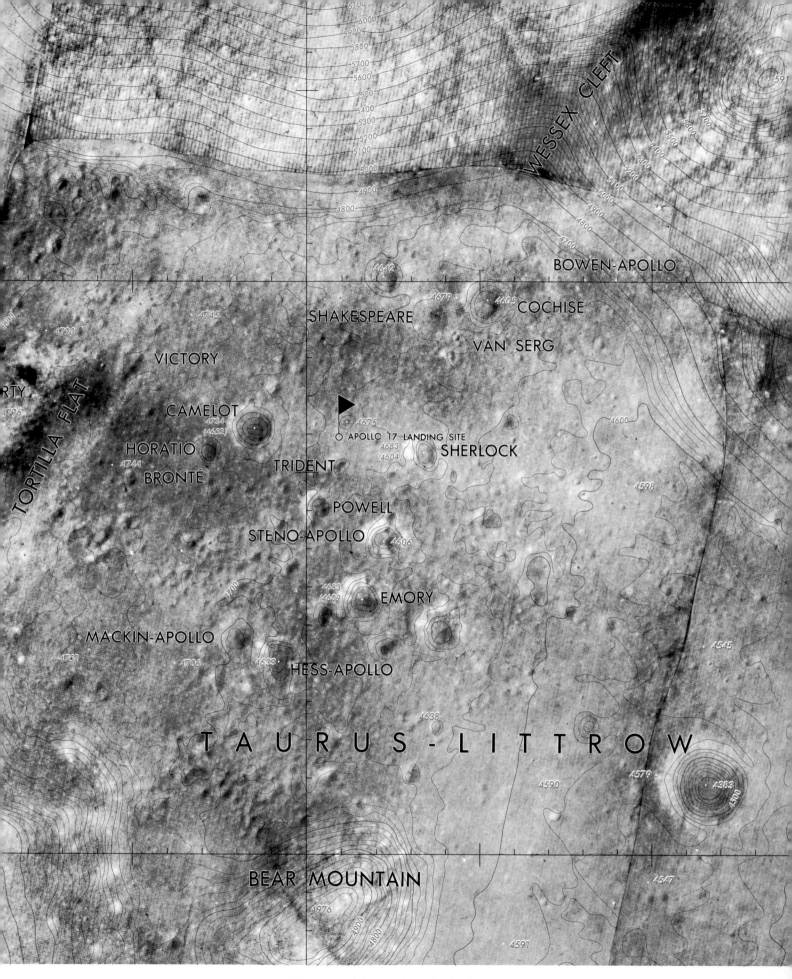

FIGURE 170. Portion of a 1:50,000-scale lunar topophotomap of the Apollo 17 landing area. The map base is an orthophotomosaic produced from Apollo 17 panoramic photography by the Defense Mapping Agency for NASA.

Land Maps

In connection with the acquisition of land for TVA projects, land maps have been prepared for the tracts being purchased. These maps show planimetric features (roads, streams, bridges), buildings, orchards, woodland, certain pertinent contours including the purchase guide contour, and cadastral data (property lines and corners). Bearings and distances are indicated along the property lines. The owner's name, the assigned tract number, and the acreage are shown. Most of these land maps are at a scale of 1:1,200.

Reservation Maps

When a TVA project is placed in operation, lands that are deemed surplus to the effective management of the project are turned over to other Federal or State agencies for public use, leased to private persons, or sold at public auction. On completion of this land adjustment, final reservation maps are prepared as record plats of the TVA land and landrights holdings. The final reservation plats are printed in a single color at a scale of 1:12,000 or 1:15,840. The maps show the retained land and landrights, boundary lines, contours to which easements and rights were reserved, and the location of boundary monuments and other survey data required for reestablishing the boundaries should a monument be destroyed.

Navigation Charts and Maps

Navigation charts, which are published for the TVA main-river reservoirs, differ from navigation maps prepared for the tributary reservoirs chiefly in the amount of navigation information shown. The charts are much more detailed, showing the main channel sailing line, safety harbors, the general shape and elevation of the reservoir bottom, hazard areas, and other map features (fig. 171). On the tributary reservoirs, commercial navigation is of little importance and few navigation aids have been established. Consequently the maps of these reservoirs are limited to the requirements for small-craft navigation and for general recreation guidance.

Recreation Maps

Recreation maps for each of the TVA lakes make it easy for the sportsman or vacationer to locate the many recreation areas on the lakeshore and decide on the appropriate route to the selected location. Boat docks and launching sites, commercial recreation areas, public parks, and wildlife management areas are some of the features shown on the map (fig. 172). Usable roads in the vicinity of the lakes are shown along with the main roads customarily shown on road maps. The roads are named and distances between road intersections are shown.

Control Bulletins

TVA issues a series of bulletins derived from its accumulated geodetic data which are available to the public at nominal cost. Each survey control data bulletin is an 8-1/2 × 11-inch printed publication with a paper cover and the following contents: A title page, an index map of the valley region, the State coordinate system zones, the 15-minute geographic quadrangles, pages explaining the use of the bulletin, and the location descriptions and values for horizontal and vertical control markers in the particular quadrangle area.

Department of Agriculture

Cartographic activities of the U.S. Department of Agriculture (USDA) are carried out principally through three of its agencies, the Soil Conservation Service (SCS), the U.S. Forest Service (FS), and the Agricultural Stabilization and Conservation Service (ASCS).

Soil Surveys

The USDA, in cooperation with State agricultural experiment stations and other Federal and State agencies, has been making soil surveys and publishing them since 1899. These surveys furnish soil maps and interpretations needed in planning research and disseminating research results. They are used in educational programs, in technical assistance programs, and in decisionmaking about soil selection, use, and management. Sound scientific and technical standards are used in a nationwide system of soil classification, nomenclature, interpretation, and publication.

Published soil surveys contain, in addition to soil maps, general information about the agriculture and climate of the area and descriptions of each kind of soil. They include a discussion of the formation and classification of the soils in the area and also soil laboratory data when available.

Soil surveys published since 1957 contain many different kinds of interpretations for each of the different soils mapped in the area. The interpretations in these recent surveys vary with the needs of the area, but most surveys include: estimated yields of the common agricultural crops under defined levels of management, land-capability interpretations, soil-woodland interpretations, rangeland interpretations, engineering uses of soils, interpretations for community planning, suitability of the soil for drainage and irrigation, and suitability of the soil for recreation and wildlife.

Most recent soil surveys published since 1957 contain soil maps printed on a photomosaic base (fig. 173).

FIGURE 171. Portion of TVA Navigation Chart 107 for Kentucky Lake on Tennessee River. Scale: 1 inch = 1 mile (1:63,360); also published at scale of 1 inch = 1/2 mile (1:31,680).

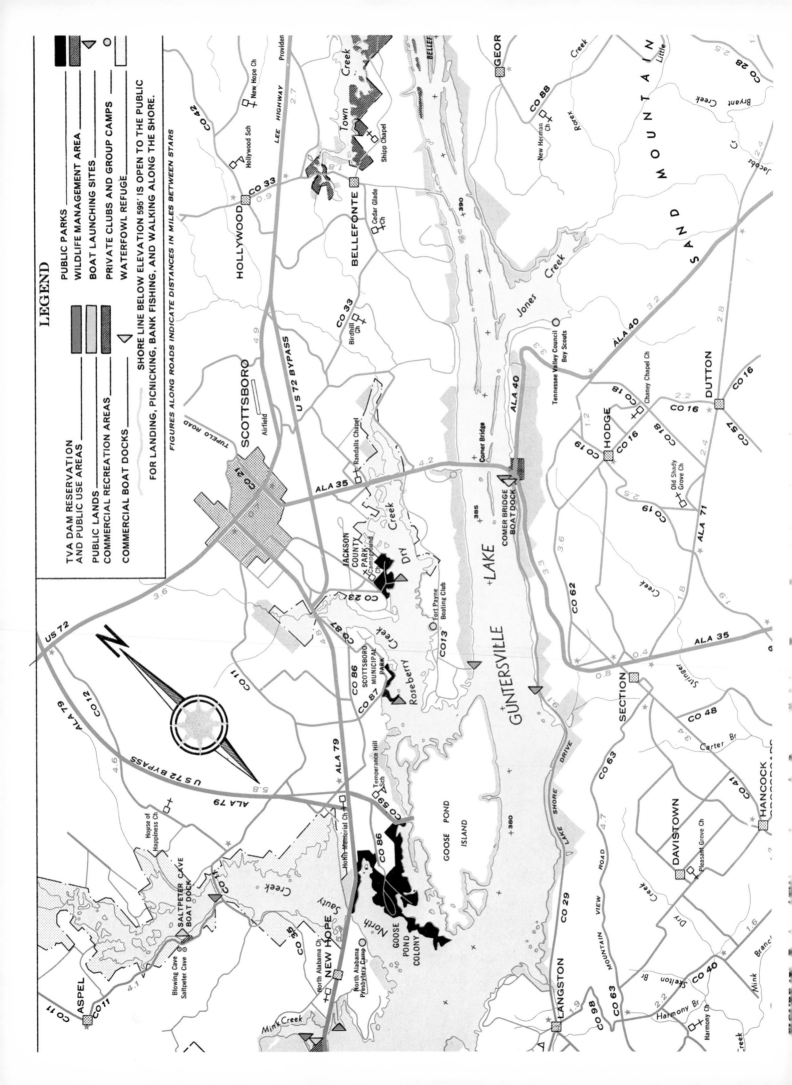

FIGURE 173. Portion of Soil Conservation Service soil survey map. (Crawford County, Pa., sheet 2.)

The usual map scale is 1:20,000 or 1:15,840, depending upon the needs of the area.

A USDA publication, *List of Published Soil Surveys,* lists surveys that have been published by the Department. A few State agencies also publish soil surveys but, except for two in Illinois, they are not included in the USDA list.

A soil survey published by the USDA that is still in print may be obtained in one of the following ways:

Δ Land users in the area surveyed and professional workers who have use for the survey can obtain a free copy from the local office of the Soil Conservation Service, from their county agent, or from their congressman.

Δ For a time after publication, copies may be purchased from the Superintendent of Documents, U.S. Government Printing Office, Washington, D.C. 20402.

Δ Many libraries keep published soil surveys on file for reference. Soil conservation district offices and county agricultural extension offices also have copies of local surveys that may be used for reference.

Most published soil surveys cover one or more counties and are so named. Where the survey covers only a part of one or more counties the word "area" is a part of the name. The date in the list is the year the fieldwork was completed for surveys made from 1899 to 1936; from 1937 on, it is the year in which the publication was issued.

National Forest Maps

The Forest Service issues two United States maps giving the location of national forests and related FS installations:

Δ Leaflet FS-13, which shows on one side a monocolor map of the United States with the title "National Forests and Forest Service Field Offices," at a scale of approximately 200 miles to the inch (fig. 174). The reverse side of the leaflet gives the addresses of FS field offices, including each regional headquarters, each national forest headquarters, and each research headquarters. Copies of leaflet FS-13 are available free from the Forest Service, Office of Information, U.S. Department of Agriculture, P.O. Box 2417, Washington, D.C. 20013.

Δ A 1:7,500,000-scale sheet of the *National Atlas of the United States* titled "National Forests and Other Lands Administered by the Forest Service." This multicolor map shows national forests, purchase units (authorized for acquisition), national grasslands, land utilization projects, regional boundaries and numbers, regional headquarters, and Forest and Range Experiment Station headquarters. The subject matter is compiled by the Forest Service on a base compiled by the Geological Survey for the *National Atlas* series.

For each national forest, the Forest Service provides a primary base series map, usually at a scale of 1:24,000, except for Alaska, which is at a scale of 1:63,360. These maps are used in administration, development, and protection of the national forests.

The primary base series maps are used to derive all other FS map products such as the forest visitor maps, forest visitor guides, wilderness maps, Special Designated Area maps, and work maps.

The forest visitor maps cover an entire geographical unit such as a national forest. The content of these maps, published at a scale of 1:126,720, is indicated by the title and legend (fig. 175). Each map also includes a tabulation and location key for points of interest and recreation sites with facilities within the mapped area.

The forest visitor guides (variable scale) are provided to the public at no charge and depict information on national forest recreation opportunities, national recreation areas, wilderness trails, and visitor information developments with text relative to resource management objectives.

Wilderness and Special Designated Area maps depict detailed information on wilderness and other areas within national forest boundaries.

Information on the availability and cost of all maps for any national forest can be obtained from FS regional offices and national forest offices.

Aerial Photographs

The uses for USDA aerial photographs have grown from major use as a quick accurate method to measure cropland acreages to encompass many other uses in nonagricultural areas. Through the Agricultural Stabilization and Conservation Service Aerial Photography Field Office (APFO) in Salt Lake City, thousands of photographs are purchased each year by Federal and local government agencies, private firms, and the general public. APFO has aerial photomaps that cover the Nation's major cropland areas.

To offset the effect of camera tilt in producing these photomaps, APFO uses simple rectification. For areas of low relief, the rectified aerial photograph is almost an orthophotographic map accurately representing ground features such as roads, streams, trees, buildings, fields, and fence lines. The rectified enlargements furnished by APFO generally meet National Map Accuracy Standards if the terrain is relatively flat. Enlargements can be obtained at a number of scales ranging from 1:20,000 to 1:2,400 and on paper ranging in size from 9-1/2 × 9-1/2 inches to 38 × 38 inches. All prints are on a water-resistant stable-base paper.

Other available products include copy negatives, glass plates, and types of film positives for light-table use and for making diazo or blueprint copies. Additional services include photographs certified as to the date of exposure and controlled or uncontrolled photomosaics.

Beginning in 1972, APFO began to acquire satellite imagery for the Department of Agriculture. This imagery is available for sale to other government agencies, private firms, and the general public. The APFO film library has on file all Landsat 1, 2, and 3 and Skylab 2, 3, and 4 imagery.

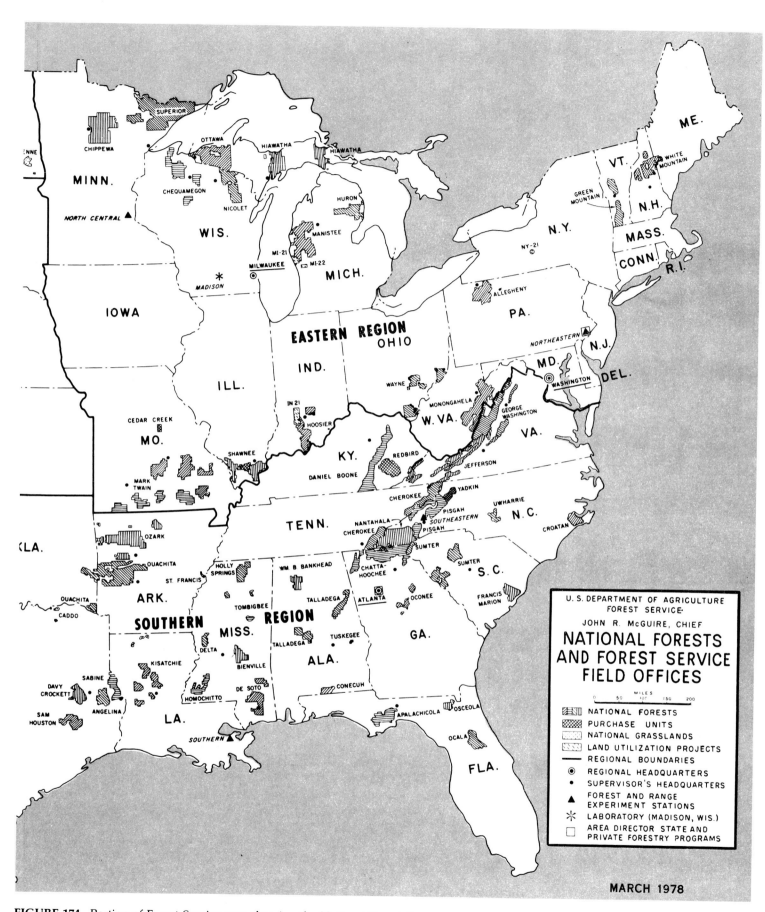

FIGURE 174. Portion of Forest Service map showing the National Forest System.

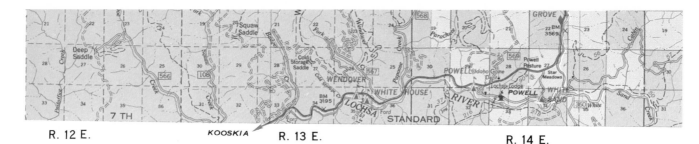

R. 12 E.   *KOOSKIA*   R. 13 E.   R. 14 E.

U.S. DEPARTMENT OF AGRICULTURE
FOREST SERVICE
JOHN R. McGUIRE, CHIEF

FOREST VISITORS MAP
LOLO NATIONAL FOREST
IDAHO AND MONTANA
BOISE MERIDIAN AND PRINCIPAL MERIDIAN MONTANA
1975

1 ½ 0   1   2   3   4   5 Miles

LEGEND

90	Interstate Highway	△	Horizontal Control Station		Forest Supervisor's Headquarters
12	U.S. Highway	⬡	Horizontal Control Station and Permanent Lookout Station	♠	District Ranger Station
		◯	Permanent Lookout Station	♠	Forest Service Station
200	State Highway	⬡ 239	Permanent Lookout Station with Aeronautical Number on Roof	⚶	Recreation Site, Forest Service
581	Forest Route	✕	Mine, Quarry or Gravel Pit	⚶	Recreation Site, other than Forest Service
	Paved Road	⊙	Located or Landmark Object		National Forest Boundary
	All Weather Road	▲	U.S. Mineral or Location Monument		Adjacent National Forest Boundary
	Primary Access Route–Normally Suitable for Automobile Travel–Travel with Caution	⊙	Gaging Station		County Line
	Dirt Road	⤙	Cave or Cavern	/////	Game or Bird Refuge Boundary
	Primitive Road	▲	Sawmill		Wilderness Boundary
	Road or Trail with Restrictions–Inquire at Local Forest Service Station	■	House, Cabin or other Building		Lolo National Forest Land
		¡	Schoolhouse		Adjacent National Forest Lands
105	Trail	¡	Church		Bureau of Land Management Land
	Railroad	♦	Point of Interest		State Land
	Power Transmission Line	▼	Sportsman's Access		U. S. Plywood Land
PIPELINE	Pipeline or Conduit	⛷	Ski Area		Burlington Northern Land
					Montana Power Company Land

TOWNSHIP AND SECTION LINE CLASSIFICATION

Surveyed, location reliable

Unsurveyed land net protraction by BLM

–FOREST SERVICE MAP CLASS A

Compiled in the Regional Office, Missoula, Montana, in 1974 from U.S. Forest Service planimetric maps and U.S. Geological Survey topographic maps constructed by photogrammetric methods. Land ownership supplied by cooperating agencies.

FIGURE 175. Reduced portion of a forest visitor's map showing title block, scale, legend, and part of Clearwater National Forest adjacent to Lolo National Forest, Idaho and Montana.

Each ASCS county office and Agricultural Service Center has a photoindex of the area it serves. The user may visit the office, select the photo needed from this index, and order on the spot. If the user is interested in aerial photography of a distant county, he may purchase an index of that county. Again, the local county ASCS office will help order the index.

Aerial photographic negatives exposed before 1942 were transferred to the National Archives. These may be ordered from National Archives and Records Service, Cartographic Archives Division, General Services Ad-

ministration, Archives Building, Pennsylvania Avenue at 8th Street, NW., Washington, D.C. 20408.

Information on all questions concerning ASCS aerial photographs may be obtained from U.S. Department of Agriculture, Agricultural Stabilization and Conservation Service, Aerial Photography Field Office, P.O. Box 30010, Salt Lake City, Utah 84125.

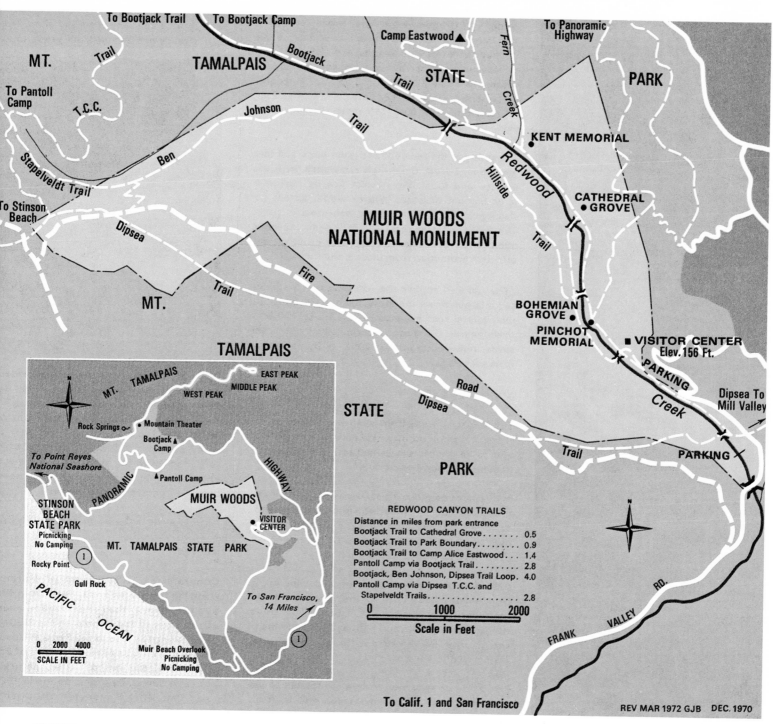

FIGURE 176. Portion of National Park Service visitor's map, Muir Woods National Monument, Calif.

National Park Service

The national park series of topographic maps is a standard Geological Survey series at various scales using contours to depict terrain relief. Some of these maps are also published in a shaded-relief edition, which creates the illusion of three-dimensional land surface (see figs. 111, 114, 116, and 124).

For the use of visitors to the national parks, monuments, and historic sites, the National Park Service issues a series of leaflets, one for each facility. These leaflets contain information on the history and characteristics of the facility, recreational opportunities, and visitor services. Generally, the principal feature of the leaflet is a simplified map to aid the visitor in using the facility. Figure 176 exemplifies a large-scale visitor's map for a relatively small facility, the Muir Woods National Monument. Figure 177 is a portion of a small-scale visitor's map of a large facility, Yellowstone National Park.

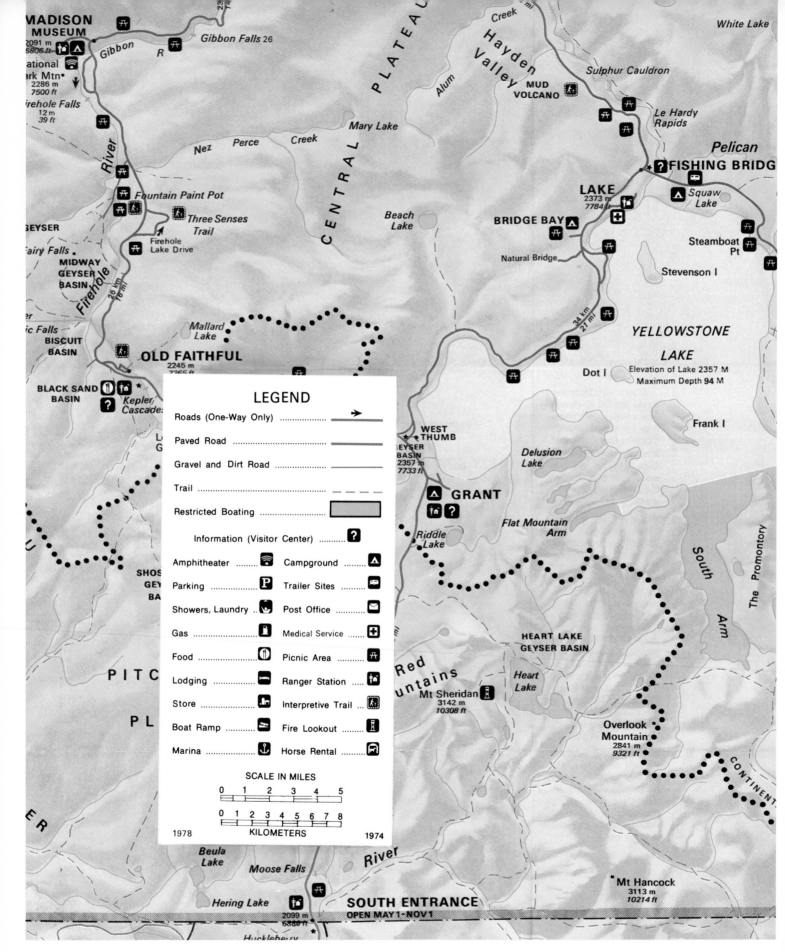

FIGURE 177. Portion of National Park Service visitor's map, Yellowstone National Park, Wyo.-Mont.-Idaho.

To provide general information on the National Park System, a leaflet is issued by the National Park Service showing on a small-scale United States map (fig. 178) the locations of national parks, seashores, lakeshores, monuments, historic sites, historical parks, military parks, memorial parks, battlefield sites, scenic riverways, and recreation areas. Also shown are the region boundaries of the National Park System and the locations of regional offices. For each of the regions of the National Park System another leaflet is available with maps at larger scale showing the locations of facilities within that region and with a brief description of each facility. Information on these maps and leaflets can be obtained from the National Park Service, Department of the Interior, Washington, D.C. 20242.

Bureau of Land Management

The rectangular-survey system for subdividing U.S. public lands and the means of recording the subdivision data on Geological Survey quadrangle maps are described in the section "Civil Boundaries" (p. 73–86). The surveying of public lands (Bureau of Land Management, 1969) and the establishment of public land subdivisions are the responsibility of the Bureau of Land Management (BLM; formerly the General Land Office).

The cadastral surveys of the public lands (Bureau of Land Management, 1973) carried out by BLM are made in conformance to statutory law and its judicial interpretation. A cadastral survey creates (or reestablishes) marks and defines boundaries of tracts of land. This includes a field-note record of the observations, measurements, and monuments descriptive of the work performed and a plat that represents the cadastral survey, all subject to the approval of the Director of BLM.

The plat is the drawing which represents the lines surveyed, established, retraced, or resurveyed, showing the direction and length of each line; the relation to the adjoining official surveys; the boundaries, description, and area of each parcel of the land; and, as far as practicable, the topography, culture, and improvements within the limits of the survey. Occasionally the plat may constitute the entire record of the survey.

Ordinarily an original survey of public lands does not ascertain boundaries; it creates them. The running of lines in the field and the platting of townships, sections, and legal subdivisions are not alone sufficient to constitute a survey. Even though a survey may have been made, if it is disapproved by the authorized administrators, the public lands which were the subject of the survey are still classed as unsurveyed.

The subdivisions are based upon and are defined by the monuments and other evidences of the controlling official surveys. As long as these evidences are in existence, the record of the survey is an official exhibit and, presumably, correctly represents the actual field conditions. If there are discrepancies, the record must give way to the evidence of the corners in place. In the absence of evidence, the field notes and plat are the best means of identification of the survey, and they will retain this purpose.

Township Plat

Figure 179 is a specimen township plat made in accordance with BLM requirements, which shows the basis of the computation of all areas. The distances noted in parentheses are the regular and fractional portions of lines that constitute the boundaries of the quarter-quarter sections and fractional subdivisions. Parenthetical distances are employed where the field notes do not indicate what was used in the calculation of areas. The same lengths are adopted proportionately in establishing sixteenth-section corners on the section boundaries and for control in the subdivision of sections.

Most township plats are maps in that they show topographic and other mappable features. Strictly speaking, a plat is a base drawing stripped of every detail nonessential to the identification of the subdivisions shown. The base drawing is always in black. It shows section boundary lines, subdivision lines of sections, lines of segregation such as mineral or other claim boundaries, and meander lines (unless shown in blue). Also shown are all lettering referring to title, names, memorandum, certificates, section numbers, lot numbers, areas, and lengths and directions of lines, as well as important improvements, works, or structures where required. The arrangement of data on all base drawings is made as nearly uniform as possible.

Mineral Surveys

Mineral surveys are made to mark the legal boundaries of mineral deposits or ore-bearing formations on the public domain where the boundaries are determined by lines other than the normal subdivision of the public lands.

Mineral surveys are required most frequently where the deposits occur in ore-bearing rock veins, known as mineral lodes, where the prospector who has made a legal discovery is permitted to stake out a claim of specified dimensions, to develop the claim to his exclusive use, and, if desired in the protection of his right, to apply for a mineral survey and obtain a patent.

The law provides that all placer-mining claims located after May 10, 1872, shall conform as nearly as practicable with the U.S. system of public land surveys and the rectangular subdivision of such surveys, and such locations shall not include more than 20 acres for each individual claimant. Surveys of placer claims are conformed to the public survey unless they are located

FIGURE 178. Portion of National Park Service map showing the National Park System.

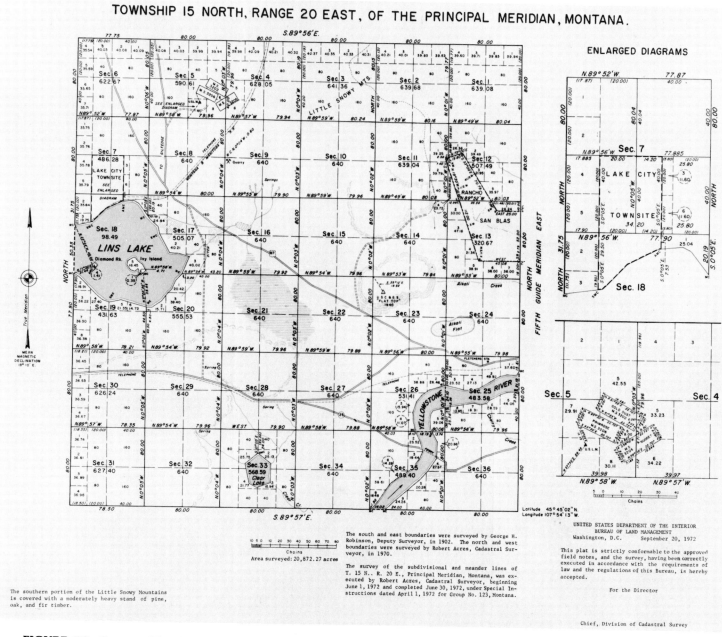

FIGURE 179. Bureau of Land Management township plat (reduced).

on unsurveyed land or the configuration of the mineral deposit makes conformation impracticable. Consequently, the mineral survey procedures apply especially to lode claims, although they are followed generally in appropriate surveys of placer claims.

Millsites embracing land occupied for milling purposes or used incidental to mining operations may be located, surveyed, and patented in a manner similar to lode claims.

Figure 180 shows a specimen mineral survey plat made in accordance with BLM requirements. A plat scale is used that is large enough to illustrate clearly the improvements, conflicts, and physical features described in the field notes, together with all courses and distances of intersecting lines and connecting lines, where space permits. Any topographic features described in the field notes tending to confuse or obscure the plat may be omitted, but as the copy of the plat posted on the claim is a notice to the public of the ground applied for, all of the roads, streams, and other objects that may aid in locating the surveyed ground are shown.

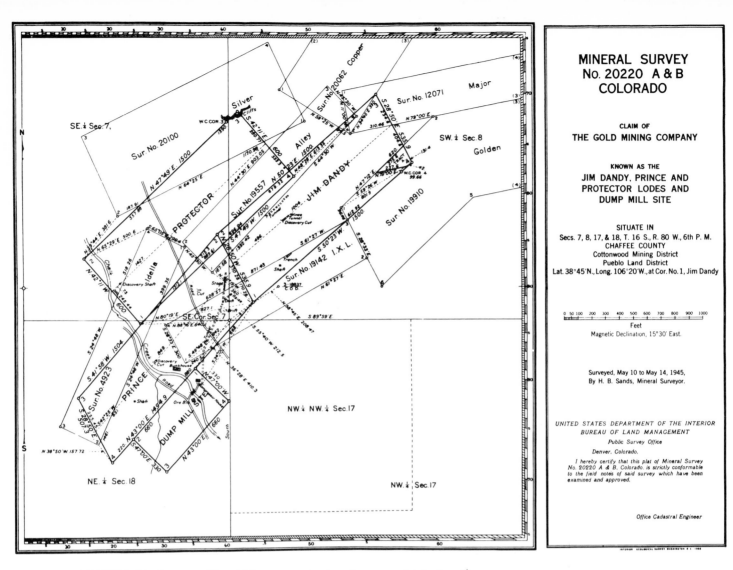

FIGURE 180. Bureau of Land Management mineral survey plat (reduced).

Availability of Plats

Plats of townships and mineral surveys are available for public distribution, as follows:

△ For Illinois, Indiana, Iowa, Kansas, Missouri, and Ohio, plats may be ordered from National Archives and Records Service, Cartographic Archives Division, General Services Administration, Archives Building, Pennsylvania Avenue at 8th Street, NW., Washington, D.C. 20408.

△ For all other public-land States, plats may be ordered from Bureau of Land Management, Eastern States Land Office, Robin Building, 7981 Eastern Avenue, Silver Spring, Md. 20910.

Department of Transportation

As an appendix to the 1976 report, *National Transportation: Trends and Choices*, the U.S. Department of Transportation issued a *U.S. Transportation Atlas*. The maps contained in this atlas are based largely on the work of the Geological Survey for the *National Atlas of the United States of America* and recent updates of that

work. These transportation maps were prepared by a commercial mapping organization. The transportation infrastructure data for the maps were furnished by the Federal Aviation Administration, Federal Highway Administration, Federal Railroad Administration, Saint Lawrence Seaway Development Corporation, Materials Transportation Bureau, the U.S. Coast Guard, the U.S. Army Corps of Engineers, and the Maritime Administration.

Separate national maps at a scale of 1:7,500,000 are included for each of the five modes of transportation: highway, railroad, aviation, marine, and pipeline. Projected information through 1990 is provided where possible. Twenty-two sectional maps covering the entire United States at a scale of 1:2,000,000 contain current transportation infrastructure in more detail. Also included are 1:7,500,000-scale U.S. maps showing Standard Metropolitan Statistical Areas (1975) and Bureau of Economic Analysis Economic Areas. Copies of this atlas can be purchased from the Superintendent of Documents, U.S. Government Printing Office, Washington, D.C. 20402.

Maps from Other Agencies

FIGURE 181. Portion of general highway map, Dallas County, Tex., prepared by the Texas Department of Highways and Public Transportation in cooperation with the U.S. Department of Transportation; scale 1:125,000.

County highway maps (fig. 181) showing all primary and secondary roads for each county in the United States can be obtained from the Federal Highway Administration, Department of Transportation, Room 4208, 400 7th Street, SW., Washington, D.C. 20590. These maps are usually prepared by the State highway department in cooperation with the Federal Highway Administration.

Department of Transportation

211

Bureau of the Census

The Bureau of the Census has published several series of maps based on the data of the 1970 Census of Population. Descriptive order forms for these maps are available free from Publications Distribution Section, Bureau of the Census, U.S. Department of Commerce, Washington, D.C. 20233.

Series GE-50 United States Maps

Measuring 42 × 30 inches on a single sheet, each GE-50 map has a scale of 1:5,000,000 with an inset map of Hawaii printed at the same scale. The inset map of Alaska has a scale of 1:10,000,000. A partial list of the maps, in this series with publication dates and series numbers, follows:

45. Population Distribution, Urban and Rural, in the United States: 1970.
47. Number of Negro Persons, by Counties of the United States: 1970.
49. Number of American Indians, by Counties of the United States: 1970.
50. Number of Chinese, by Counties of the United States: 1970.
51. Number of Japanese, by Counties of the United States: 1970.
52. Number of Persons of Spanish Origin, by Counties of the United States: 1970.
56. Median Family Income for 1969, by Counties of the United States: 1970
59. Number of Owner-Occupied Housing Units by Counties of the United States: 1970.
60. Number of Renter-Occupied Housing Units by Counties of the United States: 1970.
62. Congressional Districts for the 94th Congress.
64. Median Gross Rent by Counties of the United States: 1970.
65. Median Value of Owner-Occupied Housing Units by Counties of the United States: 1970.

Series GE-70 United States Maps

Each GE-70 map is based on a scale of 1:7,500,000 and measures 20 × 30 inches on a single sheet. Insets portray Hawaii at the same scale and Alaska at a scale of 1:17,000,000.

The first map in this series was titled "Population Distribution, Urban and Rural in the United States: 1970 (nighttime view)." The map features a unique night view of the United States, showing urban and rural areas highlighted as they would appear from a satellite (fig. 182).

Series GE-80 Urban Atlas

This series is based on data from 65 of the largest Metropolitan Areas (minimum population, 500,000). The atlases display on individual maps selected data char-

acteristics from the 1970 Census of Population for each data item; they serve as graphic supplements to individual census tract reports. The maps are drawn by computer, using micrographic mapping technology employing choropleth mapping techniques to display data for each census tract within an entire Standard Metropolitan Statistical Area (SMSA). Atlas sheets measure approximately 19 × 22 inches and are printed in color. Large SMSA's are displayed on more than one sheet to provide reasonable resolution of densely populated areas.

Annual Boundary and Annexation Survey

This annual report presents boundary changes and corporate status as of January 1 each year for incorporated places with populations of 2,500 or more.

State and Local Agencies

It is not feasible to describe all the cartographic products prepared by State, county, municipal, and regional agencies. Therefore, only the mapping program of the New York State Department of Transportation is covered, to exemplify cartographic efforts of non-Federal public agencies. In most States, information on non-Federal mapping covering areas within the State can be obtained from the State department of conservation, the State highway (or transportation) department, or the State geologist.

New York State 1:24,000-Scale 7.5-Minute Planimetric Maps

The 1:24,000-scale planimetric edition of New York State maps (fig. 183) consists of black-and-white general-purpose base maps useful for reference and for recording and displaying many types of information.

Although the 24 × 30-inch maps are based on Geological Survey topographic maps, they contain a variety of updated and additional information, including roads, route identification, railroads, airfields, water features, built-up areas, buildings, and civil boundaries. Built-up areas are shown by a gray tint similar to the light red tint used on the Geological Survey maps. Buildings shown within these areas are limited to those of landmark significance. Also shown on the maps are the State plane coordinate and New York transverse Mercator grid systems. Neither contours nor the green woodland tint used on Geological Survey maps are included on the planimetric edition.

FIGURE 182. Reduced portion of Bureau of the Census map (original scale 1:7,500,000) showing U.S. population distribution in 1970 (Map GE-70, No. 1). The map presents a simulated night view of the United States from a satellite.

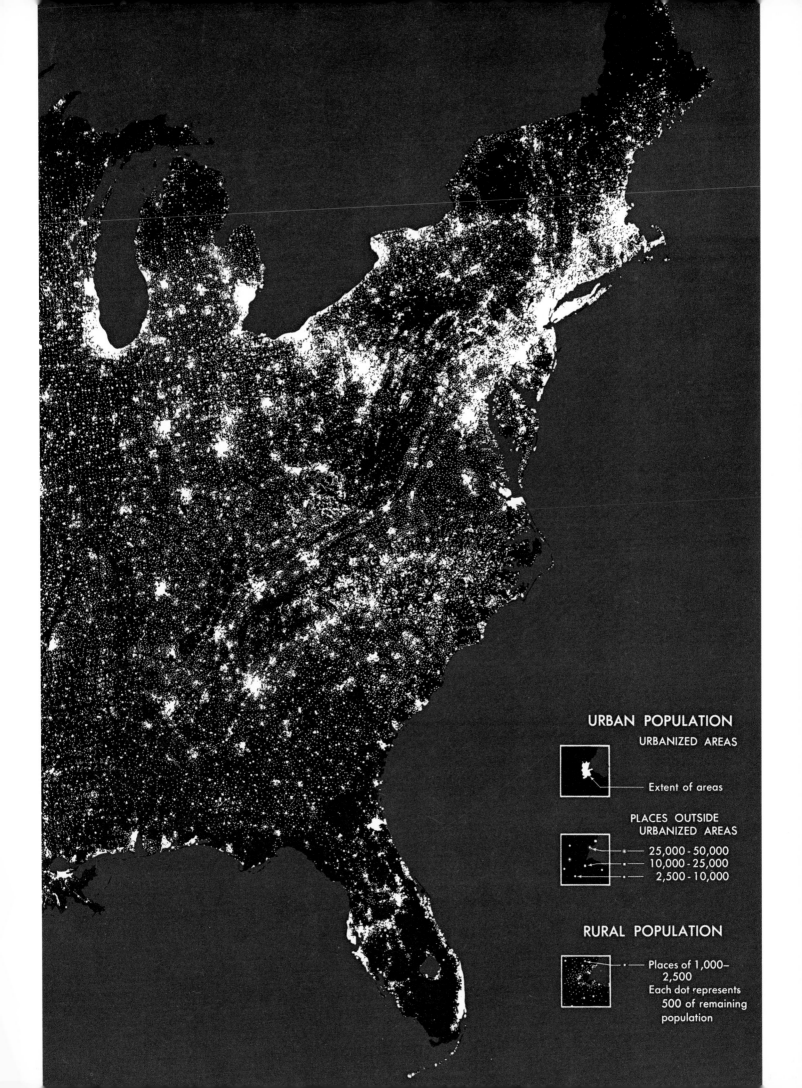

URBAN POPULATION

URBANIZED AREAS

Extent of areas

PLACES OUTSIDE
URBANIZED AREAS

25,000 - 50,000
10,000 - 25,000
2,500 - 10,000

RURAL POPULATION

Places of 1,000–
2,500
Each dot represents
500 of remaining
population

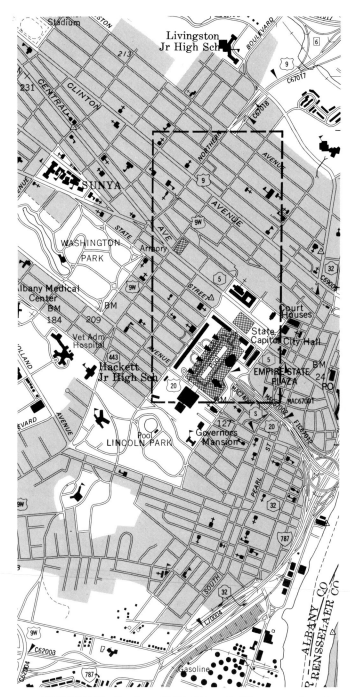

FIGURE 183. Portion of 1:24,000-scale Albany quadrangle, New York State 7.5-minute planimetric map series. The area within the dashed lines is shown at a scale of 1:9,600 in figure 184.

New York State 1:24,000-Scale 7.5-Minute Topographic Maps

This two-color edition shows in light brown the contours from the most recent Geological Survey map and in black the 7.5-minute planimetric map image. The contour lines have not been updated; therefore, these lines may not accurately represent the land surface near recently built features such as highways and reservoirs.

Topographic Maps, 1:2,400 Scale

Topographic mapping at a scale of 1:2,400 is frequently obtained by the State Department of Transportation from its in-house photogrammetric operation and from photogrammetric consultants. Although this mapping is primarily for use in the planning and preliminary design of highway projects, it is often helpful in other uses and copies are available for general sale.

The black-and-white maps are produced by photogrammetric methods generally on 30 × 54-inch sheets. Dates of maps range from 1942 to the present. Contours are shown on all maps and a 5-foot contour interval is used. The State plane coordinate system usually is shown on the maps.

New York State 1:9,600-Scale Planimetric Maps

The 1:9,600-scale planimetric maps provide large-scale coverage of all cities and villages in New York State, except New York City, and of other selected developed areas at a uniform scale of 1:9,600. These black-and-white general-purpose base maps are useful for reference and for recording and displaying many types of information. A topographic edition is not available at this scale.

The 1:9,600-scale maps are photographic enlargements of portions of the 1:24,000-scale planimetric maps, to which additional local street names have been added. To improve clarity, the gray built-up-area tint and selected building symbols from the 1:24,000-scale maps have been deleted.

Two formats are used for the 1:9,600-scale planimetric maps: (1) urban area maps and (2) village/hamlet atlases. Urban area maps (fig. 184) measure 36 × 48 inches and cover the larger urban areas of the State except New York City. Generally, each urban area map represents the north or south half of a 1:24,000-scale quadrangle. Several sheets often are needed for complete coverage of an urban area. Village/hamlet atlases include maps of smaller communities not covered by urban area maps. The atlases measure 24 × 36 inches and are published for individual counties or for regions of two or more counties.

Four-Sheet New York State Map, 1:250,000 Scale

The 1:250,000-scale New York State map provides small-scale coverage of the State on four sheets. This five-color planimetric map is an up-to-date, easily read, general-reference map suitable for display and for the recording of many types of data. The 39 × 54-inch map

Maps from Other Agencies

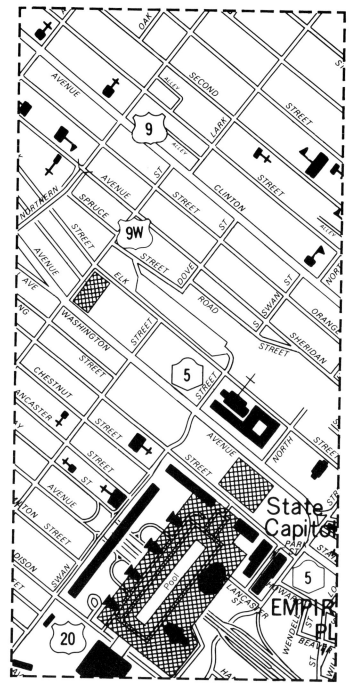

FIGURE 184. Portion of Albany (South) urban area map, New York State 1:9,600 planimetric map series.

other computer-related operations, is employed to insure a high degree of accuracy in the map's construction. The primary source for information shown on the map is the 1:24,000-scale planimetric map series. Other State and local records and plans are also used in an effort to make this map as accurate as possible.

Features shown on the map include: State highways with their State, U.S., or Interstate route numbers; parkways; most county roads; railroads; airports; canals; boundaries and names of all counties, towns, cities, villages, and Indian reservations; selected unincorporated places; State parks; Federal parks and reservations; and major drainage systems. Local roads are not shown.

New York State County Maps and Atlas, 1:250,000 Scale

These small-scale county maps are two-color adaptations of the New York State Department of Transportation's four-sheet 1:250,000 State map. They provide basically the same information as the five-color State map; however, users may find the 11 × 17-inch format of these county maps more convenient than the State map for general desk-top reference.

The colors of the county maps are gray and green. All 62 counties are shown on the 45 maps in this series, with two or more counties shown on a single page in several instances. The maps are available as either a bound atlas of all counties or as individual sheets. A cover sheet with legend information is included with each atlas.

Commercial and Geographic Organizations

Many types of maps, charts, atlases, and globes are available from commercial firms that make, publish, or distribute cartographic products. Names and addresses of such organizations can be obtained from the American Congress on Surveying and Mapping (210 Little Falls Street, Falls Church, Va. 22046) or the American Society of Photogrammetry (105 North Virginia Avenue, Falls Church, Va. 22046).

National associations such as the American Automobile Association (8111 Gatehouse Road, Falls Church, Va. 22042) and the National Geographic Society (17th and M Streets, NW., Washington, D.C. 20036) produce and distribute a variety of maps and related materials. The American Geographical Society (Broadway at 156th Street, New York, N.Y. 10032) engages in scholarly activities in the field of cartography but has recently discontinued the sale of books and maps. Detailed information on the kinds of cartographic products or services available may be obtained directly from each firm or national association.

sheets overlap adjoining sheets and, when joined together, form a State map that measures approximately 111 × 87 inches.

A statewide precision grid, compatible with the map projection and with automatic data plotting as well as

9:

Cartographic Information Sources

Information on cartographic products of Federal and other agencies can be obtained from a number of sources, including the National Cartographic Information Center, the National Geodetic Information Center, the Environmental Data Service, the EROS Data Center, the Library of Congress, and the various map-producing agencies.

National Cartographic Information Center

The National Cartographic Information Center (NCIC), established by the Geological Survey in 1974, provides a national information service to make cartographic data of the United States more easily accessible to the public and to various Federal, State, and local agencies. At present, more than 30 Federal agencies collect and prepare cartographic data. These data include more than 1.5 million maps and charts, 25 million aerial and space photographs, records on 1.5 million geodetic control points, and a growing collection of map data in computer-compatible form.

These data have innumerable applications relating to the Earth and its resources, including energy resource exploration and development, the construction of highways and other public works, the classification and mapping of vegetation, land use planning, and protection of the environment. NCIC uses the latest techniques of microphotography and computer technology (fig. 185) to manage the vast amount of information and to provide a focal point for information on data produced and distributed by many Federal sources. NCIC also provides information on some Federal plans for future data collection, to help eliminate duplication of effort.

NCIC does not obtain the cartographic data from present holders; rather it collects and organizes descriptive information about the data, tells where they are located, ensures their availability, and provides ordering assistance. Government and private data centers continue to hold and distribute cartographic data. Some of these centers also provide for local users direct access to NCIC information through their public service facilities; thus many government and private organizations are cooperating with the Geological Survey in forming a network of NCIC facilities.

The Geological Survey and the National Oceanic and Atmospheric Administration are the principal affiliates in the network. The network functions as summarized below.

The Geological Survey through:

▲ The National Mapping Division—
   △ Houses, funds, and manages NCIC.
   △ Maintains and distributes topographic, ortho-photo, and land use map compilation materials; digital map data; and other closely related cartographic data.
   △ Operates a system for indexing and cataloging maps and charts in cooperation with the Geography and Map Division, Library of Congress.
   △ Distributes printed topographic, hydrologic, geologic, and other maps published by the Geological Survey.
▲ The EROS (Earth Resources Observation Systems) Data Center—
   △ Stores, reproduces, and disseminates aerial and space imagery and electronic data originally acquired by NASA, various bureaus of the Department of the Interior, and some other Federal agencies.
   △ Operates and maintains an automated information and ordering system for aerial photography and space imagery and provides selected users with direct telecommunication access to the system.

FIGURE 185. The National Cartographic Information Center uses CRT computer terminals (*above*) and microfilm viewing devices (*right*) to provide fast access to information on millions of maps, charts, and aerial photographs.

The National Oceanic and Atmospheric Administration through:

▲ The National Geodetic Survey—
△ Operates and maintains the automated National Geodetic Control File.
△ Evaluates, classifies, stores, and disseminates geodetic data and provides an indexing service for geodetic data.

Some other cooperating Federal agencies with major cartographic holdings are:

▲ Agricultural Stabilization and Conservation Service—aerial photography.
▲ Bureau of Land Management—cadastral survey data, maps, and aerial photography.
▲ Cartographic Division, National Archives and Records Service—historic maps, charts, cadastral plats, aerial photography, and other related data.
▲ Geography and Map Division, Library of Congress—reference library of current and historic maps, charts and related literature.
▲ National Ocean Survey, National Oceanic and Atmospheric Administration—nautical and aeronautical charts, maps, and aerial photography.
▲ Soil Conservation Service—soil survey and other maps and aerial photography.
▲ U.S. Forest Service—maps, aerial photography, and survey data.

In addition to these major Federal affiliates, NCIC has signed agreements, as of 1980, with 27 State governments to distribute State-oriented data directly to the States. In return, each State affiliate sets up and staffs an office to distribute the information to the public and to acquire State and local cartographic data for inclusion in NCIC's data bases.

NCIC provides different levels of service for the various types of cartographic data. For general-purpose data—topographic maps and aerial photographs—the objective is to provide complete service, including the identification of specific products and assistance in ordering these products. On the other hand, only general information and referral service are provided for special-purpose cartographic data. The types of cartographic data for which NCIC offers assistance are listed below:

▲ Multiuse maps and charts including:

Aeronautical charts
Bathymetric maps
City maps
Extraterrestrial maps
Flood-plain maps
Forest maps
Geologic maps
Highway maps
Land use maps
Map and chart feature separates
Nautical charts
Orthophotomaps and orthophotoquads
River surveys and damsite maps
Slope maps
Soil maps
Topographic maps
U.S. maps
World maps

▲ Survey data including:

First- and second-order control from any source
Third-order control from any source that is useful
Selected fourth-order control
Photogrammetrically derived control
Selected private control
Land plats
Census subdivisions

▲ Aerial and space imagery from Federal, State, and private sources including:

Photographs
Satellite computer-compatible tapes
Photomosaics
Other remote-sensor data

▲ Closely related data such as:

Cartographic educational materials, atlases, gazetteers, and other related literature
Digital data representing detail on maps and charts
Geographic names

Aerial Photography Summary Record System

In 1979, the Map and Chart Information System and the Cartographic Catalog System became operational. These computer-based and microfilm-supported systems contain detailed information on all topographic map series of the National Mapping Program, as well as other major map series such as the Federal Highway Administration's County and Metropolitan Highway Series. Information from NCIC's systems is available in a standard graphical form called State-Based Graphics, in comfiche listings, and in custom searches of the system data bases.

In 1976 the Aerial Photography Summary Record System (APSRS) was developed by NCIC to provide information on aerial photography. It catalogs the planned, in-progress, and completed aerial photographic missions in the United States so that informed decisions on photograph acquisition can be made.

Inquiries should be addressed to the National Cartographic Information Center, U.S. Geological Survey National Center, Reston, Va. 22092.

National Geodetic Information Center

The National Geodetic Survey (NGS), a part of the National Ocean Survey of the National Oceanic and Atmospheric Administration, is responsible for establishing and maintaining the Nation's horizontal and vertical control networks. Control survey data are available from the National Geodetic Information Center. In addition to information on NGS control, the information center now receives input from a number of Federal agencies, including the Geological Survey, and from some State agencies. Assistance in acquiring control survey data may be obtained directly from National Geodetic Information Center, National Geodetic Survey, C18, National Ocean Survey, National Oceanic and Atmospheric Administration, Rockville, Md. 20852.

Environmental Data and Information Service

The national environmental data and information resources of NOAA's Environmental Data and Information Service (EDIS) are essential to environment-related coastal-zone programs. This service provides basic knowledge needed to plan, design, build, operate, and monitor the environmental impact of energy facilities, such as drilling rigs, supertanker ports, and floating nuclear powerplants, and to provide a level against which

Environmental Data Service

to measure pollution and its impact upon the coastal environment. EDIS data are also needed for assessing the natural state of the coastal environment for planning and management programs. EDIS works with Federal, State, and local agencies to determine coastal-zone environmental data and information needs and develops the data products necessary to meet these needs. In addition, EDIS provides experiment design and data management expertise as well as referral to data and information holdings not in its own files. Finally, to meet NOAA's obligations under the Deepwater Ports (DWP) Act of 1974, EDIS evaluates and prepares recommendations regarding DWP license applications, related environmental impact statements, and adjacent coastal States statutes as specified in the act. Assistance in obtaining these data is available from Director, Environmental Data and Information Service, National Oceanic and Atmospheric Administration, Page Building 2, 3300 Whitehaven Street, NW., Washington, D.C. 22023.

EROS Data Center

The EROS Data Center (EDC), near Sioux Falls, S. Dak., is operated by the Earth Resources Observation Systems (EROS) Program of the Department of the Interior and managed by the Geological Survey Land Information and Analysis Office. It provides access to Landsat imagery, Skylab and aerial photography, NASA aircraft data, and other remote-sensing products. Facilities are available for storage, retrieval, reproduction, and distribution, as well as for user assistance and training. The EROS Data Center reproduces and distributes (as sale items) copies of imagery, photographs, other geophysical data, and computer products collected by 16 different organizations.

Assistance in selecting imagery or in placing an order is available from User Services Unit, EROS Data Center, U.S. Geological Survey, Sioux Falls, S. Dak. 57198.

Several EROS Applications Assistance Facilities have been established. They have microfilm copies of imagery held at the EROS Data Center and provide computer terminal inquiry and order capability. Scientific personnel are available for assistance in applying the data to a variety of resource and environmental problems and for assistance in ordering data from EDC.

EROS data reference files have been established to hold microfilm copies of the data available from EDC and to provide guides to help a user review and order copies. Help is not provided at the offices where only the reference files are located. Files can be viewed at the EROS Applications Assistance Facilities and at various other locations.

Geological Survey Maps

Indexes of topographic maps published for each State, Puerto Rico, the American Virgin Islands, Guam, and American Samoa are available free on request to the Eastern Distribution Branch, U.S. Geological Survey, 1200 South Eads Street, Arlington, Va. 22202, or Western Distribution Branch, U.S. Geological Survey, P.O. Box 25286, Denver Federal Center, Denver, Colo. 80225. The indexes contain lists of special maps, addresses of local map reference libraries, local map dealers, and Federal map distribution centers. An order blank and detailed instructions for ordering maps are supplied with each index.

Mail orders for State maps may be sent to the Arlington address for areas east of the Mississippi River or to the Denver address for areas west of the river. Payment may be made by money order or check payable to the Geological Survey.

In 1980, a new system was adopted for listing and describing the products available from the National Mapping Program. Under this system, an index booklet (in a new format) and a companion catalog are planned for each State. The index booklet (fig. 186) shows the map coverage for five map categories:

Δ 7.5-minute series.
Δ 1:100,000-scale series.
Δ 1:250,000-scale series.
Δ International Map of the World series.
Δ Sectional map series and State map series.

Indexes and catalogs in the new format have been completed for Ohio and nearly completed for several other States.

The catalog of the published maps for each State contains:

Δ An alphabetical listing of topographic maps, orthophotoquads, and orthophotomaps (grouped by map scale), including map date, type, and location.
Δ List describing other county, State, national park, and special-purpose maps.
Δ List describing products of wider interest, such as U.S. and selected *National Atlas* maps.
Δ List of map reference libraries and commercial map dealers located in the State.
Δ Order forms for maps and open-file products.

National Ocean Survey

Nautical Chart Catalogs

The National Ocean Survey (NOS) issues nautical chart catalogs of the nearly 1,000 different charts available for American coastal waters. The following nautical chart catalogs are available free from Distribution Division, C64, National Ocean Survey, National Oceanic and Atmospheric Administration, Riverdale, Md. 20840:

Δ **Nautical Chart Catalog 1,** Atlantic and gulf coasts, including Puerto Rico and the Virgin Islands.
Δ **Nautical Chart Catalog 2,** Pacific coast, including Hawaii, Guam, and Samoa.
Δ **Nautical Chart Catalog 3,** Alaska, including the Aleutian Islands.
Δ **Great Lakes** and adjacent waterways.

Figure 187 shows part of the nautical chart index map for Hawaii, from *Nautical Chart Catalog 2.*

A separate free publication, *Dates of Latest Editions of Nautical Charts,* is issued quarterly to aid mariners in obtaining up-to-date charts. NOS also provides information and indexes on the following lake and river charts:

Δ **Lakes**—Cayuga, Champlain, Great Lakes, Mead, Minnesota-Ontario border lakes, Okeechobee, Oneida, Pend Oreille, Franklin D. Roosevelt, Seneca, Tahoe.
Δ **Rivers**—Caloosahatchee, Columbia, Connecticut, Delaware, Hudson, James, Kennebec, Neuse, New, New York State Barge Canal, Pamlico, Penobscot, Potomac, Rappahannock, Savannah, St. Johns, St. Lawrence to Cornwall, York, and others.

List of World, United States, and Historical Maps

A list of *Frequently Used Federal Government World, United States, and Historical Maps* is available free from the Map Information Office, Map Library, C513, National Ocean Survey, Rockville, Md. 20852. For each map on the list, the identifying number, description (including projection, scale, size, and map characteristics), publisher, and price are given.

Also included are several projections for small-scale maps.

TO LOCATE SPECIFIC AREA OF INTEREST

1. **Refer to the State diagram shown on the opposite page to locate the block covering your** *general area* **of interest**

2. **Refer to the page indicated in the block to locate your** *specific area* **of interest**

3. **Refer to the coded list of available maps for the name of the map you desire. Refer to the** *Catalog of Published Maps* **for the dates of available maps**

Example: *General area* **of interest—Chillicothe**

Example: *Specific area* **of interest—Dundas**

Example: *Name of map* **desired—McArthur**

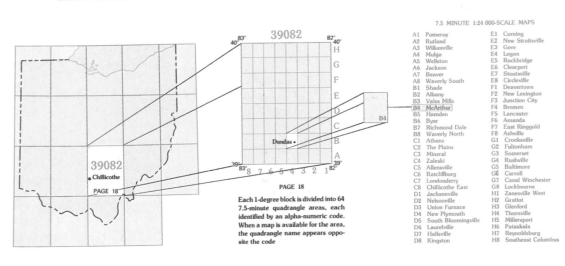

7.5 MINUTE 1:24 000-SCALE MAPS

A1	Pomeroy	E1	Corning
A2	Rutland	E2	New Straitsville
A3	Wilkesville	E3	Gore
A4	Mulga	E4	Logan
A5	Wellston	E5	Rockbridge
A6	Jackson	E6	Clearport
A7	Beaver	E7	Stoutsville
A8	Waverly South	E8	Circleville
B1	Shade	F1	Deavertown
B2	Albany	F2	New Lexington
B3	Vales Mills	F3	Junction City
B4	McArthur	F4	Bremen
B5	Hamden	F5	Lancaster
B6	Byer	F6	Amanda
B7	Richmond Dale	F7	East Ringgold
B8	Waverly North	F8	Ashville
C1	Athens	G1	Crooksville
C2	The Plains	G2	Fultonham
C3	Mineral	G3	Somerset
C4	Zaleski	G4	Rushville
C5	Allensville	G5	Baltimore
C6	Ratcliffburg	G6	Carroll
C7	Londonderry	G7	Canal Winchester
C8	Chillicothe East	G8	Lockbourne
D1	Jacksonville	H1	Zanesville West
D2	Nelsonville	H2	Gratiot
D3	Union Furnace	H3	Glenford
D4	New Plymouth	H4	Thornville
D5	South Bloomingville	H5	Millersport
D6	Laurelville	H6	Pataskala
D7	Hallsville	H7	Reynoldsburg
D8	Kingston	H8	Southeast Columbus

Each 1-degree block is divided into 64 7.5-minute quadrangle areas, each identified by an alpha-numeric code. When a map is available for the area, the quadrangle name appears opposite the code

STATE MAP SERIES
1:500 000 AND 1:1 000 000 SCALE

1 X 2 DEGREE SERIES
1:250 000 SCALE

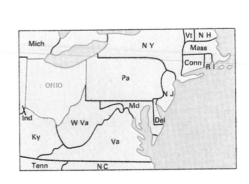

SECTIONAL MAP SERIES
1:2 000 000 SCALE
National Atlas Sheet 8: Middle Atlantic States

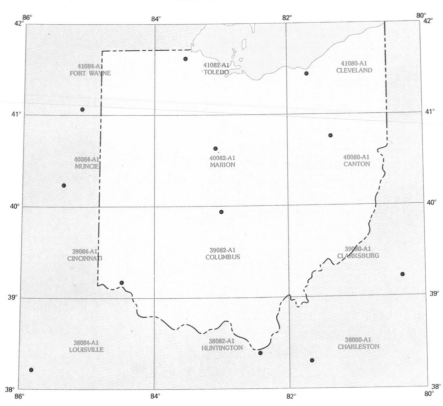

See companion *Catalog of topographic and other Published Maps* for types, dates, and prices of available maps and instructions for ordering

Refer to the State location map (opposite) which is shown divided into 1 degree blocks of latitude and longitude, with each block identified with its origin at the southeast corner.

Example: Chillicothe is located in block 3982 (39° latitude and 82° longitude) which is shown in detail on page 18.

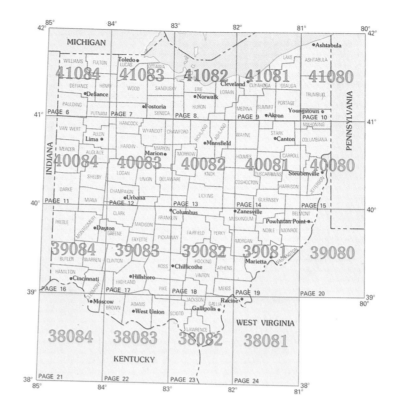

FIGURE 186. Excerpts from Ohio index booklet of topographic and other map coverage, reduced here to approximately two-thirds size.

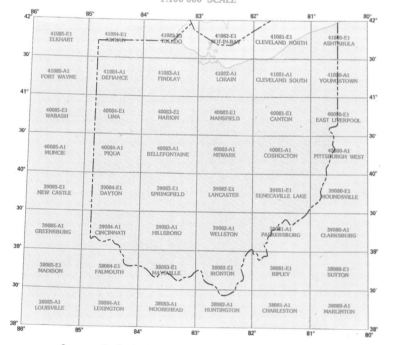

See companion *Catalog of topographic and other Published Maps* for types, dates, and prices of available maps and instructions for ordering

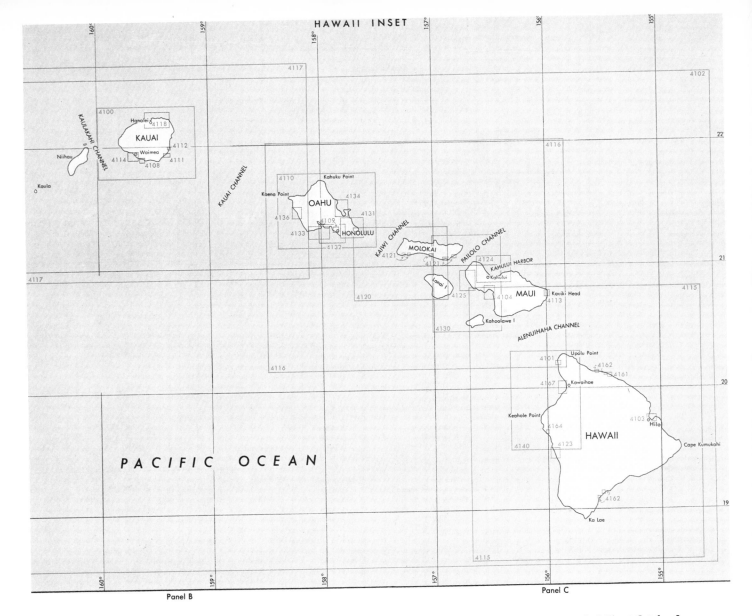

FIGURE 187. Index (reduced) of nautical charts of Hawaii, from National Ocean Survey *Nautical Chart Catalog 2.*

Aeronautical Chart Catalog

The National Ocean Survey publishes and frequently revises a *Catalog of Aeronautical Charts and Related Publications.* This catalog (fig. 188) contains index maps showing coverage for the following kinds of charts:

Δ Sectional and VFR (visual flight rules) terminal area charts.
Δ World aeronautical charts.
Δ En route low-altitude charts.
Δ En route high-altitude and RNAV (area navigation) charts.
Δ Alaska en route charts.
Δ Aircraft position charts.
Δ Planning charts.
Δ Instrument approach procedure charts.
Δ World aeronautical and operational navigation charts (published by DMAAC—Defense Mapping Agency Aerospace Center).
Δ Jet navigation charts (published by DMAAC).
Δ Global navigation charts (published by DMAAC).

The catalog also describes:

Δ Airport taxi charts.
Δ SID (standard instrument departure) and STAR (standard terminal arrival route) charts.
Δ Alaska terminal publication.
Δ Related publications.
Δ Auxiliary charts.

To insure that only the latest charts are used, regularly revised lists titled *Dates of Latest Editions* are published for the several series of aeronautical charts. These lists, as well as the latest *Catalog of Aeronautical Charts and Related Publications,* are available free from the Distribution Division of NOS.

Cartographic Information Sources

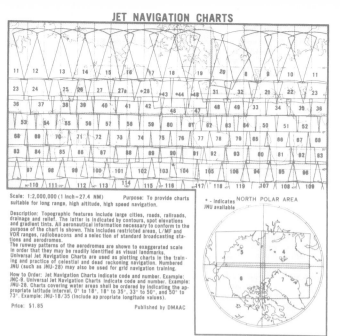

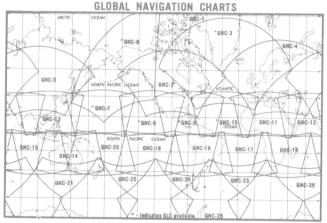

FIGURE 188. Page from National Ocean Survey *Catalog of Aeronautical Charts and Related Publications.*

Geodetic Control Diagrams

The National Geodetic Survey (NGS) and the Geological Survey cooperate to publish a series of geodetic control diagrams (fig. 189) showing the location and quality of geodetic control, with additional control data from other Government agencies as deemed necessary. These geodetic control diagrams provide a cartographic index as to the availability of geodetic data and are used extensively by Federal, State, local, and private organizations involved in land planning, surveying and mapping, and civil engineering projects. They are published at a scale of 1:250,000, each diagram spanning 1 degree latitude and 2 degrees longitude or an average of about 6,500 mi² (16,800 km²) each.

The cooperative agreement between NOS (for NGS) and the Geological Survey requires that each agency appraise its control data and summarize the information to be shown on the diagrams. All the control is plotted and shown in approximately its true geographic location on the diagram. This control consists of all triangulation stations; located objects such as water tanks, church spires, courthouse steeples, forest fire lookout towers; level lines and nets; measured base lines; and various types of traverse surveys. When the Geological Survey receives the plotted data from the contributing agencies, plastic overlays are prepared and scribed. Press-plate film negatives are then prepared and forwarded to the NGS where the diagrams are printed.

The diagram base, printed in blue, depicts the same planimetric features as shown on the Geological Survey 1:250,000-scale series topographic maps. Horizontal and vertical control, established or adjusted by the National Geodetic Survey, is shown in black, and an outline of its 30-minute quadrangle designation is shown in gray. Horizontal and vertical control, established by the Geological Survey, is shown in solid and screened red, and each 15-minute quadrangle area is outlined and numbered in red. Other Federal agency control is shown in brown or buff.

Marginal information includes symbols designating the order and type (horizontal or vertical) control established by each agency; the geodetic control quadrangle reference systems used by the National Geodetic Survey and Geological Survey, as well as ordering instructions; and various other information such as county, State, and international boundaries, plane coordinates zones, road and railroad data, names, bar scales, location diagrams, and compilation data.

Indexes of the published diagrams are available free of charge from the National Cartographic Information Center, U.S. Geological Survey, Mail Stop 507, National Center, Reston, Va. 22092, or the National Geodetic Survey, National Geodetic Information Center, C18, Rockville, Md. 20852.

Tennessee Valley Authority

Indexes of topographic maps of the Tennessee Valley watershed show the availability of several classes of maps:

Δ Standard 7.5-minute TVA-USGS topographic maps.
Δ Preimpoundment maps (showing underwater contours mapped prior to completion of dams).
Δ Project maps (showing proposed pools for dams under construction or planned).
Δ Large-scale topographic maps for reservoirs.

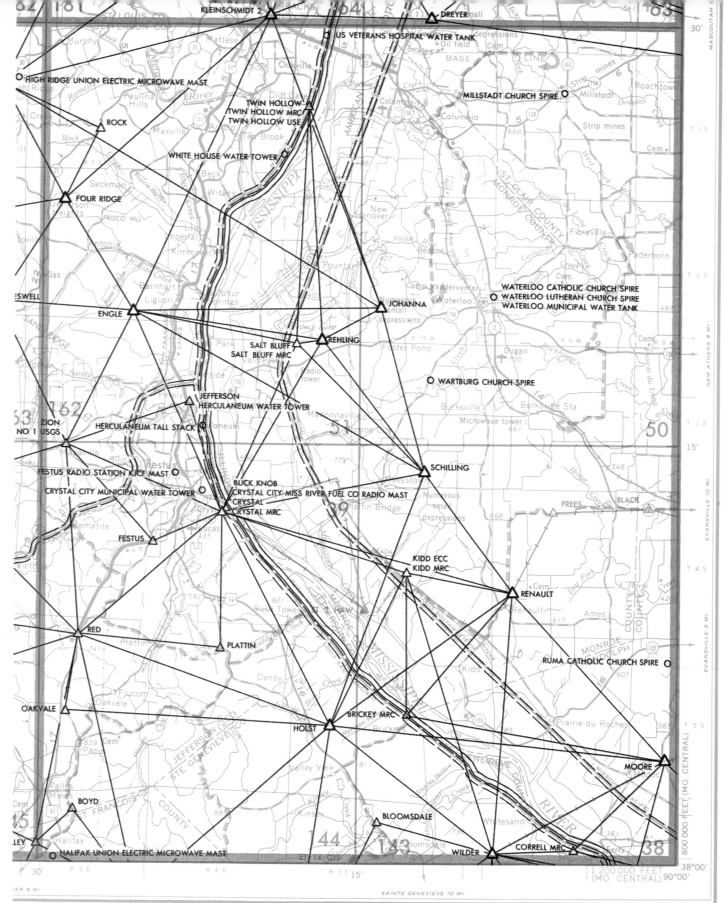

USCOMM – NOAA – DC   MAY 1971   A-5584

FIGURE 189. Portion of a 1:250,000-scale geodetic control diagram. This portion covers a 30-minute quadrangle; the entire diagram covers eight 30-minute quadrangles. (St. Louis, Missouri-Illinois, quadrangle.)

Cartographic Information Sources

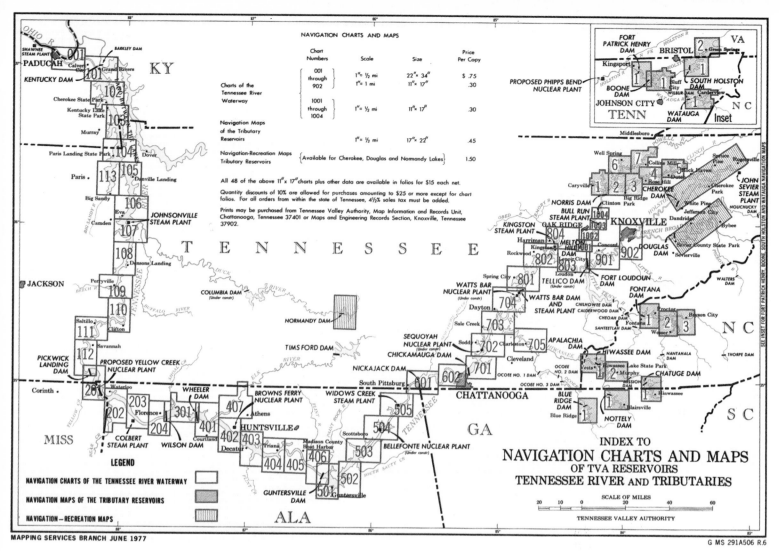

FIGURE 190. Index (reduced) to TVA navigation charts and maps.

TVA also publishes an *Index to Navigation Charts and Maps of TVA Reservoirs* (fig. 190) and an *Index to Recreation Maps—Tennessee Valley Lakes*. A price catalog and indexes may be obtained free from Mapping Services Branch, Tennessee Valley Authority, 200 Haney Building, Chattanooga, Tenn. 37401. Control data bulletins may be obtained from the same address.

Defense Mapping Agency

General information on the maps available from the Defense Mapping Agency (DMA) is given in the *Price List of Maps and Charts for Public Sale,* available free from DMA Topographic Center, 6500 Brookes Lane, Attn: 55510, Washington, D.C. 20315. This publication describes nine small-scale topographic map series (covering foreign and worldwide areas) and two plastic relief map series (worldwide and Puerto Rico). Plastic relief maps at 1:250,000 scale of the continental United States and Hawaii are not sold by DMA but may be purchased from T. N. Hubbard Scientific Company, 2855 Shermer Road, Northbrook, Ill. 60062.

A complete listing of nautical charts available from DMA is tabulated in the DMA Hydrographic Center (DMAHC) *Numerical Listing of Charts* (Pub. 1–N–L). Names and addresses of the DMAHC sales agents and ordering instructions are given in the DMAHC *Catalog of Nautical Charts* (Pub. 1–N–A). These are available free of charge from the Defense Mapping Agency Depot, Clearfield, Utah 84016, or 5801 Tabor Avenue, Philadelphia, Pa. 19120.

The *Catalog of Nautical Charts* covers nine regions:

Region	Area of coverage and chart numbers listed
1	United States and Canada: charts 11000–19999.
2	Central and South America and Antarctica: charts 21000–29999.
3	Western Europe, Iceland, Greenland and the Arctic: charts 31000–39999.
4	Scandinavia, Baltic, and USSR: charts 41000–49999.
5	Western Africa and the Mediterranean: charts 51000–59999.
6	Indian Ocean: charts 61000–69999.
7	Australia, Indonesia, and New Zealand: charts 71000–79999.
8	Oceania: charts 81000–89999.
9	East Asia: charts 91000–99999.
1–N–A	Miscellaneous and special-purpose navigational charts, sheets, and publications: charts 1–9999.

The DMA Aerospace Center (DMAAC) publishes aeronautical charts covering foreign areas. These charts, as well as domestic aeronautical charts, are sold to civilian users by NOS.

Library of Congress

The Library of Congress Geography and Map Division has on file many maps and publications covering a great variety of cartographic subjects. The *List of Publications* issued free by this division provides information on the kinds of maps and other cartographic materials available at the Library of Congress.

U.S. Army Corps of Engineers

Information on nautical charts of rivers showing water depths and navigation data and indexes showing water areas and number of charts required to cover them may be obtained from the district offices of the U.S. Army Corps of Engineers as listed below:

▲ Louisville District, P.O. Box 59, Louisville, Ky. 40201.
  Δ Rivers: Ohio and tributaries.
▲ Huntington District, P.O. Box 2127, Huntington, W. Va. 25721.
  Δ Rivers: Big Sandy, Kanawha, Ohio.
▲ Pittsburgh District, 1000 Liberty Avenue, Federal Building, Pittsburgh, Pa. 15222.
  Δ Rivers: Allegheny, Monongahela, Upper Ohio.
▲ Nashville District, P.O. Box 1070, Nashville, Tenn. 37202.
  Δ Rivers: Cumberland, Tennessee.
▲ Chicago District, 219 South Dearborn Street, Chicago, Ill. 60604.
  Δ Rivers: Middle and Upper Mississippi and Illinois Waterway to Lake Michigan.
▲ Omaha District, 6014 USPO and Courthouse, 215 North 17th Street, Omaha, Nebr. 68102.
  Δ River: Missouri.
▲ Kansas City District, 700 Federal Building, Kansas City, Mo. 64106.
  Δ River: Missouri.

▲ Vicksburg District, P.O. Box 60, Vicksburg, Miss. 39180.
  Δ Rivers: Atchafalaya, Big Sunflower, Calcasieu, Lower Mississippi and Illinois Waterway to Lake Michigan.
▲ Other: Navigation map of the Gulf Intracoastal Waterway.

State and Local Sources

Mapping programs of State and local jurisdictions are in various stages of development; map information services available from these jurisdictions vary likewise in extent. The State of New York exemplifies the more extensive State programs. The following statement appears on an announcement of New York's map information services:

Information on map and aerial photo coverage of New York State is available to the general public through the Map Information Unit. Although sales by this Unit are limited to Department of Transportation maps, it maintains files on other coverage of New York available from State, Federal, and local governments and commercial firms. A wide variety of material is covered, including planimetric and topographic base mapping, geologic and soils mapping, aeronautical charts, tax mapping, hydrographic charts, satellite imagery, and aerial photography. Index/status maps and other materials are available on request for selected map and photo materials. In addition, the Unit maintains a map/photo collection which the public is welcome to use in the Unit's office.

If you need information on sources of map and photo coverage for New York State direct your inquiries to the Map Information Unit at the following address, or visit the Unit's office on the State Campus: Map Information Unit, New York State Department of Transportation, State Campus, Building 4, Room 105, Albany, N.Y. 12232.

Inquiries concerning cartographic programs in other States and local jurisdictions should be directed either to the cognizant State or local agency or to the National Cartographic Information Center.

CARTOGRAPHIC PRODUCTS. Customers being served at the public map sales counter in the Geological Survey's Denver Branch of Distribution, Central Region.

10:

Future Trends in Cartography

New tools already in hand include automation techniques, digital applications, inertial navigation systems, remote-sensing technology, and applications of space science. In the future we shall certainly use them more effectively, and inevitably develop other technologies to meet changing requirements for cartographic products.

As the techniques for surveying and mapping change with new technology, so too will cartographic products change to exploit the new scientific tools and to meet changing requirements for map data. New tools that we have in hand include electronic computers, automation techniques, digital applications, electronic distance-measurement procedures, inertial navigation systems, remote-sensing technology, and applications of space science. We are just beginning to learn how to use these tools; in the future we shall certainly use them more effectively, and inevitably we shall develop other technologies. By extrapolating from state-of-the-art developments, it is not too risky to make some predictions.

Map Format and Symbolization

It can be expected that the classical form of maps, in which features are represented by lines and symbols, will eventually be supplemented or replaced to a large extent by photoimage maps or sensor-image maps. Map formats and symbolization will be changed radically to accommodate techniques of cartographic automation (fig. 191). Maps of the future, especially image maps, will tend to erode the user's dependence on standard map symbols as the medium of communication. The map user will become a photointerpreter; he will recognize the narrow white thread on the image map as a highway and will not need a double-line black symbol to identify the road. In this sense, the role of the standard map symbol will be a declining one.

In another sense, however, there will be a need for a new set of standard symbols. These will be automatable symbols—symbols that can be programed into an automatic plotter or that can be identified by an automatic character-recognition device. A change to such symbols requires that mapmakers and map users accept the idea of flexibility in the esthetic standards for cartography.

The question of esthetics will doubtless remain a debatable issue. Does the map have eye appeal? Does it have an attractive, well-balanced collar? Does it have beauty of color and line and texture? The answers to these questions are matters of subjective judgment.

There is a school of thought which holds that it is not worth one penny to make the map more attractive, so long as it is readable and clearly communicates the desired information. Why not use a typewritten map collar, the argument runs, instead of typesetting it? Conversely, the very thought of a typewritten map collar may dismay a veteran cartographer or discriminating map user.

Map Content

Maps of the future will have a diversity of content far exceeding that of the present. Thematic maps, many of them automatically produced, will cover a broad and crowded spectrum of cartographic representations involving a wide variety of disciplines (fig. 192). Cartographic information will be compiled and stored in digital form at a central data bank which can be queried at distant points through computer terminals to provide needed information (in either digital or graphic form), or to provide special products such as tactual maps for the blind (figs. 193 and 194).

The image map of the future will offer a new standard for completeness. Whereas the line map or data bank will supply only the data that have been selected, the image map will supply everything that the camera or other sensor can record.

FIGURE 191. Portion of an experimental map on a grid format. New symbols and line weights simplify drafting and lend themselves to digitizing; for example, dots are eliminated from spot and linear symbols. (San Juan, Puerto Rico, 1:20,000-scale quadrangle.)

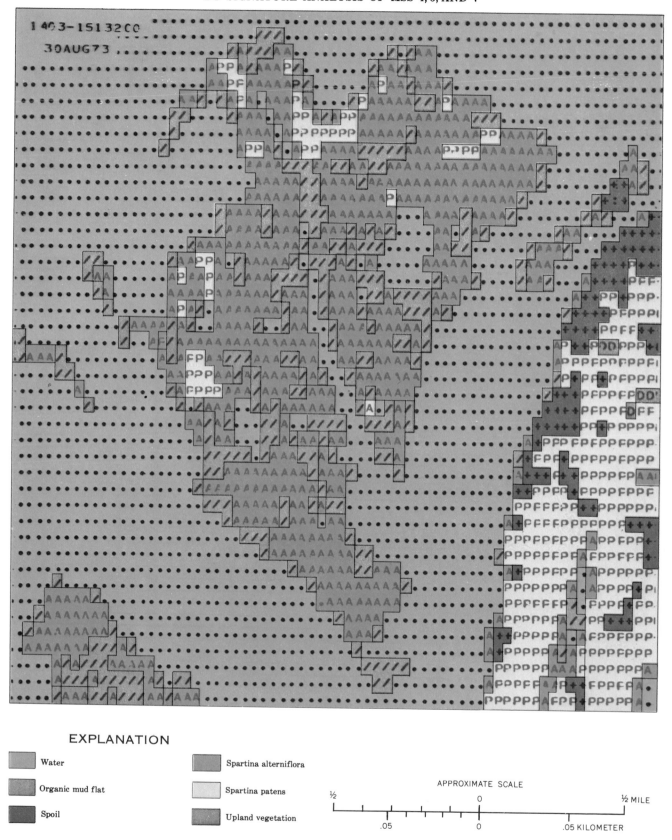

CHINCOTEAGUE MARSH, VA.
PLOT OF WETLAND CLASSES DETERMINED
BY SIGNATURE ANALYSIS OF MSS 4, 5, AND 7

EXPLANATION

Water

Organic mud flat

Spoil

Spartina alterniflora

Spartina patens

Upland vegetation

APPROXIMATE SCALE

½   0   ½ MILE

.05   0   .05 KILOMETER

FIGURE 192. Computer-processed wetland map of the Chincoteague Bay salt-marsh complex, Virginia Eastern Shore.

Map Content

229

FIGURE 193. This experimental tactual map, produced at the University of Washington, has raised representations of features. Names are given in braille so that the blind reader can read both the name and the shape of each feature.

FIGURE 194. Portion of braille edition of Geological Survey 1:24,000-scale map of metropolitan Washington, D. C., showing raised representations of linear cultural features such as principal streets and traffic circles. Parks are indicated by a raised area pattern. Major features are identified in braille (shown here at 1:32,000-scale).

The ability to maintain the currency of a map will be greatly enhanced by the use of new automated techniques for updating map content. An orthophotoquad, in particular, has a great advantage over a conventional line map with respect to timeliness; the orthophotoquad can be updated frequently at relatively low cost through the use of new photography.

Reference Systems

It can be expected that, in the future, survey and map data will be expressed in terms of a universally accepted system of rectangular coordinates that is mathematically relatable to the Earth's surface. Computerized land data records will be accepted as legal descriptions, and property transactions will be computerized.

In anticipation of the need to achieve compatibility with future trends in mapping, the Survey issued the following statement, dated August 23, 1974, on "Reference Systems for the National Mapping Program":

The Geological Survey recognizes the importance and utility of the following reference systems for recording and using position data pertaining to identified points or objects:

1. Geographic coordinates (latitude and longitude).
2. Universal Transverse Mercator (UTM) rectangular coordinates.
3. State Plane Coordinates.
4. Other plane rectangular coordinate systems that are mathematically relatable to geodetic positions via defined map projections.
5. Public Land Surveys.

Although different systems will be used to meet different needs, there are obvious advantages to the maximum use of a single plane coordinate reference system. For compatibility with future trends in mapping, the system should be in metric units and should require a minimum number of zones without compromising cartographic accuracy. Accordingly, the Geological Survey intends to encourage the adoption of the Universal Transverse Mercator system as the basic reference for use with the products of the National Mapping Program.

To implement this philosophy, the Geological Survey will show a full fine-line UTM grid on its published maps at scale 1:1,000,000 or larger, except in special cases for which it is not appropriate or not justified. Public land lines and marginal indicators of State Plane Coordinates will continue to be shown on those Geological Survey maps where they are now shown. Other recognized reference systems will be shown by marginal indicators to the extent justified and practical.

The Geological Survey advocates that the UTM reference system be used to the maximum extent feasible on maps made by other organizations, and for data collections which are related to maps.

To expedite convenient use of the recognized reference systems, the Geological Survey will provide information for conversion of positions from other recognized systems to the UTM system and vice versa.

The system of describing the positions of control points on the Earth's surface will probably undergo a radical change in the future to be compatible with new techniques that will be used to determine these positions. The new system, based on a unified world datum ellipsoid and geoid, may be a geocentric coordinate system with positions of points expressed in three dimensions—latitude and longitude (easily converted to acceptable rectangular coordinate systems) and elevation (expressed as a radial distance from the center of the Earth).

Measurement System

As the United States converts from the customary to the metric system of measurement, American maps are being published in the metric system. In a few years, maps will be considered nonstandard and outdated if they are not so constructed.

The metric system poses no great difficulties for mapmakers and map users. The Geological Survey maps of Puerto Rico have for many years been produced in the metric system at scales of 1:30,000 and 1:20,000. In 1974 the Survey produced 7.5-minute topographic quadrangle maps in the metric system for areas of Alaska, and the 1:100,000-scale series started in 1975 was constructed in the metric system from its inception. The Survey now shows a full fine-line UTM (metric) grid on its published maps at scale 1:1,000,000 or larger. There will undoubtedly be some growing pains in the transition, and it will be necessary to educate the map-using community in the use of the new measurement standard.

Geological Survey Policy on Metric Base Maps

Following the passage of the Metric Conversion Act of 1975, the Survey adopted a policy in 1977 for the systematic conversion of its National Mapping Program to the metric system. Details of the policy were worked out over a considerable period of time with consideration given not only to in-house production problems of conversion but also to the impact conversion will have on the map-using community. Advice and comments were solicited from a broad cross-section of users including all States, some 40 Federal agencies, educators, private surveying and mapping firms, and professional societies. The policy is flexible with regard to the timing of conversion in the various States since the situation varies from State to State, some being willing to convert immediately while others prefer to have their quadrangle mapping completed at a common scale before conversion. The policy is concerned primarily with new mapping and revision work and does not fully address the problem of how to convert the 40,000 published quadrangle maps. This major conversion is being considered and will be the subject of a subsequent policy statement. The current Survey policy (1979) is:

In accord with the national intent to convert to the metric system, the Geological Survey will pursue a policy of proceeding with metrication as rapidly as possible, compatible with production goals and objectives and with due consideration for map user needs. All new and completely revised small-scale and intermediate-scale maps will be prepared using the International System of Units (SI). Completely revised standard quadrangle maps formerly prepared in the English system will now be prepared in the metric system. New standard quadrangle maps will be prepared in either one or a combination of the systems for the time being, depending on the unique situation in each state. The objective is to ultimately prepare all products of the National Mapping Program in the metric system.

The map elements to be shown in metric units are contours, elevations and distances, bathymetric contours and soundings, and the Universal Transverse Mercator (UTM) rectangular coordinate reference system:

Map Scales. The scales for maps prepared in the metric system will be 1:25,000, 1:50,000, 1:100,000, 1:250,000, 1:500,000, and 1:1,000,000. The Puerto Rico series will continue to be prepared at 1:20,000 scale.

Contour Intervals. The basic contour intervals for the various map scales will be 1, 2, 5, 10, 20, 50, and 100 meters.

Elevations and Distances. Elevations will be shown in meters. Distances will be shown in kilometers.

Bathymetric Contours and Soundings. Bathymetric contours will be shown in meters at intervals appropriate to map scale. Soundings will be shown in meters.

Universal Transverse Mercator (UTM) Grid. The full-line UTM grid will be shown in meters in accordance with provisions contained in the Statement on Reference Systems, dated August 23, 1974.

Planning for conversion to the metric system of the various map series will be accomplished in accordance with the following guidelines and will be coordinated with the States and other Federal agencies as appropriate.

Complete Metrication—preparation of fully metric maps, i.e., all map elements are shown in the metric system. Included in this category are:

Δ New 1:25,000-scale 7.5-minute maps on agreement with the state.

Δ Remapping, at 1:25,000 scale, of areas presently covered by 1:24,000-scale 7.5-minute maps.

Δ New 1:50,000-scale and 1:100,000-scale county and standard-format maps (exception may be granted for ongoing county mapping program if States insist).

Δ Complete revision of 1:250,000-scale series maps and 1:50,000-scale State base series maps.

Δ New and complete revision of maps in the National Park Series and other special area maps.

Δ All feature new-series national base maps.

Partial Metrication—preparation of maps where one or more map elements is in the metric system. Included in this category are:

Δ New 1:24,000-scale 7.5-minute maps prepared with metric contours and elevations in States that prefer metrication but where it is agreed that 1:24,000-scale maps are needed temporarily to maintain scale continuity.

Δ Standard and interim revision and reprints of existing 1:24,000-scale maps published at 1:25,000 scale on agreement with the State.

Deferred Metrication—partial or complete metrication deferred. Maps in this category include:

Δ New 7.5-minute 1:24,000-scale maps prepared with foot-unit contours in States that prefer delaying converting to the metric system until complete 1:24,000-scale coverage is available for that State.

To implement this policy on metrication, the Survey produced its first 1:25,000-scale metric topographic map in 1978 (fig. 195). The map has a double-quad format depicting the same area as two of the 1:24,000-scale maps; the long dimension of the 7.5- by 15-minute format is in the east-west direction. Several cartographic innovations with respect to symbology, typography, and colors are introduced in this new series (fig. 196). The series is designed for both a flat edition and a folded edition which comes in a zip-lock resealable plastic pouch. Maps in this series also include a set of additional geographic coordinate ticks shown at the four map corners. These ticks indicate the predicted change in coordinates from the North American datum of 1927 to the new North American datum of 1983 which is now in preparation.

Role of Research

The task of matching the ever-growing demand for new and better map products with the sophisticated tools of modern science falls to the researchers. Working at universities, in government agencies, and in private companies, research engineers and scientists have advanced the cartographic art from the crude methods of the past to the relatively advanced methods of the 1970's. Much remains to be done before mapmaking can become a completely automated procedure and before the catalog of cartographic products meets with universal satisfaction.

FIGURE 195. Portion of a 7.5 × 15-minute metric topographic map. The face side of the folded version is indicated by the light green panel (*upper right*). The dashed corner ticks (*arrow*) show the movement necessary to place the map on the projected North American datum of 1983. (Lake Placid, N.Y., 1:25,000-scale quadrangle.)

7.5X15 MINUTE SERIES (TOPOGRAPHIC)

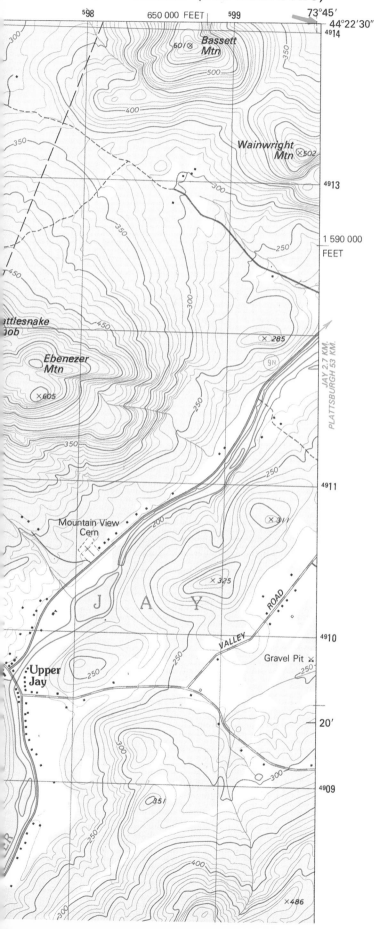

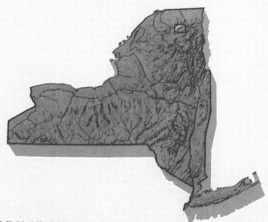

4473–231–T25

1:25 000-scale *metric* topographic map of

Lake Placid
NEW YORK

7.5 X 15 MINUTE QUADRANGLE SHOWING

- Contours and elevations in meters
- Highways, roads and other manmade structures
- Water features
- Woodland areas
- Geographic names

GEOLOGICAL SURVEY

1979

Produced by the United States Geological Survey

Control by USGS and NOS/NOAA

Compiled by photogrammetric methods from aerial photographs taken 1976. Field checked 1976
Limited field revision 1979. Map edited 1979

Projection and 1000-meter grid, zone 18: Universal Transverse Mercator
10,000-foot grid ticks based on New York coordinate system, east zone. 1927 North American Datum
To place on the predicted North American Datum 1983 move the projection lines 2 meters south and 32 meters west as shown by dashed corner ticks

There may be private inholdings within the boundaries of the National or State reservations shown on this map

This area also covered by 1:25 000-scale orthophotoquad

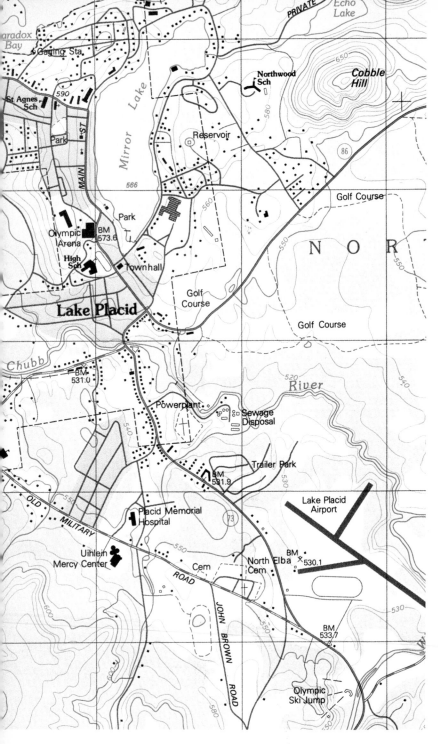

FIGURE 196. Innovations in symbology, typography, and colors shown in built-up area on 7.5 × 15-minute metric topographic map. (Lake Placid, N.Y., 1:25,000-scale quadrangle.)

By extrapolating from developments already conceived, one can forecast the research paths that are likely to lead to better and more economical maps and related materials (for example, see ITEK,1981,for a study of Mapsat concept). Some developments for which extensive research should prove fruitful are:

Δ Increased use of sensors other than optical photography, made practicable by substantial improvements in the quality of imagery from those sensors.

Δ Improvement of inertial survey systems to the point where they can give the precise position and elevation of a sensor at any desired instant.

Δ Use of inertial positioning and height-finding systems in the field and automated aerotriangulation in the office to reduce the cost of ground control needed for surveys.

Δ Improvement in air and space technology so that basic imagery and other data can increasingly be acquired by high-altitude aircraft and space vehicles.

Δ Improvement of automated systems for simultaneously producing orthophotographs, contours, and digital terrain models.

Δ Improvement of systems for theme extraction, automatic classification, and derivation of specialized information by manipulation of images from various sensors.

Δ Development of a completely automated mapping process.

Δ Development of new cartographic products in graphic, digital, or image form.

Δ Complete conversion of map products to the metric system.

Δ Adoption of a universally accepted map reference system.

Δ Modification of standards for maps including symbology, format, and styles to make them more compatible with modern requirements.

None can say with certainty what the fruits of scientific research will be in the year 2000 or 1990 or even next year. Moreover, none can say what technological progress will spring forth from research already completed; where we need no new scientific breakthrough but only practical and efficient applications of the knowledge already in hand. Who can doubt that in the near future you will be able to feed the name of a place, a desired map scale, and a selected theme into a computer input device and almost immediately have a map of that area showing the desired theme at the specified scale displayed on the computer console or printed on a map sheet? All the basic research needed for developing the technology of such a system has been completed. We need only to supply the engineering, the funds, and the incentive to construct the needed data bank and the system hardware and software.

New basic research—often in fields that seem remote from cartography—is bound to produce possibilities for rapid automated cartography, especially in the production of thematic maps. The concept that seems distant today will be the prevailing practice of tomorrow. Only two decades ago, the concept of measuring distances by means of electromagnetic waves was considered far out and was sometimes ridiculed. Today, surveyors and mapmakers use electronic distance-measuring systems as a routine practice. Who knows what new concepts will evolve in the next few years? One can be sure only that there will indeed be new concepts applied to mapmaking and that they will result in cheaper, more accurate, and more useful maps.

Future Trends in Cartography

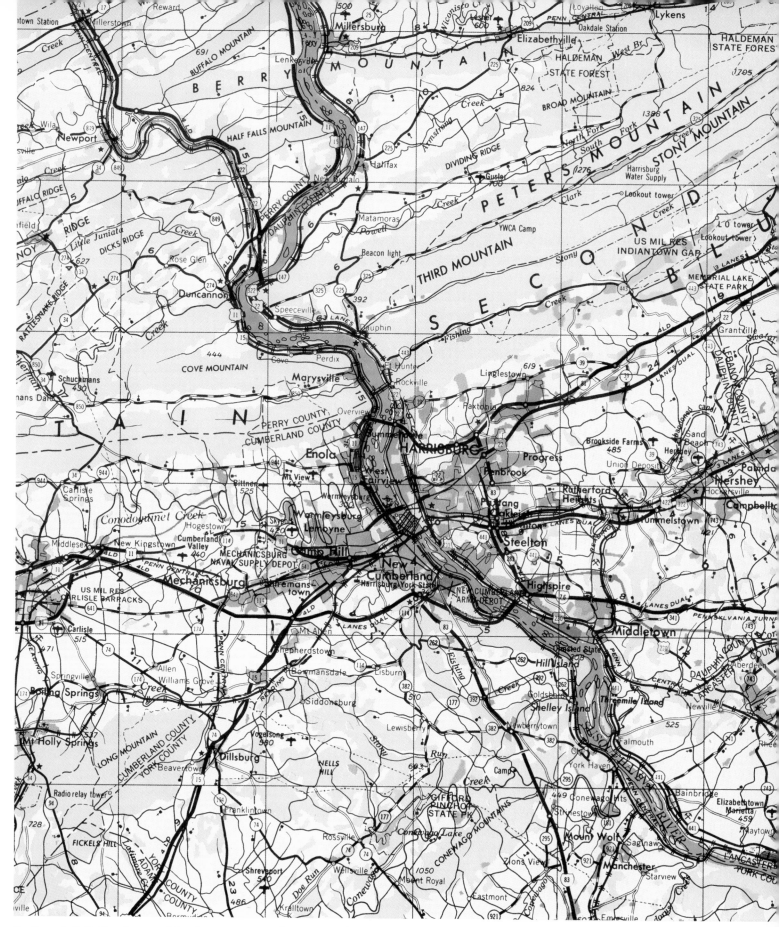

Portion of digital land use and land cover map, scale 1:250,000 (Harrisburg, Pa., 1°×2° quadrangle). The USGS Level II land use tints, plotted automatically on a large-format laser plotter, replace hundreds of polygon boundaries and numerical labels that otherwise would be applied manually.

Role of Research

235

Portion of computer-plotted polygon-style map of land use and land cover for Three Mile Island and vicinity, with census tracts, scale 1:100,000. Following the March 1979 nuclear accident at Three Mile Island, a basic unannotated map of the area was prepared. Because of the use of digital techniques, preparation of the map required only one evening's time.

Map Projections, Reference Systems, and Geodetic Control

Only a globe, or a portion of one, can truly portray the Earth's surface. The obvious inconvenience of such a curved surface for mapping has led mathematicians and cartographers to devise projection systems (McDonnell, 1979). The following are fundamental to the concepts of map projections and reference systems:

Δ **Map projection.** A system to portray all or part of the round Earth on a plane surface. Some systems are projected geometrically; others, mathematically.

Δ **Graticule.** A network of lines or ticks representing the geographic parallels and meridians forming the map projection.

Δ **Grid.** Two sets of parallel lines intersecting at right angles, forming a rectangular Cartesian coordinate system superimposed on a map projection. Sometimes the term "grid" is used loosely to mean the projection system itself rather than the rectangular system superimposed on the projection.

The basic problem of map projection is to reduce to the map plane the terrestrial properties of true areas, shapes, distances, and directions. This includes the condition that the meridians pass through the Earth's poles and that they intersect all parallels at right angles (see fig. 197).

Since it is impossible to preserve all these properties simultaneously, it is necessary to select a projection preserving the property most desired, usually correct areas or correct shapes. The factors in this selection are:

Δ **Areas.** Any area on the Earth's surface should be represented by the same area at the scale of the map; that is, a coin placed anywhere on such a map would always cover the same-size area of the Earth's surface as represented on the map. Such projections are termed "equal-area" or "equivalent."

Δ **Distances.** The distances between points on the Earth should be correctly represented on the map. This can be done only on some favored line or lines, such as the Equator; or in the case of polar projection, on all the meridians. Such projections are termed "equidistant."

FIGURE 197. Earth encircled by meridians and parallels. True scale in all directions can be obtained only on a globe (*A*). Projection for a flat map is selected according to property most desired. In *B*, scale is true along all parallels but not along all meridians. *C* shows scale true along all meridians but not along all parallels. In *D*, the scale changes along both parallels and meridians. (After Strahler, *Introduction to Physical Geography*, 3rd ed., copyright 1973, John Wiley & Sons, Inc., New York.)

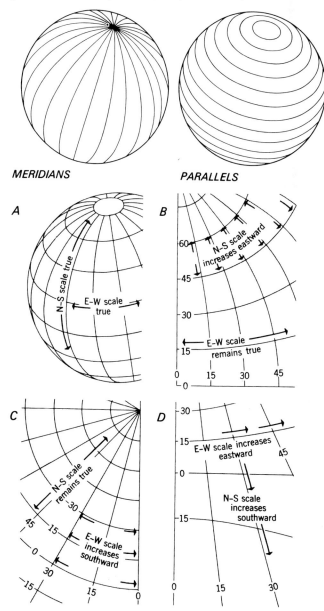

Δ **Directions.** The azimuths from a point to other points on the Earth should be correct on the map. This property is usually limited to a center point of the projection, and the graticule about that point must necessarily be symmetrical. Such projections are termed "azimuthal" or "zenithal."

Δ **Shapes.** The shape of any relatively small figure, such as a lake, should be represented truly. This requires that the parallels and meridians meet at right angles, and that the scale about any point be constant in any azimuth. Such projections are termed "conformal."

The cone and the cylinder are most frequently used to illustrate the transfer of detail of the globe projected to the plane needed for mapping. The cone and cylinder usually are "developed" by cutting the former along its slant length, and the latter along an element (meridian), and laying them flat.

The kind of projection that results depends on the system of projection used to transfer the detail from the globe to the developable surface. For the cylinder, we may have the Mercator, the transverse Mercator, Lambert's cylindrical equal-area, or other projections. For the cone, we may have the Lambert's conformal conic with two standard parallels, Bonne's conical equal-area, Lambert's conical equal-area, Albers' equal-area with two standard parallels, or other projections.

A tangent plane needs no development, and therefore it is used to illustrate the transfer of detail from the globe. The kind of projection that results depends on the position of the origin of projecting lines. With the plane tangent at a pole (polar case), the origin at the opposite pole results in the stereographic projection; the origin at the globe's center results in the gnomonic projection. Parallel rays projecting the globe's detail to the plane (origin infinitely far from the plane) result in the orthographic projection.

Placing a cone or cylinder so that it is not tangent to a parallel of the globe results in the oblique case of some projection systems. Similarly, a plane may be placed in an oblique position, producing a "horizon" case..When a plane is placed tangent to the Equator, we have a "meridional" case. When the cylinder is placed on the globe so that it is tangent to a meridian, we have the "transverse" case.

Regardless of which case occurs, the polar, oblique, or meridional, the properties of a particular projection system remain the same; only the appearance of the graticule changes. A conformal system remains conformal and an equal-area system is still equal-area.

Mercator Projection

The projection most used in navigation is the Mercator in which the meridians and parallels appear as lines crossing at right angles. In this projection, based on a cylinder tangent to the Equator, a table of meridional parts may be used to expand the distances between parallels as they increase in latitude from the Equator, in exactly the same proportion as the meridians

are expanded, since the meridians do not converge as they do on the spheroid. This projection is not a geometric projection; the table of meridional parts is obtained mathematically and is a function of the adopted spheroid. (See Deetz and Adams, 1934, p. 124.)

The Mercator is the only projection on which a rhumb line (a line which crosses successive meridians at constant angle) appears as a straight line. The gnomonic projection (origin at center of the globe) is used to lay out sailing courses on the Mercator, since a straight line on the gnomonic chart represents the great circle arc (the shortest distance) between two points. This line on the gnomonic is then plotted by segment lines on the Mercator to obtain the shortest sailing route between the two points. For general mapping, the Mercator projection has little value, except near the Equator.

Projections Used by the Geological Survey

The Geological Survey uses the Albers equal-area projection with standard parallels at 29.5° and 45.5° for its U.S. base map at 1:2,500,000 and other scales; the Lambert conformal conic projection with standard parallels at 33° and 45° for its State base maps at 1:500,000 scale; the Universal Transverse Mercator projection (UTM) for its 1:250,000-scale series, 1:100,000-scale series, and Alaska 1:63,360-scale series; and State coordinate systems (Lambert and transverse Mercator) for its 15- and 7.5-minute series.

For Antarctica, the Survey uses the polar stereographic projection with standard parallel at 71° for its 1:500,000-scale sketch maps; the World Aeronautical Charts Lambert conformal conic projections with two standard parallels (4° bands) for its 1:250,000-scale reconnaissance series; and a polar stereographic projection with the standard parallel at 80°14' for the same scale series between 80° and the South Pole.

For nearly all projections used by the Survey the Earth is assumed to have the shape of an ellipsoid of revolution—the Clarke spheroid of 1866 for the United States and possessions (see U.S. Coast and Geodetic Survey, 1946). For Antarctica maps, the international (Hayford) ellipsoid is used (see United Nations, 1963, p. 59).

There are many ways in which map projections can be classified: by their manner of development, such as cylindrical or conic; by their properties, such as conformal, azimuthal, or equal-area; or by their inventors' names, such as Mercator or Lambert.

Albers Conical Equal-Area Projection with Two Standard Parallels

The Albers conical equal-area projection with two standard parallels is used by the Survey for its U.S. base maps at 1:2,500,000 and smaller scales. The standard parallels are 29.5° and 45.5°. This is a conic projection which has straight-line meridians and arcs of concentric circles for parallels (see Adams, 1927). The scale along the meridians between the standard parallels is expanded over the nominal scale; the scale on the meridians above 45.5° and below 29.5° is compressed. Although the parallels are concentric arcs, the radii do not have a center at the North Pole. Instead, this projection may be thought of as developed on a truncated cone. All the other attributes of conic development remain.

The scale factor of any parallel is the reciprocal of the scale factor on the meridian at the point. This satisfies the equal-area condition. On the map of the conterminous United States, the maximum scale error is only 1.25 percent. The strength of the Albers projection lies in its two standard parallels, which account for the small scale error. It would be possible to produce sectional maps on this system and have perfect joins to the neighboring sheets. Figure 198 illustrates how a given figure retains the same area although its shape might vary in different parts of the map.

FIGURE 199. Diagrams (below) show development of the Lambert, transverse Mercator, and polyconic projections and type and location of principal distortions, all highly exaggerated. Each differential strip of the developed surface is shown in its true shape (uniform scale). To fit the adjacent strips together so that they are entirely contiguous on the flat map surface, the true shapes must be distorted. This results in areas of compression, where the map scale is too small, and areas of stretching, where the map scale is too large.

FIGURE 198. Equal-area diagram.

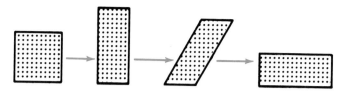

Lambert Conformal Conic Projection with Two Standard Parallels

The Lambert conformal conic projection with two standard parallels has very wide application since any two parallels may be chosen as standard, and the best scale may be placed where needed (fig. 199). The wide-band Lambert conformal conic with standard parallels at 33° and 45° is used by the Survey for its State base series at the scale of 1:500,000 (see Adams, 1918).

The Defense Mapping Agency Aerospace Center has published 4° bands-of-latitude tables for mapping between 80° S. and 84° N. The polar caps are mapped on stereographic projections. These Lambert tables are used for the International Map of the World at 1:1,000,000 scale and are based on the International ellipsoid (see United Nations, 1963, p. 27). More than half the State coordinate systems use the Lambert projection; the others use the transverse Mercator. Alaska also uses the oblique Mercator.

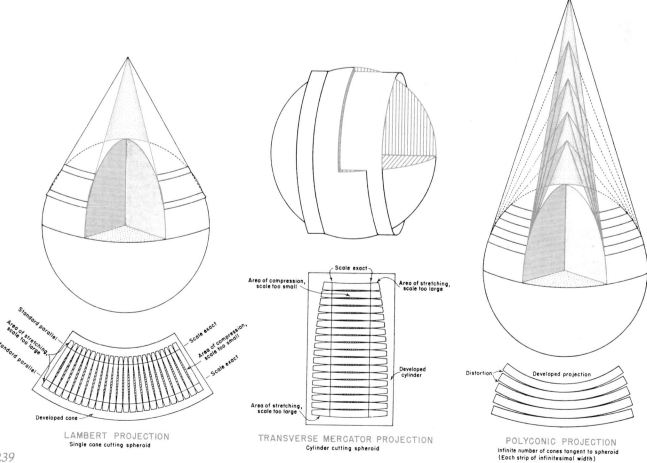

LAMBERT PROJECTION
Single cone cutting spheroid

TRANSVERSE MERCATOR PROJECTION
Cylinder cutting spheroid

POLYCONIC PROJECTION
Infinite number of cones tangent to spheroid
(Each strip of infinitesimal width)

Maps based on a conformal projection show the shape of a small feature, such as a lake, in the same form in which it appears in nature. This requires that angles be shown the same as they are on the surface of the Earth and that distances around a point be consistently mapped in any direction. Thus, the scale factor at any point on the projection is the same in any azimuth. All conditions are met by the Lambert projection except at the poles.

The Lambert projection is best used for a map having dimensions extensive in longitude and relatively narrow in latitude, since the scale along any parallel remains constant. The standard parallels are selected near but between the upper and lower limits of intended use. Between the standard parallels the scale is compressed; outside them the scale is expanded.

The Lambert conformal conic projection is easy to construct and use with available tables. The Lambert does not have the rhumb line property, but straight lines between points approximate great circle arcs. Scale factors can be easily found for all latitudes.

Transverse Mercator Projection

When the cylinder of the regular Mercator projection (tangent to the Equator) is turned 90° about an axis through the Equator and the center of the globe, it becomes tangent to a meridian. The Earth's graticule is projected in an entirely different aspect from the regular Mercator projection. All the properties of the regular Mercator are preserved, except the straight rhumb line. The projection is conformal. The parallels are no longer straight lines but curves. Likewise, the meridians are not straight, but complex curves. The line of true scale is no longer the Equator, but the central meridian of the projection, to which the cylinder is tangent. Consequently, the transverse Mercator projection system is suited for mapping a large extent of latitude having a relatively restricted longitude. This system, therefore, lends itself well to "universal" application in repeated columns of longitude.

Universal Transverse Mercator Projection

A special case (fig. 199) of the Transverse Mercator projection is the Universal Transverse Mercator (UTM) projection, which is used as the basis for the UTM grid. The UTM system consists of 60 north-south zones, each 6° wide in longitude, with the longitude of the boundary edges integral multiples of 6°. The longitudes of the central meridians are therefore odd multiples of 3°. The zones are numbered consecutively, starting with zone 1 between 180° and 174° W. longitude and increasing eastward to zone 60 between 174° and 180° E. longitude (fig. 200).

FIGURE 200. UTM grid zone designations for the world.

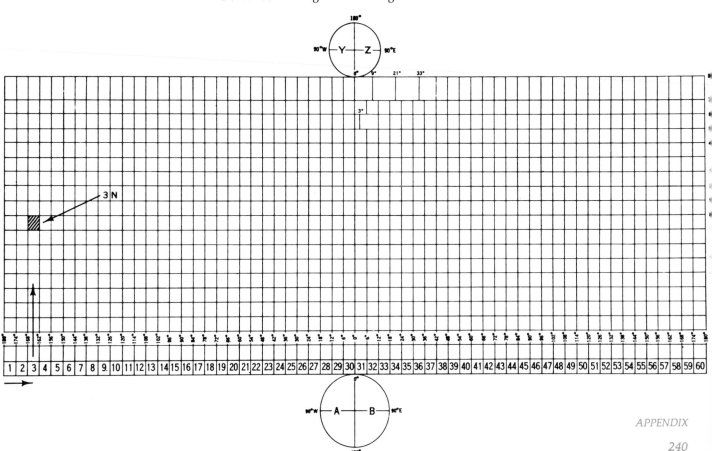

Five spheroids are used in the UTM system to cover various portions of the world. The Clark 1866 spheroid (U.S. Coast and Geodetic Survey, 1946) is used for the United States and its possessions. The cylinder is not tangent to the spheroid at the central meridian as in the nominal transverse Mercator system, but cuts the spheroid along two meridians that are equidistant from the central meridian. The scale factor of the central meridian of each zone is 0.9996. This produces a scale factor of 1 along two grid lines 180,000 m east and west of the central meridian, and produces two lines of true scale in each zone, instead of just one. The unit of measure is the meter, and the origin for each zone is the intersection of the central meridian and the Equator. The false coordinates of the origin are 500,000 m easting and 0 m northing for the Northern Hemisphere; 10,000,000 m northing for the Southern Hemisphere. The Survey uses the UTM graticules and grids for its map series at 1:63,360 (in Alaska), 1:100,000 and 1:250,000 scales. It also applies UTM grids to its series at 1:24,000, 1:62,500, 1:500,000 (State base maps), and 1:1,000,000 scales.

The UTM is used for latitudes between 80° S. and 84° N. The Universal Polar Stereographic (UPS) system is used for the south and north polar caps.

Polyconic Projection

As its name implies, the polyconic projection is derived from the elements of a multiplicity of cones tangent to the Earth at each parallel (fig. 199). A central meridian is chosen, upon which the parallels are truly spaced. Each parallel is the arc of a circle which is developed on its own tangent cone. The apexes of the cones lie on the extension of the central meridian. The arcs of the parallels are not concentric, since they are described by radii which decrease as the cotangents of the latitudes. The arcs of the developed parallels are subdivided true to scale, and the meridians are drawn through the corresponding subdivisions. Consequently the scale of the straight-line central meridian is correct, as is the scale of all the parallels. All lines of the graticule except the central meridian and the Equator are curves, and the meridians and parallels intersect at oblique angles except at the central meridian. The other meridians are concave toward the central meridian.

Although not conformal nor equal-area, the polyconic projection is an excellent compromise of desirable properties over a limited area; it has been widely used for topographic mapping. For many years, the Survey used the polyconic projection for its 7.5-minute map series before changing to the State coordinate systems.

A variation of this projection results in a polyconic projection with two standard meridians, used until recently for the International Map of the World (IMW) series, 1:1,000,000 scale. (See Deetz and Adams, 1934, p. 65.) In this modified polyconic, the central meridian is reduced to make the meridians 2° east and west of the central meridian true to scale, within the 6° of longitude and 4° of latitude of each sheet. All the meridians are straight lines, and every sheet can be joined to its four neighbors. In 1962, the 4°-band Lambert conformal conic projection was adopted to replace the modified polyconic projection for the IMW series, whenever practicable (see United Nations, 1963, p. 9–10).

State Coordinate Systems

For over a hundred years the National Ocean Survey (formerly U.S. Coast and Geodetic Survey) has determined precise geographic positions throughout the United States. Beginning in 1933 these positions were made available to surveyors, engineers, and others in a form they could easily use; namely, as rectangular coordinates on a plane derived from a special projection system for a specific State, or a zone in a specific State.

The National Ocean Survey has published projection tables, in feet, for both basic and 2.5-minute intersections, for all the States. The projection tables are based on either a Lambert conformal conic projection with two standard parallels or a transverse Mercator projection. (One zone in Alaska is on an oblique Mercator projection.) Most States have projections for two or more zones. A few have a single projection for the whole State. (See Mitchell and Simmons, 1945, p. 45–47.)

All the projections are based on the Clarke spheroid of 1866, except for Michigan, which has had its original State coordinate system changed from three transverse Mercator projections to three Lambert conformal conic projections. These are based on a new "Michigan spheroid" which is an enlarged Clarke spheroid of 1866, producing a reference surface at lat. 44° N. approximately 800 feet above the Clarke spheroid of 1866. (See U.S. Coast and Geodetic Survey Pub. 65–3.)

The Lambert conformal conic projection with two standard parallels has been used for States having large east-west extents, while transverse Mercator projections have been used for States which are large from north to south. In almost all cases, the number of zones for a State has been chosen to hold the central parallels of the Lambert or the central meridians of the transverse Mercator to a scale reduction of not more than 1 part in 10,000. In States having more than one zone, the limits of a zone follow the county boundaries. That is, each county lies wholly within one zone.

For many years it has been the practice of the National Ocean Survey to compute its survey points on the appropriate State system. This makes it possible to transfer them directly to a map or grid based on that system.

The Geological Survey indicates the State grids on most of its maps by ticks along the neatlines. Appendix table A1 shows the spacing at different scales for State plane coordinate grid ticks and the UTM full grid.

TABLE A 1. Reference system spacing

| Map scale | State plane coordinate | | | UTM | | |
	Tick spacing (ft on ground)	Spacing (on map) inches	Spacing (on map) mm	Grid spacing (m on ground)	Spacing (on map) inches	Spacing (on map) mm
1:20,000	10,000	6.0	152.4	1,000	1.97	50.0
1:24,000	10,000	5.0	127.0	1,000	1.64	41.6
1:25,000	10,000	4.8	122.0	1,000	1.57	40.0
1:50,000	20,000	4.8	122.0	5,000	3.94	100.0
1:62,500	20,000	3.84	97.5	5,000	3.15	80.0
1:63,360	20,000	3.78	96.0	5,000	3.10	78.7
1:100,000	50,000	6.0	152.4	10,000	3.94	100.0
1:250,000	100,000	4.8	122.0	10,000	1.57	40.0
1:500,000	200,000	4.8	122.0	50,000	3.94	100.0
1:1,000,000	500,000	6.0	152.4	100,000	3.94	100.0

FIGURE 201. Templet CR-1, used by the Geological Survey for map coordinate reading with various metric scales. Tinted area shows extent of templet, which is printed on clear plastic.

Universal Transverse Mercator Grid

A full fine-line Universal Transverse Mercator (UTM) grid is shown on new Geological Survey maps at scales of 1:1,000,000 and larger. To make the best use of the map reference system it should be kept in mind that the grid is the physical representation of a Cartesian coordinate system which ties all the map detail to itself.

The Survey has developed two metric coordinate readers for use with grids at standard scales. These are transparent templets for quick scaling of grid coordinates of points or objects on the map. Figure 201 shows templet CR–1, designed for general use with metric scales. Templet CR–2, designed for scales used most frequently by the Survey is shown in figure 202.

Often the term "grid" is used loosely to mean the projection system itself rather than the system of squares superimposed over a graticule made on that projection. Thus, the phrase "Universal Transverse Mercator grid" may refer to (1) the network of two families of uniformly spaced straight parallel lines intersecting at right angles or (2) the specific transverse Mercator projection system, which has all the attributes of the Universal Transverse Mercator projection with a scale factor of 0.9996,

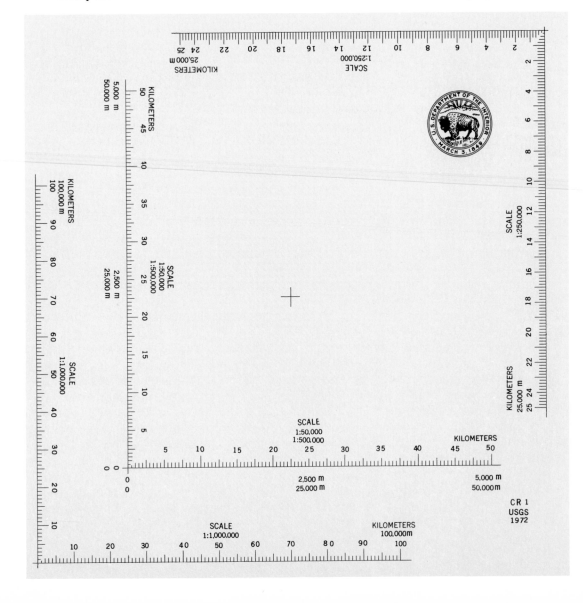

a false easting of 500,000 m on the central meridian of each zone, and an origin at its intersection with the Equator, which has a false northing of 0 m for the Northern Hemisphere.

Geological Survey maps at 1:250,000 scale are cast on the Universal Transverse Mercator projection. Since each sheet covers 1° of latitude by 2° of longitude, there are three sheets in each 1° band of latitude within a zone: a center sheet, a left wing sheet, and a right wing sheet. The central meridian of each zone is also the central meridian of the center sheet, and its graticule is symmetrical about it. The right wing graticule is the mirror image of the left wing graticule. In the case of a center sheet, the outside meridian is about 0.005 cm (0.002 inch) longer than the central meridian.

Only the center sheet of the 1:250,000-scale UTM graticules in a zone is symmetrical about its central meridian. The outer meridian of a wing sheet is larger than the inner meridian, as shown in appendix table A2.

TABLE A 2. UTM meridian lengths in centimeters at 1:250,000 scale

Latitude	Central meridian	1°Out (Inner meridian)	3°Out (Outer meridian)
30 ° – 31 °	44.325	44.330	44.371
35 ° – 36 °	44.361	44.365	44.402
40 ° – 41 °	44.399	44.403	44.435
45 ° – 46 °	44.439	44.442	44.470
50 ° – 51 °	44.478	44.481	44.503
55 ° – 56 °	44.516	44.518	44.536
60 ° – 61 °	44.551	44.553	44.567
65 ° – 66 °	44.583	44.585	44.594
70 ° – 71 °	44.611	44.612	44.618
75 ° – 76 °	44.633	44.634	44.637
79 ° – 80 °	44.647	44.647	44.649

FIGURE 202. Templet CR-2, used for map coordinate reading with scales most frequently used by the Geological Survey. Tinted area shows extent of templet, which is printed on clear plastic.

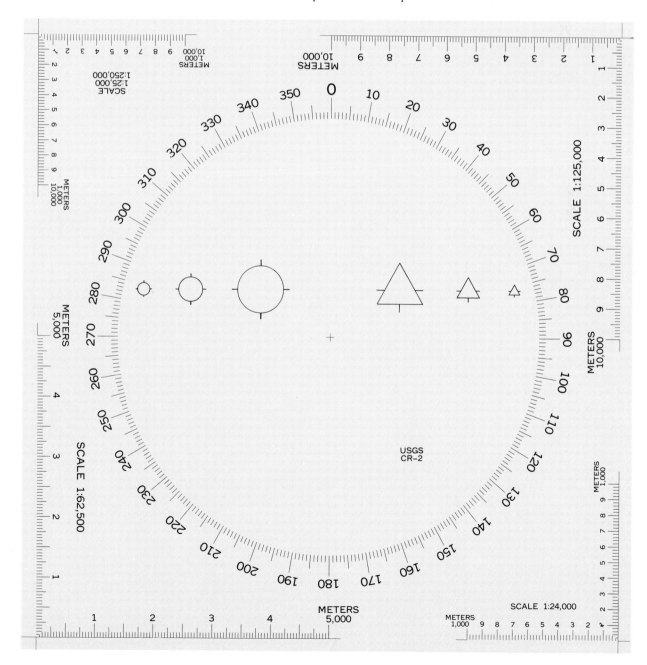

For a right or left wing sheet, the outside meridian is about 0.037 cm (0.015 inch) longer than the inside one, in conterminous United States latitudes.

Scaling on the UTM Grid

To find the grid distance between points A and B on a UTM grid: Scale the eastings and northings of the positions A and B, using a metric coordinate reader or a centimeter scale or a coordinatograph, measuring from the nearest grid lines to the left of and below the points. Record the easting and northing of each point. Solve for the grid distance by the Pythagorean equation

$$L = \sqrt{\Delta E^2 + \Delta N^2}$$

where L is the grid length, ΔE and ΔN are the differences in eastings and northings between A and B, as scaled. (This procedure can be used for any grid, substituting Δx and Δy for ΔE and ΔN.) To find the ground distance corresponding to the grid distance, divide by the approximate scale factor of the midpoint of the two eastings. A scale factor is the quantity by which a ground distance must be multiplied to obtain the corresponding grid distance and by which a grid distance must be divided to obtain the corresponding ground distance.

Auxiliary Use of UTM Tables

The Department of the Army has published UTM tables (U.S. Army, 1967) for the transformation of coordinates from geographic to grid, and grid to geographic; 5-minute intersection tables for the five spheroids used in the UTM system—Clarke 1866, Clarke 1880, Everest, Bessel, and the International (Hayford); and 7.5-minute intersections on the Clark 1866 spheroid. For cartographic use it is sometimes necessary to know the length of the terrestrial arc of the meridian between two latitudes, or the length of the arc of the parallel for a difference of longitude on a stated parallel.

The polyconic tables (U.S. Coast and Geodetic Survey, 1946) give the length of the parallel for every minute of latitude from the Equator to the pole, for seconds, minutes, and degrees on Clarke's spheroid of 1866. The tables also give the arc of the meridian for seconds and minutes between the 1°-latitude lines. A longer arc requires summing.

The length of a meridian arc or a parallel arc from the Equator to 80° may be found on the other four spheroids in the UTM system, in this manner: Use the volume *Transformation of Coordinates from Geographic to Grid* (U.S. Army Corps of Engineers, 1958) to find the pertinent spheroid. The function (I) lists the northing coordinate for every minute of latitude from the Equator to 80°. This is the value on the central meridian, which has a scale factor of 0.9996. The terrestrial arc then is equal to the difference in northings between two latitudes, divided by 0.9996. The result is accurate.

For the arc of the parallel, function (IV) is used for the desired latitude, listed for every minute. The value of (IV) is multiplied by the constant 0.360144058 to get the terrestrial arc of 1° on that parallel. The arc for a degree will be correct within about 2 m.

As technology improves, the use of these tables is being superseded largely by computer programs.

Grid Fitting

The only grid that can be shown correctly on a graticule is the grid based on the same projection system which produced that graticule. Therefore, if one wanted to show a UTM grid or some other grid on a polyconic graticule or some state coordinate system graticule, the grid would not be perfect, at least in theory. In practice the errors would be insignificant for scales of 1:24,000 or larger. For smaller scales, the problem is more difficult because of the larger areas of the Earth's surface that are involved in each map.

The name "grid fitting" is given to the procedure to best position the individual lines of an "alien grid" on a map. For large-scale maps, such as the 1:24,000 scale, a "templet" type of best-fit grid placement can be used. For smaller scale maps, it is necessary to follow a more complex procedure, often requiring internal distortion of the grid lines. Chapman (1974) describes such a procedure.

Geodetic Control

Geodetic control consists of the coordinated and correlated elevation or position data that form the framework to which detailed surveys are adjusted. Basic control may be either horizontal or vertical; it is usually executed with greater precision and accuracy than is required for subsequent surveys which depend on it for accurate positioning. Both horizontal and vertical control are fundamental to mapping and charting. Permanent monuments (fig. 203) whose geographic position and elevation are accurately determined are the cornerstones of modern maps. Except for operations directly referenced to tidal datums, both horizontal and vertical control for accurate mapping are established by geodetic surveying methods. The shape and size of the Earth are thereby taken into account, and accumulation of errors caused by distortions which accompany plane surveying techniques is avoided (National Research Council, 1978).

There are two geodetic control networks in the United States—the national horizontal control network and the national vertical control network. Both are maintained by the National Ocean Survey through its National Geodetic Survey. Other Federal agencies, such as the Geological Survey, Bureau of Reclamation, and the Corps of Engineers, as well as many State agencies, establish geodetic control in the accomplishment of their missions. Whenever a specific mission dictates a requirement for second-order or higher accuracy (see Federal Geodetic Control Committee, 1974), the instruments, methods, and techniques used to establish such control meet the criteria set by the National Ocean Survey. The records and observations acquired by the establishing agency are accepted by the National Ocean Survey and adjusted to the appropriate national network. The national horizontal control network, based on the North American datum of 1927, covers the conterminous United States and Alaska; this new network is being adjusted for incorporation into the North American datum of 1983. The State of Hawaii and the oceanic islands are covered by independent networks. The national vertical control network covers the conterminous United States only; independent networks cover Alaska, Hawaii, and the oceanic islands.

FIGURE 203. The control monument consisting of this bronze disk set in a concrete post is one of a network of permanent survey monuments to which surveys for mapping and other purposes can be referenced.

HORIZONTAL CONTROL. Horizontal control makes it possible for the cartographer to orient and scale a map accurately, to position it properly on the Earth and to datum, and to compile details on the map in their correct positions and relationship. Basic horizontal control may be of first-, second-, or third-order accuracy. The network maintained by the National Ocean Survey usually provides sufficient control for mapping and

charting. The few gaps that occur in the basic schemes can, in most instances, be filled by the use of modern photogrammetric techniques, to avoid the expense of establishing additional control by conventional field methods.

VERTICAL CONTROL. Vertical control is needed to relate relief features and elevation data to an accepted vertical datum. The national geodetic vertical datum of 1929 is the one most suitable for this purpose in the conterminous United States and Alaska. However, this datum has not been extended to Hawaii or to the Pacific Islands, Puerto Rico, and the Virgin Islands. Local datums are therefore used in these areas, each based upon tidal datums established at selected tide stations, and the datum involved is specified in the geodetic control data provided for each of these areas.

Vertical control of great significance to mapping operations is provided by tidal observations. The type of tidal datum computed depends on the tidal characteristics present. In general the tide along the Atlantic Coast is classified as semidiurnal, with two high waters of nearly equal heights each day, and similarly, two low waters each day. Data are provided for mean high water, half-tide level, mean sea level, and mean low water, with the elevations of tidal bench marks referred to mean low water. In the Gulf of Mexico and the Pacific Ocean the tide is classified either as diurnal (one high water and one low water each day) or as mixed. The mixed tide is similar to the semidiurnal except that there is a marked difference in the height of the two high waters and (or) in the height of the two low waters each day (called "diurnal inequality"). For many tide stations in the Gulf of Mexico, along the Pacific Coast, Alaska, Hawaii, and the Pacific Islands, data are provided for mean higher high water, mean high water, half-tide level, mean sea level, mean low water, and mean lower low water, with tidal bench marks along the Gulf Coast referred to mean low water, and along the Pacific Coast to mean lower low water. Mean sea level at any point may be defined simply as the mean level of the sea at that point; it is the arithmetic mean of hourly water elevations observed over a specific 19-year metonic cycle (the National Tidal Datum Epoch). Mean sea level is the primary tidal datum, and all the other tidal datums are derived with reference to it. As it is a local tidal datum and may be valid only at that locality, local mean sea level should not be confused with the national geodetic vertical datum of 1929 (previously called "mean sea level 1929") which is a geodetic vertical datum most often used in conjunction with engineering projects and which is the vertical reference datum for Geological Survey maps.

Information concerning available horizontal and vertical control data can be obtained from the National Cartographic Information Center, or from the National Geodetic Information Center as explained in the chapter, "Cartographic Information Sources." ▲

STANDARD SERIES MAPS

Standard quadrangle maps cover systematically subdivided areas of latitude and longitude, and are published at various scales depending on the size of the area mapped

Standard quadrangle formats range from 7.5x7.5 minutes covering geographic areas of 49 to 71 square miles to 1x2 degrees covering areas of 4580 to 8669 square miles

Standard quadrangle map scales range from 1:24 000 (one inch on the map represents 2000 feet on the ground) to 1:250 000 (one inch on the map represents approximately 4 miles on the ground)

Other quadrangle maps are published at scales of 1:20 000 (Puerto Rico) to 1:63 360 (Alaska) and 1:1 000 000 (International Map of the World)

Special area maps are published at scales of 1:50 000 and 1:100 000 (County, Regional, and National Park Maps), and 1:500 000 (State Base Maps).

MAP SERIES COMPARISON

Illustrated opposite is the relative comparison of the size of the area covered by the various map series. Comparatively, the number of maps required to cover an area of 1 degree latitude by 2 degrees longitude is:

128 — 7.5 minute maps
64 — 7.5x15 minute maps
32 — 15 minute maps
4 — 30x60 minute maps
1 — 1x2 degree map

The amount of detail shown on a map is proportionate to the scale of the map; the larger the map scale, the more detail that is shown. For example, individual houses are shown on 1:24 000-scale 7.5-minute maps, whereas only landmark buildings are shown on 1:100 000-scale 30x60-minute maps.

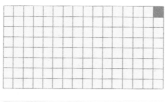

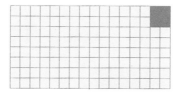

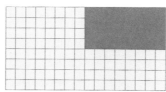

7.5 MINUTE SERIES

Map scale[1] 1:24 000
Map to ground ratio ....1 inch represents 2000 feet
Area covered ....49–71 square miles
Paper size (approx.) ....22"x27"
Contours and elevations[2] ....shown in feet

7.5 X 15 MINUTE SERIES

Map scale 1:25 000
Map to ground ratio ....1 inch represents 2083 feet
Area covered ....100–140 square miles
Paper size (approx.) ....24"x40"
Contours and elevations ....shown in meters

15 MINUTE SERIES

Map scale[3] 1:62 500
Map to ground ratio ......1 inch represents about 1 mile
Area covered ....197–282 square miles
Paper size (approx.) ....18"x22"
Contours and elevations[2] ....shown in feet

30 X 60 MINUTE SERIES

Map scale 1:100 000
Map to ground ratio ....1 inch represents 1.6 miles
Area covered ....1578–2167 square miles
Paper size (approx.) ....29"x44"
Contours and elevations[2] ....shown in meters

1 X 2 DEGREE SERIES

Map scale 1:250 000
Map to ground ratio .....1 inch represents about 4 miles
Area covered ....4580–8669 square miles
Paper size (approx.) ....22"x32"
Contours and elevations[2] ....shown in feet

[1]1:25 000 scale on selected maps
[2]Shown in meters on selected maps
[3]1:50 000 scale on selected maps

ADDRESSES OF AGENCIES

[See table 1, p. 18–19, for map products available from these agencies.]

Agricultural Stabilization and Conservation Service (ASCS)
Aerial Photography Field Office
Agricultural Stabilization and Conservation Service
Department of Agriculture
(2222 West, 2300 South)
P.O. Box 30010
Salt Lake City, Utah 84125

Bonneville Power Administration (BPA)
Bonneville Power Administration
Department of Energy
(1002 NE. Holladay Street)
P.O. Box 3621
Portland, Oreg. 97208

Bureau of the Census (BC)
Users Service Staff
Data Users Services Division
Bureau of the Census
Department of Commerce
Washington, D.C. 20233

Bureau of Indian Affairs (BIA)
Bureau of Indian Affairs
Department of the Interior
18th and C Streets, NW.
Washington, D.C. 20240

Bureau of Land Management (BLM)
Bureau of Land Management
Department of the Interior
18th and C Streets, NW.
Washington, D.C. 20240

Bureau of Mines (BM)
Environmental Affairs Field Office
Bureau of Mines
Department of the Interior
Room 3323
Penn Place
20 North Pennsylvania Avenue
Wilkes-Barre, Pa. 18701

Mine Map Repository
Bureau of Mines
Department of the Interior
Building 20
Denver Federal Center
Denver, Colo. 80225

Bureau of Mines (BM) *(continued)*
Mine Map Repository
Bureau of Mines
Department of the Interior
4800 Forbes Avenue
Pittsburgh, Pa. 15213

Defense Mapping Agency (DMA)
Defense Mapping Agency
Building 56
U.S. Naval Observatory
Washington, D.C. 20305

Delaware River Basin Commission (DRBC)
Executive Director
Delaware River Basin Commission
(25 State Police Drive)
Post Office Box 7360
West Trenton, N.J. 08628

Department of Energy (DOE)
Public Affairs Director
Department of Energy
1000 Independence Avenue, SW.
Washington, D.C. 20585

Department of State (DOS)
Office of the Geographer
Bureau of Intelligence and Research
Department of State
8742 NS INR/GE
Washington, D.C. 20520

Environmental Protection Agency (EPA)
Office of Public Awareness
Environmental Protection Agency
401 M Street, SW.
Washington, D.C. 20460

Federal Energy Regulatory Commission (FERC)
Office of Public Information
Federal Energy Regulatory Commission
825 North Capital Street, NE.
Washington, D.C. 20426

Federal Highway Administration (FHWA)
Office of Public Affairs
Federal Highway Administration
Department of Transportation
Room 4208
400 7th Street, SW.
Washington, D.C. 20590

Federal Highway Administration (*continued*)
Aerial Surveys Branch
Highway Design Division
Federal Highway Administration
Department of Transportation
Room 3130A
400 7th Street, SW.
Washington, D.C. 20590

Federal Insurance Administration (FIA)
National Flood Insurance Program
Federal Insurance Administration
Federal Emergency Management Agency
P.O. Box 34294
Bethesda, Md. 20034

Heritage Conservation and Recreation Service (HCRC)
(formerly Bureau of Outdoor Recreation)
Federal Land Planning Division
Heritage Conservation and Recreation Service
130 Interior South Building
18th and C Streets, NW.
Washington, D.C. 20240

International Boundary and Water Commission, United States and Mexico (IBWC)
U.S. Commissioner
International Boundary and Water Commission, United States and Mexico
United States Section
(4110 Rio Bravo, Executive Center)
P.O. Box 20003
El Paso, Tex. 79998

International Boundary Commission, United States and Canada (IBC)
U.S. Commissioner
International Boundary Commission, United States and Canada
United States Section
Room 150
425 I Street, NW.
Washington, D.C. 20001

Library of Congress (LC)
Geography and Map Division
Library of Congress
Washington, D.C. 20540

Mississippi River Commission (MRC)
Executive Assistant
Mississippi River Commission
(Mississippi River Commission Building)
U.S. Army Corps of Engineers
P.O. Box 60
Vicksburg, Miss. 39180

National Aeronautics and Space Administration (NASA)
Contact the facility office of the installation concerned.

National Archives and Records Service (NARS)
Cartographic Archives Division
National Archives and Records Service
General Services Administration
Archives Building
Pennsylvania Avenue at 8th Street, NW.
Washington, D.C. 20408

National Oceanic and Atmospheric Administration (NOAA)

Environmental Data and Information Service (EDIS)
National Oceanic and Atmospheric Administration
Department of Commerce
Page Building 2
3300 Whitehaven Street, NW.
Washington, D.C. 22023

Environmental Research Laboratories (ERL)
Environmental Research Laboratories
National Oceanic and Atmospheric Administration
Department of Commerce
3100 Marine Avenue
Boulder, Colo. 80302

National Ocean Survey (NOS)

Aerial photographs and shoreline maps:
Coastal Mapping Division, C3415
National Ocean Survey
National Oceanic and Atmospheric Administration
Department of Commerce
Rockville, Md. 20852

Chart sales:
Washington Science Center 1, C5131
National Oceanic and Atmospheric Administration
Department of Commerce
Rockville, Md. 20852

Charts:
Distribution Division, C64
National Ocean Survey
National Oceanic and Atmospheric Administration
Department of Commerce
Riverdale, Md. 20840

General cartographic information:
Physical Science Services Branch, C513
National Ocean Survey
National Oceanic and Atmospheric Administration
Department of Commerce
Rockville, Md. 20852

Geodetic control data:
National Geodetic Information Center, C18
National Ocean Survey
National Oceanic and Atmospheric Administration
Department of Commerce
Rockville, Md. 20852

National Weather Service (NWS)

National Meteorological Center
National Weather Service
National Oceanic and Atmospheric Administration
Department of Commerce
5200 Auth Road
Camp Springs, Md. 20233

National Park Service (NPS)
Office of Communications
National Park Service
3043 Interior Building
18th and C Streets, NW.
Washington, D.C. 20242

Soil Conservation Service (SCS)
Cartographic Division
Soil Conservation Service
Department of Agriculture
Federal Building
6505 Belcrest Road
Hyattsville, Md. 20782

State Geologic Agencies (SGA)
Contact the State Geologist or
other cognizant official in each State.

Tennessee Valley Authority (TVA)
Mapping Services Branch
Tennessee Valley Authority
200 Haney Building
Chattanooga, Tenn. 37401

U.S. Air Force (USAF)
Contact the information officer of the base concerned.

U.S. Army (USA)
Contact the commander of the base concerned.

U.S. Army Corps of Engineers (USCE)
Office of Chief of Engineers
U.S. Army Corps of Engineers
Washington, D.C. 20314

U.S. Coast Guard (USCG)
Oceanographic Unit
U.S. Coast Guard
Building 159E, Washington Navy Yard Annex
Washington, D.C. 20590

U.S. Fish and Wildlife Service (FWS)
Division of Realty
U.S. Fish and Wildlife Service
Department of the Interior
555 Matomic Building
1717 H Street, NW.
Washington, D.C. 20240

U.S. Forest Service (FS)
U.S. Forest Service
Office of Information
Department of Agriculture
P.O. Box 2417
Washington, D.C. 20013

U.S. Geological Survey (USGS)

All cartographic data:

Branch of User Services
National Cartographic Information Center (NCIC)
U.S. Geological Survey
Department of the Interior
MS 507, National Center
(12201 Sunrise Valley Drive)
Reston, Va. 22092

Photographs and remote sensor imagery:
User Services Unit
EROS Data Center **(EDC)**
U.S. Geological Survey
Department of the Interior
Sioux Falls, S. Dak. 57198

Maps and control data by mail:

Alaska
Distribution Section
U.S. Geological Survey
Department of the Interior
101 12th Avenue
Fairbanks, Alaska 99701

States east of Mississippi River plus Puerto Rico
Eastern Distribution Branch
U.S. Geological Survey
Department of the Interior
1200 South Eads Street
Arlington, Va. 22202

States west of Mississippi River plus Hawaii, Guam, and American Samoa
Western Distribution Branch
U.S. Geological Survey
Department of the Interior
MS 306, Box 25286
Denver Federal Center
Denver, Colo. 80225

Commercial dealers are listed on sales indexes which can be obtained from any of the above three offices.

U.S. Government Printing Office (GPO)
Assistant Public Printer
(Superintendent of Documents)
U.S. Government Printing Office
North Capitol and H Streets, NW.
Washington, D.C. 20402

U.S. Marine Corps (USMC)
Contact the commander of the base concerned.

U.S. Navy (USN)
Contact the commander of the base concerned.

Water and Power Resources Service (WPRS)
Chief, Publications and Photography Branch
General Services Division
7442 Interior Building
18th and C Streets, NW.
Washington, D.C. 20240

GLOSSARY

accuracy Degree of conformity with a standard. Accuracy relates to the quality of a result and is distinguished from precision which relates to the quality of the operation by which the result is obtained.

adjustment Process designed to remove inconsistencies in measured or computed quantities by applying derived corrections to compensate for random or accidental errors.

adjustment, land-line Positioning land lines on a map to indicate their true, theoretical, or approximate location relative to the adjacent terrain and culture, by reconciling the information shown on Bureau of Land Management plats and field records with the ground evidence of the location of the lines.

adjustment, standard-accuracy Adjustment of a survey resulting in values for positions and (or) elevations that comply with the National Map Accuracy Standards.

aerotriangulation (bridging) The process of developing a network of horizontal and (or) vertical positions from a group of known positions using direct or indirect measurements from aerial photographs and mathematical computations.

alidade Instrument, or part of an instrument, for determining direction, either horizontal or vertical. In its simplest form, a peepsight or telescope mounted on a straightedge and used for plotting directions graphically. In such instruments as transits and theodolites, the alidade is the part containing the telescope and its attachments.

altimeter Instrument for measuring altitudes or elevations with respect to a reference level, usually mean sea level. The most common type is an aneroid barometer. A radar altimeter determines the height of an aircraft above the terrain by measuring the time required for an electromagnetic pulse to travel from aircraft to the ground and back.

azimuth Horizontal direction reckoned clockwise from the meridian plane.

backshore Part of a beach that is usually dry and is reached only by the highest tides; by extension, a narrow strip of relatively flat coast bordering the sea.

base map *See* **map, base.**

bathymetric map *See* **map, bathymetric.**

bathymetry Science of measuring water depths (usually in the ocean) to determine bottom topography.

beach (seabeach) Zone of unconsolidated material that extends landward from the low water line to the place where there is marked change in material or physiographic form, or to the line of permanent vegetation (usually the effective limit of storm waves). A beach includes foreshore and backshore.

bench mark Relatively permanent material object, natural or artificial, bearing a marked point whose elevation above or below an adopted datum is known.

boundary monument Material object placed on or near a boundary line to preserve and identify the location of the boundary line on the ground.

boundary survey Survey made to establish or to reestablish a boundary line on the ground, or to obtain data for constructing a map or plat showing a boundary line.

cadastral map *See* **map, cadastral.**

cadastral survey Survey relating to land boundaries, made to create units suitable for title transfer or to define the limitations of title. Derived from "cadastre" meaning a register of land quantities, values, and ownerships used for levying taxes, the term "cadastral survey" is used to designate the surveys of the public lands of the United States. Although the term may properly be applied to surveys of a similar nature outside the public lands, such surveys are more commonly called "land surveys" or "property surveys."

cartography Science and art of making maps and charts. The term may be taken broadly as comprising all the steps needed to produce a map: planning, aerial photography, field surveys, photogrammetry, editing, color separation, and multicolor printing. Mapmakers, however, tend to limit use of the term to the map-finishing operations, in which the master manuscript is edited and color separation plates are prepared for lithographic printing.

chain Unit of length equal to 66 feet, used especially in the U.S. public land surveys. The original measuring instrument (Gunter's chain) was literally a chain consisting of 100 iron links, each 7.92 inches long. Steel-ribbon tapes began to supersede chains around 1900, but surveying tapes are often still called "chains" and measuring with a tape is often called "chaining." The chain is a convenient unit in cadastral surveys because 10 square chains = 1 acre.

chart Special-purpose map designed for navigation or to present specific data or information. The term "chart" is applied chiefly to maps made primarily for nautical and aeronautical navigation, and to maps of the heavens, although the term is sometimes used to describe other special-purpose maps.

chart, aeronautical Chart designed to meet requirements of aerial navigating, produced in several series, each on a specified map projection and differing in scale, format, and content, for use as dictated by type of aircraft and whether flight is to be conducted under visual or instrument flight rules.

chart, bathymetric *See* **map, bathymetric.**

chart, nautical Representation of a portion of the navigable waters of the Earth and adjacent coastal areas on a specified map projection and designed specifically to meet requirements for marine navigation. Included on most nautical charts are depths of water, characteristics of the bottom, elevations of selected topographic features, general configuration and characteristics of the coast, the shoreline (usually the mean high water line), dangers, obstructions and aids to navigation, limited tidal data, and information about magnetic variation in the charted area.

choropleth map *See* **map, choropleth.**

clinometric map *See* **map, slope.**

color separation Process of preparing a separate drawing, engraving, or negative for each color required in the printing production of a map or chart.

compilation Preparation of a new or revised map or chart, or portion thereof, from existing maps, aerial photographs, field surveys, and other sources.

continuous tone Image not broken into dots by photographic screen; contains unbroken gradient tones from black to white, and may be either in negative or positive form. Aerial photographs are examples of continuous-tone prints. Contrasted with halftone (screened) and line copy.

contour Imaginary line on the ground, all points of which are at the same elevation above or below a specified datum.

contour interval Difference in elevation between two adjacent contours.

control, mapping Points of established position or elevation, or both, which are used as fixed references in positioning and correlating map features. Fundamental control is provided by stations in the national networks of triangulation and traverse (horizontal control) and leveling (vertical control). Usually it is necessary to extend geodetic surveys, based on the fundamental stations, over the area to be mapped, to provide a suitable density and distribution of control points.

    Supplemental control points are those needed to relate the aerial photographs used for mapping with the system of ground control. These points must be positively photo-identified; that is, the points on the ground must be positively correlated with their images on the photographs.

control station Point on the ground whose position (horizontal or vertical) is known and can be used as a base for additional survey work.

coordinates Linear and (or) angular quantities that designate the position of a point in relation to a given reference frame.

coordinates, origin of Point in a system of coordinates which serves as a zero point in computing the system's elements or in prescribing its use.

culture Features constructed by man that are under, on, or above the ground which are delineated on a map. These include roads, trails, buildings, canals, sewer systems, and boundary lines. In a broad sense, the term also applies to all names, other identification, and legends on a map.

datum (*pl.* **datums**) In surveying, a reference system for computing or correlating the results of surveys. There are two principal types of datums: vertical and horizontal. A vertical datum is a level surface to which heights are referred. In the United States, the generally adopted vertical datum for leveling operations is the national geodetic vertical datum of 1929 (differing slightly from mean sea level). The horizontal datum, used as a reference for position, is defined by: the latitude and longitude of an initial point, the direction of a line between this point and a specified second point, and two dimensions which define the spheroid. In the United States, the initial point for the horizontal datum is station Meades Ranch, in Kansas.

datum, national geodetic vertical *See* **national geodetic vertical datum of 1929.**

declination In astronomy, the angular distance of a celestial body above (north, plus) or below (south, minus) the celestial Equator. Magnetic declination is the angular difference between magnetic north and true (geographic) north at the point of observation; it is not constant but varies with time because of the ''wandering'' of the magnetic north pole.

depth curve Line on a map or chart connecting points of equal depth below the datum.

diazo process Rapid method for copying documents in which the image is developed by exposure to ammonia.

dike Bank of earth or stone used to form a barrier, frequently and confusingly interchanged with levee. A dike restrains water within an area that normally is flooded. *See* **levee.**

electronic distance measuring (EDM) devices Instruments that measure the phase difference between transmitted and reflected or retransmitted electromagnetic waves of known frequency, or that measure the round-trip transit time of a pulsed signal, from which distance is computed.

elevation Vertical distance of a point above or below a reference surface or datum.

ellipsoid *See* **spheroid.**

engineering map *See* **map, engineering.**

ER–55 plotter Double-projection plotting instrument (*see* fig. 20*B*) utilizing ellipsoidal reflectors for light projection.

erosion Group of natural processes including weathering, dissolution, abrasion, corrosion, and transportation that remove material from any part of the Earth's surface.

estuary That portion of a stream influenced by the tide of the body of water into which it flows; an arm of the sea at a river mouth.

feature separation Process of preparing a separate drawing, engraving, or negative for selected types of data in the preparation of a map or chart.

flood control map *See* **map, flood control.**

flood plain Belt of low flat ground bordering a stream channel that is flooded when runoff exceeds the capacity of the stream channel.

forestry map *See* **map, forestry.**

formlines Lines, resembling contour lines, drawn to present a conception of the shape of the terrain without regard to a true vertical datum or regular spacing.

geodesy Science concerned with the measurement and mathematical description of the size and shape of the earth and its gravitational field. Geodesy also includes the large-scale, extended surveys for determining positions and elevations of points, in which the size and shape of the earth must be taken into account.

geoid Figure of the Earth visualized as a mean sea level surface extended continuously through the continents. It is a theoretically continuous surface that is perpendicular at every point to the direction of gravity (the plumbline).

geologic map *See* **map, geologic.**

graticule Network of parallels and meridians on a map or chart.

graticule, geographic System of coordinates of latitude and longitude used to define the position of a point on the surface of the Earth with respect to the reference spheroid. (Note that use of the word ''grid'' with ''geographic'' in this application is incorrect.)

grid Network of uniformly spaced parallel lines intersecting at right angles. When superimposed on a map, it usually carries the name of the projection used for the map—that is, Lambert grid, transverse Mercator grid, universal transverse Mercator grid.

hachure Any of a series of lines used on a map to indicate the general direction and steepness of slopes. The lines are short, heavy, and close together for steep slopes; longer, lighter, and more widely spaced for gentle slopes.

halftone A picture in which the gradations of light are obtained by the relative darkness and density of tiny dots produced by photographing the subject through a fine screen.

high water Maximum height reached by a rising tide. The height may be due solely to the periodic tidal forces or it may have superimposed upon it the effects of prevailing meteorological conditions. Use of the term "high tide" is discouraged.

high water line Intersection of the land with the water surface at an elevation of high water.

high water mark Line or mark left upon tidal flats, beach, or alongshore objects indicating the elevation or the intrusion of high water.

hydrographic survey Survey of a water area, with particular reference to submarine relief, and any adjacent land. See **oceanographic survey.**

hydrography Science that deals with the measurement and description of the physical features of the oceans, seas, lakes, rivers, and their adjoining coastal areas, with particular reference to their use for navigation.

hydrology Scientific study of the waters of the Earth, especially with relation to the effects of precipitation and evaporation upon the occurrence and character of ground water.

hypsographic map See **map, hypsographic.**

hypsography Topography referred to the national geodetic vertical datum of 1929. The science or art of describing heights of land surfaces with reference to this datum.

hypsometric map See **map, hypsometric.**

hypsometry Science or art of determining terrain relief, by any method.

imagery Visible representation of objects and (or) phenomena as sensed or detected by cameras, infrared and multispectral scanners, radar, and photometers. Recording may be on photographic emulsion (directly as in a camera or indirectly after being first recorded on magnetic tape as an electrical signal) or on magnetic tape for subsequent conversion and display on a cathode ray tube.

infrared scanner (thermal mapper) Instrument that detects infrared radiation and converts the detected energy to an electrical signal for recording on photographic film or magnetic tape.

isogonic chart Chart showing isogonic lines properly labeled with their magnetic declinations.

isogonic line Line joining points on the Earth's surface having equal magnetic declination as of a given date.

isopleth map See **map, isopleth.**

Kelsh plotter Double-projection plotting instrument (see fig. 20B) utilizing swinging lamps to transmit light through contact-size diapositives (positive transparencies).

land use classification system Coding system of categories and subcategories designed for use on a map to designate land or water use.

land use map See **map, land use.**

landmark Monument or material mark or fixed object used to designate a land boundary on the ground; any prominent object on land that may be used to determine a location or a direction in navigation or surveying.

latitude Angular distance, in degrees, minutes, and seconds, of a point north or south of the Equator.

lead line Line weighted with lead for making depth soundings in water.

levee Artificial bank confining a stream channel or limiting adjacent areas subject to flooding; an embankment bordering a submarine canyon or channel, usually occurring along the outer edge of a curve.

level surface Surface which at every point is perpendicular to the plumbline or the direction in which gravity acts.

leveling Surveying operation in which heights of objects and points are determined relative to a specified datum.

line copy (line drawing) Map copy suitable for reproduction without the use of a screen; a drawing composed of lines as distinguished from continuous-tone copy.

line map See **map, line.**

longitude Angular distance, in degrees, minutes, and seconds, of a point east or west of the Greenwich meridian.

low water Minimum height reached by a falling tide. The height may be due solely to the periodic tidal forces or it may have superimposed upon it the effects of meteorological conditions.

low water line Intersection of the land with the water surface at an elevation of low water. Not to be confused with mean low water line.

magnetic declination See **declination.**

map Graphic representation of the physical features (natural, artificial, or both) of a part or the whole of the Earth's surface, by means of signs and symbols or photographic imagery, at an established scale, on a specified projection, and with the means of orientation indicated.

map, base Map on which information may be placed for purposes of comparison or geographical correlation. The term "base map" was at one time applied to a class of maps now known as outline maps. It may be applied to topographic maps, also termed "mother maps" that are used in the construction of other types of maps by the addition of particular data.

map, bathymetric Map delineating the form of the bottom of a body of water, or a portion thereof, by the use of depth contours (isobaths).

map, cadastral Map showing the boundaries of subdivisions of land, often with the bearings and lengths thereof and the areas of individual tracts, for purposes of describing and recording ownership. It may also show culture, drainage, and other features relating to land use and value. See **plat.**

map, choropleth Thematic map in which areas are colored, shaded, dotted, or hatched to create darker or lighter areas in proportion to the density of distribution of the theme subject.

map digitization Conversion of map data from graphic to digital form.

map, engineering Map showing information that is essential for planning an engineering project or development and for estimating its cost. It usually is a large-scale map of a small area or of a route. It may be entirely the product of an engineering survey, or reliable information may be collected from various sources for the purpose, and assembled on a base map.

map, flood control Map designed for studying and planning control projects in areas subject to flooding.

map, forestry Map prepared principally to show the size, density, kind, and value of trees in a designated area.

map, geologic Map showing the structure and composition of geologic features.

map, hypsographic Map showing relief with elevations referred to the national geodetic vertical datum of 1929.

map, hypsometric Map showing relief by any convention, such as contours, hachures, shading, or tinting.

map, isopleth Map consisting of lines connecting places of equal value of distribution for a given theme such as rainfall or temperature.

map, land use Map showing by means of a coding system the various purposes for which parcels of land are being used by man.

map, line Map composed of lines as distinguished from photographic imagery.

map, orthophotographic See **orthophotographic map.**

map, photographic See **photomap.**

map, planimetric Map that presents only the horizontal positions for features represented; distinguished from a topographic map by the omission of relief in measurable form. The features usually shown on a planimetric map include rivers, lakes, and seas; mountains, valleys, and plains; forests, and prairies; cities, farms, transportation routes, and public utility facilities; and political and private boundary lines. A planimetric map intended for special use may present only those features essential to the purpose to be served.

map projection Orderly system of lines on a plane representing a corresponding system of imaginary lines on an adopted terrestrial or celestial datum surface. Also, the mathematical concept of such a system. For maps of the Earth, a projection consists of (1) a graticule of lines representing parallels of latitude and meridians of longitude or (2) a grid.

map series Family of maps conforming generally to the same specifications and designed to cover an area or a country in a systematic pattern.

map, slope (clinometric map) Map showing the degree of steepness of the Earth's surface by the use of various colors or shading for critical ranges of slope.

map, soil Map that shows the constitution, structure, and texture of the soil and identifies ongoing erosion.

map, storm evacuation Map designed to identify coastal areas subject to flooding, to indicate recommended areas of refuge, and to emphasize available evacuation routes.

map, thematic Map designed to provide information on a single topic, such as geology, rainfall, population.

map, topographic Map that presents the horizontal and vertical positions of the features represented; distinguished from a planimetric map by the addition of relief in measurable form.

marsh, coastal Area of salt-tolerant vegetation in brackish and (or) saline-water habitats subject to tidal inundation.

marsh, freshwater Tract of low wet ground, usually miry and covered with rank vegetation.

mean high water Tidal datum that is the arithmetic mean of the high water heights observed over a specific 19-year Metonic cycle (National Tidal Datum Epoch). For stations with shorter series, simultaneous observations are made with a primary control tide station to derive the equivalent of a 19-year value. Use of "mean high tide" is discouraged.

mean high water line Intersection of the land with the water surface at the elevation of mean high water. See **shoreline.**

mean low water Tidal datum that is the arithmetic mean of the low water heights observed over a specific 19-year Metonic cycle (the National Tidal Datum Epoch). For stations with shorter series, simultaneous observations are made with a primary control tide station in order to derive the equivalent of a 19-year value. Use of the synonymous term "mean low tide" is discouraged.

mean low water line Intersection of the land with the water surface at the elevation of mean low water.

mean sea level Tidal datum that is the arithmetic mean of hourly water elevations observed over a specific 19-year Metonic cycle (the National Tidal Datum Epoch). Shorter series are specified in the name; that is, monthly mean sea level and yearly mean sea level. See **datum.**

meander line Metes-and-bounds traverse approximately along the mean high water line of a permanent body of water. By following the sinuosities of the bank or shoreline, the meander line provides data for computing the area of land remaining after the water area has been segregated. A meander line differs from other metes-and-bounds surveys in that it does not ordinarily determine or fix boundaries.

meanderable Capable of being depicted by reference to a meander line.

meridian Great circle on the surface of the Earth passing through the geographical poles and any given point on the Earth's surface. All points on a given meridian have the same longitude.

metes and bounds Method of describing land by measure of length (metes) of the boundary lines (bounds).

Metonic cycle Period of 235 lunations or about 19 years. Devised by Meton, an Athenian astronomer (5th century B.C.) for the purpose of obtaining a period at the end of which the phases of the Moon recur in the same order and on the same days as in the preceding cycle.

metric system Decimal system of weights and measures based on the meter as a unit length and the kilogram as a unit mass.

monoscopic Pertaining to the observation of a single photograph or other view.

monument (surveying) Permanent physical structure marking the location of a survey point. Common types of monuments are inscribed metal tablets set in concrete posts, solid rock, or parts of buildings; distinctive stone posts; and metal rods driven in the ground.

mosaic, aerial Assembly of aerial photographs whose edges usually have been torn or cut selectively and matched to the imagery on adjoining photographs to form a continuous representation of a portion of the Earth's surface.

multiplex Stereoplotter of the double-projection type characterized by its use of reduced-scale diapositives and stationary lamphouses with condensing lenses (*see* fig. 20B).

multispectral scanner (MSS) Device for sensing radiant energy in several channels of the electromagnetic spectrum.

national geodetic vertical datum of 1929 Reference surface established by the U.S. Coast and Geodetic Survey in 1929 as the datum to which relief features and elevation data are referenced in the conterminous United States; formerly called "mean sea level 1929."

National Map Accuracy Standards Specifications promulgated by the U.S. Office of Management and Budget to govern accuracy of topographic and other maps produced by Federal agencies.

navigable waters Waters usable, with or without improvements, as routes for commerce in the customary means of travel on water.

neatline Line separating the body of a map from the map margin. On a standard quadrangle map, the neatlines are the meridians and parallels delimiting the quadrangle.

oceanographic survey Survey or examination of conditions in the ocean or any part of it, with reference to animal or plant life, chemical elements present, temperature gradients, etc. See **hydrographic survey.**

offshore Comparatively flat zone of variable width that extends from the outer margin of the rather steeply sloping shoreface to the edge of the continental shelf.

orientation Establishing correct relationship in direction with reference to points of the compass; the state of being in correct relationship in direction with reference to the points of the compass.

origin of coordinates Point in a system of coordinates that serves as a zero point in computing the system's elements or in prescribing its use.

orthophotograph Photograph having the properties of an orthographic projection. It is derived from a conventional perspective photograph by simple or differential rectification so that image displacements caused by camera tilt and terrain relief are removed.

orthophotographic map Map produced by assembling orthophotographs at a specified uniform scale in a map format.

orthophotomap Orthophotographic map with contours and cartographic treatment, presented in a standard format, and related to standard reference systems.

orthophotomosaic Assembly of orthophotographs forming a uniform-scale mosaic.

orthophotoquad Monocolor orthophotographic map presented in a standard quadrangle format and related to standard reference systems. It has no contours and little or no cartographic treatment.

orthophotoscope Photomechanical device used in conjunction with a double-projection stereoplotter for producing orthophotographs.

overedge Any portion of a map lying outside the nominal map border (neatline).

overlay Printing or drawing on a transparent or translucent medium intended to be placed in register on a map or other graphic and which shows details not appearing or requiring special emphasis on the base material.

overprint New material printed on a map or chart to show data of importance or special use, in addition to those data originally printed.

parallel of latitude A circle, or approximation of a circle, on the surface of the Earth, parallel to the Equator, and connecting points of equal latitude; a circle of the celestial sphere parallel to the ecliptic, and connecting points of equal celestial latitude.

photogrammetry Science or art of obtaining reliable measurements or information from photographs or other sensing systems.

photomap (photographic map) Map made by adding marginal information, descriptive data, and a reference system to a photograph or asssembly of photographs.

plain Region of uniform general slope, comparatively level, of considerable extent, and not broken by marked elevations and depressions (it may be an extensive valley floor or a plateau summit); an extent of level or nearly level land; a flat, gently sloping, or nearly level region of the sea floor.

planetable Instrument consisting essentially of a drawing board on a tripod and some type of sighting device (alidade) with attached straightedge, used for plotting the lines of survey directly from observation in the field.

planimetric map See **map, planimetric.**

planimetry Plan details of a map—those having no indications of relief or contour.

plat Diagram drawn to scale showing all essential data pertaining to the boundaries and subdivisions of a tract of land, as determined by survey or protraction. As used by the Bureau of Land Management, the drawing which represents the particular area included in a survey, such as

township, private land claim, or mineral claim, and the lines surveyed, established, or retraced, showing the direction and length of each such line; the relation to the adjoining official surveys; the boundaries, descriptions, and area of each parcel of land subdivided; and, as nearly as may be practicable, a representation of the relief and improvements within the limits of the survey.

prime meridian Meridian of longitude 0°, used as the origin for measurements of longitude. The meridian of Greenwich, England, is the internationally accepted prime meridian on most charts. However, local or national prime meridians are occasionally used.

projection, map See **map projection.**

public land system Public lands are subdivided by a rectangular system of surveys established and regulated by the Bureau of Land Management. The standard format for subdivision is by townships measuring 6 miles (480 chains) on a side. Townships are further subdivided into 36 numbered sections of 1 square mile (640 acres) each.

quad-centered photograph Middle exposure of a phototriplet (three consecutive aerial photographs) taken so that the middle photograph is exposed directly above the center of the quadrangle and the preceding and following photographs are exposed directly above the boundaries of the quadrangle. The flying height is set such that the quad-centered photograph covers the entire quadrangle.

quadrangle Four-sided area, bounded by parallels of latitude and meridians of longitude used as an area unit in mapping (dimensions are not necessarily the same in both directions). Also, a geometric figure of significance in geodetic surveying.

radial-line plotting Determination of the location of points by the successive intersection and resection of direction lines radiating from the radial centers of overlapping aerial photographs.

rectification, differential The process of scanning and reprojecting a photograph onto a horizontal plane in differential elements to remove displacements caused by tilt and relief. The process may be accomplished by any one of a number of instruments developed specifically for the purpose.

rectification, simple Projection of an aerial photograph (mathematically, graphically, or photographically) from its plane onto a horizontal plane by translation, rotation, and (or) scale change to remove displacement due to tilt of the camera.

relief Elevations and depressions of the land or sea bottom.

relief shading Technique for making hypsography on a map appear three dimensional by the use of graded shadow effects. Generally, the features are shaded as though illuminated from the northwest.

remote sensing Process of detecting and (or) monitoring chemical or physical properties of an area by measuring its reflected and emitted radiation.

representative fraction Scale of a map or chart expressed as a fraction or ratio that relates unit distance on the map to distance measured in the same unit on the ground.

reproduction Summation of all the processes involved in printing copies from an original drawing. A printed copy of an original drawing made by the processes of reproduction.

scale Relationship existing between a distance on a map, chart, or photograph and the corresponding distance on the Earth.

sea level (water level) Height of the surface of the sea at any time.

section Unit of subdivision of a township; normally a quadrangle 1 mile square with boundaries conforming to meridians and parallels within established limits, and containing 640 acres as nearly as practicable.

sensor Technical means, usually electronic, to extend man's natural senses by detecting emitted or reflected energy. The energy may be nuclear, electromagnetic (including the visible and invisible portions of the spectrum), chemical, biological, thermal, or mechanical.

shoreline Intersection of the land with the water surface. The shoreline shown on charts represents the line of contact between the land and a selected water elevation. In areas affected by tidal fluctuations, this line of contact is usually the mean high water line. In confined coastal waters of diminished tidal influence, the mean water level line may be used.

slope map See **map, slope.**

soil map See **map, soil.**

spheroid Mathematical figure closely approaching the geoid in form and size and used as a surface of reference for geodetic surveys. A reference spheroid or ellipsoid is a spheroid determined by revolving an ellipse about its shorter (polar) axis and used as a base for geodetic surveys of a large section of the Earth (such as the Clarke spheroid of 1866 which is used for geodetic surveys in the United States).

spot elevation Point on a map or chart whose height above a specified datum is noted, usually by a dot or a small sawbuck and elevation value. Elevations are shown, on a selective basis, for road forks and intersections, grade crossings, summits of hills, mountains and mountain passes, water surfaces of lakes and ponds, stream forks, bottom elevations in depressions, and large flat areas.

stadia Technique of distance measurement wherein the observer reads the intercept subtended on a graduated rod between two marks on the reticle of the telescope.

standard-accuracy adjustment See **adjustment, standard-accuracy.**

state plane coordinate systems Coordinate systems established by the U.S. Coast and Geodetic Survey (now the National Ocean Survey), usually one for each State, for use in defining positions of points in terms of plane rectangular (x, y) coordinates.

stereocompilation Production of a map or chart manuscript from aerial photographs and geodetic control data by means of photogrammetric instruments.

stereoplotter Instrument for plotting a map by observation of stereomodels formed by pairs of photographs.

stereoscopic Pertaining to the use of binocular vision for observation of a pair of overlapping photographs or other perspective views, giving the impression of depth.

storm evacuation map See **map, storm evacuation.**

subsidence Decrease in the elevation of land surface due to tectonic, seismic, or artificial forces, without removal of surface material.

survey Orderly process of determining data relating to any physical or chemical characteristics of the Earth. The associated data obtained in a survey. An organization engaged in making a survey.

tacheometer (tachymeter) Surveying instrument designed for use in the rapid determination of distance, direction, and difference of elevation from a single observation, using a short base which may be an integral part of the instrument.

thematic map See **map, thematic.**

theodolite Precision surveying instrument for measuring horizontal and vertical angles.

tide Periodic rise and fall of the water resulting from gravitational interactions between the Sun, Moon, and Earth. The vertical component of the particulate motion of a tidal wave. Although the accompanying horizontal movement of the water is part of the same phenomenon, it is preferable to designate this motion as tidal current.

topographic map See **map, topographic.**

topography Configuration (relief) of the land surface; the graphic delineation or portrayal of that configuration in map form, as by contour lines; in oceanography the term is applied to a surface such as the sea bottom or a surface of given characteristics within the water mass.

township Unit of survey of the public lands of the United States, normally a quadrangle approximately 6 miles on a side with boundaries conforming to meridians and parallels within established limits, containing 36 sections. Also, in certain parts of the country, the term designates a minor governmental subdivision.

transit Precision surveying instrument; a theodolite in which the telescope can be reversed in direction by rotation about its horizontal axis.

traverse Sequence of lengths and directions of lines connecting a series of stations, obtained from field measurements, and used in determining positions of the stations.

triangulation Method of extending horizontal position on the surface of the Earth by measuring the angles of triangles and the included sides of selected triangles.

trilateration Method of surveying wherein the lengths of the triangle sides are measured, usually by electronic methods, and the angles are computed from the measured lengths. Compares with triangulation.

Universal Transverse Mercator (UTM) grid Military grid system based on the transverse Mercator projection, applied to maps of the Earth's surface extending from the Equator to 84° N. and 80° S. latitudes.

upland Highland; ground elevation above the lowlands along rivers or between hills.

zenith telescope Instrument for observing stars near the zenith (a point on the celestial sphere directly above the observer's position).

SELECTED REFERENCES

Adams, O. S., 1918, Lambert projection tables for the United States: U.S. Coast and Geod. Survey Spec. Pub. 52.
——1927, Tables for Albers projection: U.S. Coast and Geod. Survey Spec. Pub. 130.
Agnew, A. F., 1975, The U.S. Geological Survey: Committee Print, 94th Cong., 1st Sess., Senate Committee on Interior and Insular Affairs, Washington, U.S. Govt. Printing Office, p. 1–44.
American Society of Civil Engineers-American Congress on Surveying and Mapping, 1972, Definitions of surveying and associated terms: Am. Soc. Civil Engineers Manual 34, 205 p.
American Society of Photogrammetry, 1939, Report on recommended map-accuracy standards: Photogramm. Eng., v. 5, no. 1, p. 26–29.
Anderson, J. R., 1976, Land use and land cover map and data compilation in the U.S. Geological Survey: Paper presented at Pecora Memorial Symposium, Sioux Falls, S. Dak. [Available from U.S. Geological Survey, MS 520, Reston, Va. 22092.]
Anderson, J. R., Hardy, E. E., Roach, J. T., and Witmer, R. E., 1976, A land use and land cover classification system for use with remote sensor data: U.S. Geol. Survey Prof. Paper 964, 28 p.

Bartlett, R. A., 1962, Great surveys of the American West: Norman, Univ. Oklahoma Press, 408 p.
Breed, C. B., and Hosmer, G. L., 1953, Higher surveying, vol. II *of* The principles and practice of surveying: New York, John Wiley, 675 p.
Brown, L. A., 1949, The story of maps: New York, Bonanza Books, 393 p.
Bureau of Land Management, 1969, Surveying our public lands: Bur. Land Management leaflet, 16 p.
——1973, Manual of instructions for the survey of the public lands of the United States: Bur. Land Management Tech. Bull. 6, 333 p.

Cazier, Lola, 1976, Surveys and surveyors of the public domain—1785–1975: Bur. Land Management, 228 p.
Chapman, W. H., 1974, Gridding of ERTS images: Washington, Am. Cong. Surveying and Mapping, Fall Proc., p. 15–19.
Chief of Engineers, 1878, Report of the Chief of Engineers to the Secretary of War on May 10, 1878: H. Ex. Doc. no. 88, 45th Cong., 2d Sess., p. 4.
Colvocoresses, A. P., 1975, Evaluation of the cartographic application of ERTS–1 imagery: Am. Cartographer, v. 2, no. 1, p. 5–18.
Crone, D. R., 1953, The accuracy of topographical maps: Empire Survey Rev., v. 12, no. 88.

Darrah, W. C., 1951, Powell of the Colorado: Princeton, N.J., Princeton Univ. Press, 460 p.
Deetz, C. H., and Adams, O. S., 1934, Elements of map projection: U.S. Coast and Geod. Survey Spec. Pub. 68, 200 p.
Doyle, F. J., 1975, Cartographic applications of satellite imagery: U.S. Geol. Survey, 21 p. [Available as separate from U.S. Geological Survey, MS 520, Reston, Va. 22092.]
Dupree, A. H., 1957, Science in the Federal government—A history of policies and activities to 1940: Cambridge, Belknap Press of Harvard Univ. Press, 460 p.

Edelen, G. W., Jr., 1976, National program for managing flood losses—Guidelines for preparation, transmittal and distribution of flood-prone area maps and pamphlets: U.S. Geol. Survey open-file rept., 30 p.
Ellis, M. Y., ed., 1978, Coastal mapping handbook: NOAA–USGS, 200 p.

Federal Geodetic Control Committee, 1974, Classification, standards of accuracy, and general specifications of geodetic control surveys: National Ocean Survey, 12 p.

Gilman, C. R., Richter, C. W., and Brownworth, F. S., 1972, Slope maps—A new USGS product: Am. Soc. Photogramm., Proc. 1972 Fall Convention, p. 384–397.
Goetzmann, W. H., 1959, Army exploration in the American West 1803–1863: New Haven, Yale Univ. Press, 509 p.
——1966, Exploration and empire—The explorer and the scientist in the winning of the American West: New York, Alfred A. Knopf, 656 p.
Grant, R. S., and Duerk, M. D., 1973, Floods in Capron quadrangle, northeastern Illinois: U.S. Geological Survey Hydrol. Inv. Atlas HA–498, scale 1:24,000 [1974].

Hendrickson, W. B., 1943, David Dale Owen, pioneer geologist of the Middle West: Indianapolis, Indiana Historical Bureau, 180 p.
Howell, J. V., 1959, Geology plus adventure—The story of the Hayden Survey: Washington Acad. Sci. Jour., v. 49, no. 7, p. 220–224.

ITEK, 1981, Conceptual design of an automated mapping satellite system (MAPSAT), Final Technical Report, ITEK Corporation, Lexington, Mass., 299 p., 124 figs., 55 tables.

Jackson, W. T., 1952, Wagon roads West—A study of Federal road surveys and construction in the trans-Mississippi West 1846–1869: Berkeley and Los Angeles, Univ. California Press, 442 p.
Jacobson, H. L., 1976, Charting a Nation's course—Two hundred years of military mapping: Washington, Am. Cong. Surveying and Mapping, Proc. 36th Ann. Mtg.

King, Clarence, 1880, First annual report of the U.S. Geological Survey, 1880. Washington, U.S. Govt. Printing Office.
Kissam, Philip, 1956, Surveying for civil engineers: New York, McGraw-Hill, 716 p.

Lenzen, V. F., 1968, Benjamin Pierce and the U.S. Coast Survey: San Francisco, San Francisco Press, 54 p.
Lowman, P. D., Jr., 1969, Geologic orbital photography: Experience from the Gemini Program: Photogrammetria 24 (1969), p. 77–106.

Manning, T. G., 1967, Government in science—The U.S. Geological Survey 1867–1894: Lexington, Univ. Kentucky Press, 257 p.
Marsden, L. E., 1960, How the National Map Accuracy Standards were developed: Surveying and Mapping, v. XX, no. 4, p. 427–439.
McDonnell, P. W., 1979, Introduction to map projections: New York, Marcel Dekker, 184 p.
McEwen, R. B., 1980, USGS digital cartographic applications program: Journ. of Surveying and Mapping Div., ASCE, v. 106, no. SU1, p. 13–22.

McEwen, R. B., and Schoonmaker, J. W., 1975, ERTS color-image maps: Photogramm. Eng. and Remote Sensing, v. 41, no. 4, p. 479–489.

McEwen, R. B., and Tyler, D. A., 1972, Application of extraterrestrial surveying and mapping: Jour. of Surveying and Mapping Div., ASCE, v. 98, no. SU2, Proc. Paper 9383, p. 201–218.

Merrill, G. P., 1924, The first one hundred years of American geology: New Haven, Yale Univ. Press. [Reprinted in facsimile by Hafner Publishing Co., New York and London, 1964, 773 p.]

Mitchell, H. C., and Simmons, L. G., 1945, The State coordinate systems: U.S. Coast and Geod. Survey Spec. Pub. 325, 62 p. [Revised 1974.]

Moffitt, F. H., and Mikhail, E. M., 1980, Photogrammetry (3rd ed.): New York, Harper and Row, 648 p.

National Research Council, 1978, Geodesy: Trends and prospects: Washington, D.C., National Academy of Sciences, 86 p.

Office of Management and Budget, 1973, Report of the Federal Mapping Task Force on Mapping, Charting, Geodesy and Surveying: Washington, U.S. Govt. Printing Office, 198 p.

Orth, D. J., 1978, Geographic names, in Suggestions to authors of the reports of the United States Geological Survey, sixth ed.: U.S. Geol. Survey, p. 159–166.

Powell, A. L., 1976, National Ocean Survey—The Government's first technical agency: National Ocean Survey, 95 p.

Rabbitt, M. C., 1969, John Wesley Powell: Pioneer statesman of Federal science: U.S. Geol. Survey Prof. Paper 669, p. 1–21.

———1979, Minerals, lands, and geology for the common defence and general welfare, Volume 1, Before 1879: U.S. Govt. Printing Office, 331 p.

———1980, Minerals, lands, and geology for the common defence, Volume 2, 1879–1904: U.S. Govt. Printing Office, 407 p.

Reeves, R. G., ed., 1975, Manual of remote sensing: Falls Church, Va., Am. Soc. Photogramm., 867 p.

Reingold, Nathan, ed., 1964, Science in nineteenth-century America—A documentary history: New York, Hill and Wang, 339 p. [London, Melbourne, and Toronto, Macmillan, 1966.]

Robinson, A. H., and Sale, R. D., 1969, Elements of cartography: New York, John Wiley, 415 p.

Robinson, G. D., and Spieker, A. M., 1978, Nature to be commanded—Earth-science maps applied to land and water management: U.S. Geol. Survey Prof. Paper 950, 96 p.

Roney, J. I., 1978, Design and development of the new USGS metric map series: U.S. Geol. Survey, 7 p. [Available as separate from U.S. Geological Survey, MS 520, Reston, Va. 22092.]

Sherwood, M. B., 1965, Exploration of Alaska 1865–1900: New Haven and London, Yale Univ. Press, 207 p.

Short, N. M., Lowman, P. D., and Freden, S. C., 1976, Mission to earth—Landsat views the world: NASA Spec. Pub. 360, 459 p.

Slama, C. C., ed., 1980, Manual of photogrammetry (4th ed.): Am. Soc. Photogramm., 1056 p.

Smith, D. G., 1973, Autographic theme extraction system: U.S. Geol. Survey, 10 p. [Available from U.S. Geological Survey, MS 520, Reston, Va. 22092.]

Southard, R. B., 1975, Practical applications of orthophotographs: Paper presented at Commonwealth Survey Officers Conf., Cambridge, England. [Available as separate from U.S. Geological Survey, MS 520, Reston, Va. 22092.]

Stegner, Wallace, 1954, Beyond the hundredth meridian. John Wesley Powell and the second opening of the West: Boston, Houghton-Mifflin, 438 p.

Strahler, A.N., 1973, Introduction to physical geography (3rd ed.): New York, John Wiley, 468 p.

Thompson, M. M., 1952, Development of photogrammetry in the U.S. Geological Survey: U.S. Geol. Survey Circ. 218, 24 p. [Revised 1958.]

———1960, A current view of the National Map Accuracy Standards: Surveying and Mapping, v. 16, no. 2, p. 449–457.

———1975, Surveying and mapping in the year 2000: Frankfurt, a. M. Verlag des Instituts fur Angewandte Geodasie, Karten und Vermessungswesen, p. 133–139. [Also published in Proc. Fall Convention, 1975, Am. Cong. on Surveying and Mapping, p. 362–368.]

Thomson, D. W., 1966, Men and meridians; the history of surveying and mapping in Canada, v. 1, 2, and 3: Ottawa, Dept. of Energy, Mines and Resources.

United Nations, 1963, Specifications, v. 2 of U.N. Technical Conference on the International Map of the World on the Millionth Scale (Bonn, 1962): New York, United Nations, 107 p.

U.S. Army, 1967, Grids and grid references: U.S. Army Tech. Manual 5–241–1, 192 p.

U.S. Army Corps of Engineers, 1958, Transformation of coordinates from geographic to grid, v. 1 of Universal Transverse Mercator grid tables for latitudes 0°–80°, Clarke 1866 spheroid (meters): U.S. Army Tech. Manual 5–241–4/1, 250 p.

U.S. Coast and Geodetic Survey, 1946, Tables for a polyconic projection of maps and lengths of terrestrial arcs of meridians and parallels based upon Clarke's reference spheroid of 1866: U.S. Coast and Geod. Survey Spec. Pub. 5.

———Plane coordinate projection tables for Michigan: U.S. Coast Guard and Geod. Survey Pub. 65–3. [No date.]

U.S. Geological Survey, 1960–68, Topographic instructions of the United States Geological Survey. [Selected chapters available from U.S. Geological Survey, MS 520, Reston, Va. 22092.]

———1970, The National Atlas of the United States of America: U.S. Geol. Survey, 417 p.

———1972, Publications of the Geological Survey, 1962–1970. [Also, 1879–1961; monthly and annual supplements available from U.S. Geological Survey, MS 520, Reston, Va. 22092.]

———1979, Yearbook, fiscal year 1978: U.S. Geol. Survey.

Van Zandt, F. K., 1976, Boundaries of the United States and the several States: U.S. Geol. Survey Prof. Paper 909, 191 p.

Voisin, R. L., 1976, Maps for the American people: Am. Cartographer, v. 3, no. 2, p. 101–106.

White, W. S., 1970, Geologic maps—Portraits of the Earth: U.S. Geol. Survey information leaflet.

Wilford, J. N., 1981, The mapmakers: New York, Alfred A. Knopf, 416 p.

Wilkins, Thurman, 1958, Clarence King—A biography: New York, Macmillan, 441 p.

Williams, R. S., Jr., and Carter, W. D., eds., 1976, ERTS–1—A new window on our planet: U.S. Geol. Survey Prof. Paper 929, 362 p.

Winner, M. D., Jr., 1975, Ground-water resources of the Cape Hatteras National Seashore, N.C.: U.S. Geol. Survey Hydrol. Inv. Atlas HA–540, scale 1:24,000.

Wolf, P. R., 1974, Elements of photogrammetry: New York, McGraw-Hill, 562 p.

Woods, J. W., ed., 1978, The official railway guide: New York, National Railway Publication Co., v. 4, no. 6.

INDEX

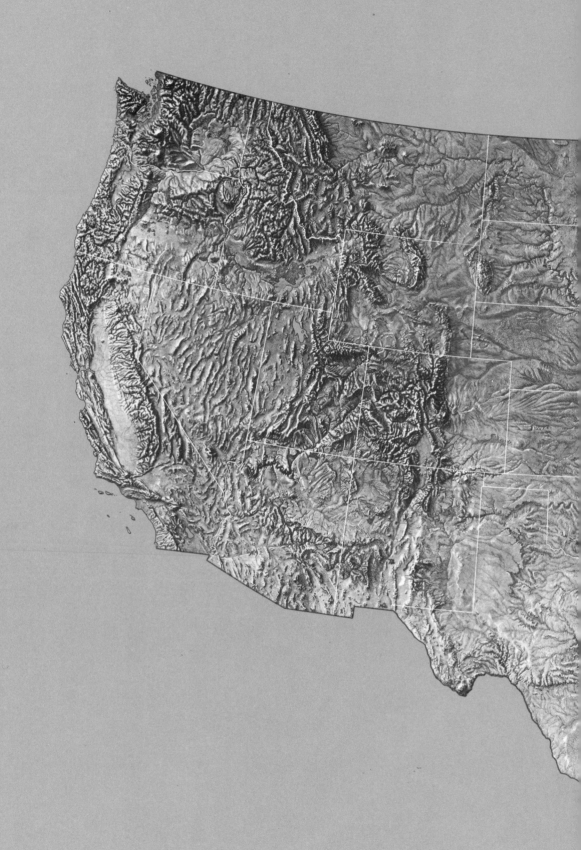